Magnetosphere - Ionosphere
Interactions

SCANDINAVIAN UNIVERSITY BOOKS
Universitetsforlaget, Oslo/Bergen/Tromsö
Munksgaard, Copenhagen
Läromedelsförlagen, Stockholm/Göteborg/Lund

UNIVERSITETSFORLAGET

Distribution offices

NORWAY
BLINDERN, OSLO 3

UNITED KINGDOM
CANNON HOUSE, PARK FARM ROAD
FOLKESTONE, KENT

UNITED STATES
BOX 142
BOSTON, MASS. 02113

Magnetosphere - Ionosphere Interactions

Proceedings of the Advanced Study Institute at
Dalseter, Norway, 14-23 April 1971

Organized by
the Norwegian Defence Research Establishment

Edited by
Kristen Folkestad

UNIVERSITETSFORLAGET

OSLO – BERGEN – TROMSÖ

DS Z

F

Andelsbogtrykkeriet i Odense

Contents

Preface

The present book contains review lectures and a few contributions on special subjects presented at a symposium arranged by the Norwegian Defence Research Establishment at Dalseter, Norway, from 15 to 22 April 1971.

The conference was largely concerned with the multifarious mechanisms governing the interaction between the magnetosphere and the polar ionosphere, the emphasis being on recent theoretical deductions and experimental findings. A bold reservation of part of the programme for a discussion of the chemistry and some general properties of the ionospheric D-region reflects the organizer's traditional orientation of interest. We hope that this excursion into a realm somewhat beside the main theme of the conference is compensated for by the novel results of the presentations concerning a fascinating and rapidly expanding field of atmospheric research.

In addition to the editor, Drs Thorne, Thomas, and Mæhlum have acted as programme committee.

Financially the arrangement has been partly supported by the Science Committee of NATO.

The Editor.

Laboratory Measurements of D-Region Ion-Molecule Reactions

E. E. FERGUSON

NOAA Environmental Research Laboratories, Boulder, Colorado 80302, U.S.A.

Abstract: The current status of laboratory measurements of D-region positive and negative ion chemistry is discussed. The laboratory derived reaction schemes are compared with available ionospheric observations. In the case of positive ion chemistry, the reactions which have been measured in the laboratory do not appear to yield the observed D-region ion composition. It is not clear at this time where the difficulty lies. In the case of negative ion chemistry, the direct ion composition measurements are as yet too sparse to critically test the detailed reaction schemes derived from laboratory studies. The first direct D-region observations offer support for the prediction from laboratory studies that NO_3^- and its hydrates play a dominant role. Some of the laboratory measurements still needed are noted.

1. INTRODUCTION

The development of even a modest understanding of D-region ion chemistry is a comparatively recent one, which can reasonably be considered to have started with the Narcisi & Bailey (1965) direct positive ion composition measurements. The first direct negative ion composition determinations have only recently been made (Narcisi et al. 1971, Arnold et al. 1971). The acquisition of relevant laboratory data on ion-neutral reaction rate constants is also of recent origin. Much of the relevant positive ion reaction data available has been acquired in the past year or so, lagging considerably behind the rocket observations. On the other hand, a substantial number of negative ion reaction rates have been published in advance of direct D-region negative ion composition measurements.

In the present discussion an attempt to review the current status of relevant laboratory reaction studies will be given, emphasizing where they seem to be compatible with direct observations and where they do not.

To anticipate the conclusions, I can say that in the case of the positive ion chemistry we have a clear incompatibility between the theoretical models and the direct observations. These models include both ion chemistry and ion production rates. In the negative ion case, the uncertainties in the D-region ion composition and neutral composition are as yet too great to allow one to establish whether or not the current ion chemistry scheme is inadequate.

2. POSITIVE ION CHEMISTRY

The outstanding D-region positive ion chemistry problem has been to explain the origin of the water cluster ions, $H_3O(H_2O)_n$ observed by Narcisi & Bailey (1965) and repeatedly verified. They found the major ion below 80 km to be $H_5O_2^+$ (37^+). For a long time it was not known how such ions could be produced at all in the ionosphere. In 1969 it was shown (Fehsenfeld & Ferguson, 1969) that reaction processes exist which convert both O_2^+ and NO^+ to hydrated hydronium ions, $H_3O^+(H_2O)_n$. The complete reaction scheme is given schematically in Fig. 1 and the relevant rate constant measurements are listed in Tables I, II, and III. The O_2^+ ions produced convert very efficiently (i.e. in a short time in the D-region) to primarily $H_3O^+(H_2O)$, an ion of mass 37^+, which is the dominant ion observed below $\sim$ 80 km. Until fairly recently we thought the O_2^+ mechanism, initiated by $O_2(^1\Delta_g)$ photoionization, was sufficient to account for the magnitude of the 37^+ concentration observed (Ferguson & Fehsenfeld 1969). However, Huffman et al. (1971) have recently shown that the original O_2^+ production rates of Hunten & McElroy (1968) were serious overestimates and it now seems quite likely that the O_2^+ scheme is quantitatively inadequate, although certainly responsible for much of the observed 37^+. Fig. 2 shows a reasonable estimate (Ferguson in press) of 37^+ production from O_2^+, using the Huffman et al. (1971) O_2^+ production rates. The calculations of Fig. 2 also include the reaction

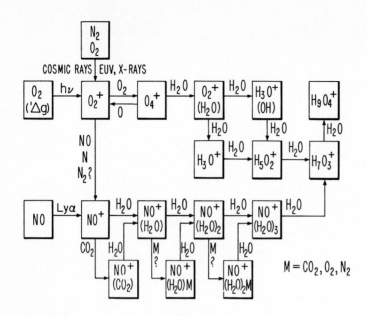

Fig. 1. Schematic diagram of D-region positive ion chemistry.

Table 1. $O_2^+ - H_2O$ reaction rate constants at 295°K

	Reaction	k*
1)	$O_2^+ + H_2O + N_2 \rightarrow O_2^+(H_2O) + N_2$	2.8(− 28)**
	$O_2^+ + H_2O + O_2 \rightarrow O_2^+(H_2O) + O_2$	1.9(− 28)†
2)	$O_2^+ + 2O_2 \rightarrow O_4^+ + O_2$	2.4(− 30)††
3)	$O_4^+ + H_2O \rightarrow O_2^+(H_2O) + O_2$	2.2(− 9),**1.3(− 9)††
4)	$O_2^+(H_2O) + H_2O \rightarrow H_3O^+ (OH) + O_2$	1.9(− 9),** 0.9(− 9)††
	$\rightarrow H_3O^+ + OH + O_2$	≤ 0.3(− 9),** 0.3(− 9)††
5)	$H_3O^+ (OH) + H_2O \rightarrow H_3O^+ (H_2O) + OH$	3.2(− 9),** > 1(− 9)††

  * Three-body rate constants in cm^6 molecule^{-2} sec^{-1}, two-body rate constants in cm^3 molecule^{-1} sec^{-1}.
** Fehsenfeld et al. 1971.
  † Howard et al. 1971.
†† Good et al. 1970.

Table 2. $NO^+ - H_2O$ reaction rate constants at 295°K

	Reaction	k_f*	k_r*
1)	$NO^+ + H_2O + M \rightleftarrows NO^+(H_2O) + M$	1.6(− 28),** 1.6(− 28),† 1.4(− 28)††	< 1(− 14)**
2)	$NO^+(H_2O) + H_2O + M \rightleftarrows NO^+(H_2O)_2 + M$	1.0(− 27),** 1.1(− 27)†	< 1(− 13),** 1.4(− 14)†
3)	$NO^+(H_2O)_2 + H_2O + M \rightleftarrows NO^+(H_2O)_3 + M$	2.0(− 27),** 1.9(− 27)†	1.3(− 12),** 1.9(− 12)†
4)	$NO^+(H_2O)_3 + H_2O \rightarrow H_3O^+(H_2O)_2 + HNO_2$	8(− 11),** 7(− 11)†	

  * k is forward rate constant, k_r is reverse rate constant for reactions a written. Three-body rate constants in cm^6 molecule^{-2} sec^{-1}, two-body rate constants in cm^3 molecule^{-1} sec^{-1}.
** Fehsenfeld et al. 1971. M = N_2.
  † Puckett & Teague. 1971. M = NO.
†† Howard et al. 1971. M = N_2.

Table 3. NO+ association rate constants (Dunkin et al. 1971)

Reaction	T($°K$)	Rate constant ($cm^6 sec^{-1}$)
$NO^+ + N_2 + He \rightarrow NO^+ \cdot N_2 + He$	200	$< 5 \quad (-33)$
$NO^+ + O_2 + He \rightarrow NO^+ \cdot O_2 + He$	200	$< 6 \quad (-34)$
$NO^+ + CO_2 + He \rightarrow NO^+ \cdot CO_2 + He$	197	$1.0 \pm 0.3 (-29)$
	235	$7.2 \pm 3.5 (-30)$
	290	$4 \quad \pm 2 \quad (-30)$
$NO^+ + CO_2 + N_2 \rightarrow NO^+ \cdot CO_2 + N_2$	200	$2.5 \pm 1.5 (-29)$
$NO^+ + CO_2 + Ar \rightarrow NO^+ \cdot CO_2 + Ar$	196	$3.1 \pm 1 \quad (-29)$
$NO^+ \cdot CO_2 + H_2O \rightarrow NO^+ \cdot H_2O + CO_2$	200	fast $(\sim 10^{-9} cm^3 sec^{-1})$

$$O_4^+ + O \rightarrow O_2^+ + O_3, \qquad (1)$$

which Fehsenfeld (private communication), finds to have a rate constant $K_1 \sim 3 \pm 2 \times 10^{-10} cm^3 sec^{-1}$. Dissociative recombination of the ions is of course also included. Without reaction (1), our earlier calculations (Ferguson & Fehsenfeld 1969) did not reproduce the steep topside dropoff in 37^+ which has repeatedly been observed. The serious problem is seen in Fig. 2 to lie below 75 km, where the O_2^+ production rapidly goes to zero, while the observed 37^+ peak did not. The disagreement at the 37^+ peak at 80 km is not as serious as it appears, since there were substantial uncertainties involved in reducing the observed rocket ion currents to ambient ion concentrations as well as in some details of the ion chemistry. The ion concentrations were almost certainly normalized to too large a value, as suggested by their magnitude. The shape reflects an altitude-dependent sensitivity factor such that the ion currents at 65 km were multiplied by almost 100 times more than those at 80 to obtain ion densities, and this is a very uncertain procedure. An estimate of the heavier cluster ions, $H_3O^+(H_2O)_n$, $n > 1$, is also shown in Fig. 2, since it is now known (Narcisi in preparation) that the rocket sampling process breaks up some of these heavy cluster ions so that some of the observed 37^+ could have arisen from 55^+ or heavier ions. However, the total reservoir of heavy cluster ions produced by O_2^+ still does not appear to be adequate to yield the observed 37^+ concentrations in the 65–75 km region.

The most reasonable way to attempt to account for the major ion observed, 37^+, is as a product of the major ion *produced*, which is NO^+. One problem here, as seen in Fig. 1 (or Table II) is that NO^+ hydration leads to the water cluster ion $H_3O^+(H_2O)_2$, mass 55^+ and not 37^+. Moreover, as Reid (in press) has shown, the time scale for the NO^+ sequence is so long that one would expect NO^+ and $NO^+(H_2O)_n$ ion concentrations to substantially exceed the $H_3O^+(H_2O)_n$ concentra_

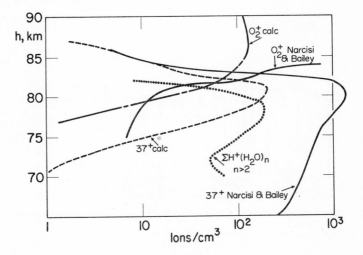

Fig. 2. Calculated and observed 37^+($H_5O_2^+$) ion concentrations in the D-region.

tions, contrary to observation. Dunkin et al. (1971) have recently shown that NO^+ hydration is accelerated by an intermediate $NO^+(CO_2)$ formation, as shown in Table III. It is quite possible that this may happen at each successive step, as suggested in Fig. 1, but this does not seem sufficient, since Reid, who included the first CO_2 step, still found $[NO^+] > [NO^+(H_2O)_n]$. The neutrals O_2 and N_2 do not appear to facilitate the hydration of NO^+ because of the low rate constants for association shown in Table III. However, they may become important in hydrating $NO^+(H_2O)$, etc., as suggested in Fig. 1.

It seems that we must be missing an essential reaction or other bit of physics in the positive ion scheme. This problem of understanding the ion composition is almost surely closely related to the problem of understanding the D-region electron density. As is well known and has been discussed in detail by Reid (in press), the production rate of electrons, i.e. Ly-α ionization of NO, leads to substantially larger electron densities than are observed. The conversion of NO^+ to $H_3O^+(H_2O)_n$ ions eases this problem somewhat because the dissociative recombination coefficients of H_3O^+ $(H_2O)_n$ ions are greater than that of NO^+. These dissociative recombination measurements are being carried out by Biondi and his students (private communication) and are as yet incomplete. They are extremely difficult to carry out because it is impossible to obtain one single water ion cluster at a time to measure – the rapid equilibration always leads to a distribution.

Two reactions not included in Fig. 1 or Tables I–III, which have not been measured but which may be significant under some circumstances, are:

$$O_4^+ + O_2(^1\Delta_g) \rightarrow O_2^+ + 2O_2 \qquad (2)$$
$$O_2^+ \cdot H_2O + O_2(^1\Delta_g) \rightarrow O_2^+ + O_2 + H_2O \qquad (3)$$

These reactions, viewed simply as charge-transfer reactions, are likely to be fast if exothermic. In almost all cases so far observed, exothermic charge-transfer to molecules is fast, typically with rate constants of the order of 10^{-10} cm^3 sec^{-1}. Reaction (2) is certainly exothermic and reaction (3) is probably exothermic, by an estimated $\sim$ 0.2 eV. On the other hand, one might not expect $NO^+ \cdot H_2O$ to be dissociated by $O_2(^1\Delta_g)$, even though the process is probably exothermic, since the charge-transfer mechanism could not operate. This should be checked experimentally in the laboratory, however.

3. NEGATIVE ION CHEMISTRY

The course of development of D-region negative ion chemistry has been very different from that of positive ion chemistry. In the latter case we had direct ion composition measurements before any relevant laboratory ion-neutral reactions had been measured, and the direction of research has been an attempt to devise reaction schemes, based on laboratory measurements, to account for the observations. We have, temporarily at least, reached an impasse in this field. We have not arrived at a satisfactory understanding of D-region positive ion chemistry and we do not have any clear idea as to where to turn next. In the negative ion chemistry case, on the other hand, we have derived fairly elaborate reaction schemes (Fehsenfeld et al. 1967, Fehsenfeld & Ferguson 1968, 1969) from laboratory measurements since 1967 and only very recently are any direct ion composition determinations becoming available for comparison (Narcisi et al. 1971, Arnold et al. 1971). I want to discuss now the present status of laboratory measurements and the extent to which

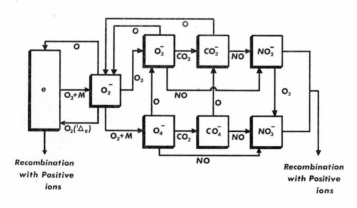

Fig. 3. Schematic diagram of D-region negative ion chemistry.

the first direct observations support or contest the present scheme.

Only qualitative comparisons are possible at present. In addition to the substantial uncertainties involved in reducing the rocket mass spectrometer data to quantitative negative ion concentrations, the negative ion chemistry is controlled largely by the concentrations of minor neutral constituents whose concentration in the D-region is so poorly known that this yields large uncertainties in computed ion concentrations. It will, in my opinion, be some time before the laboratory rate constant measurements are critically tested by ionospheric observation.

Fig. 3 shows the negative ion reactions scheme which has evolved from flowing afterglow studies. Negative ion chemistry commences, for the most part at least, by electron attachment to O_2. The chemistry can immediately be quenched here by the atomic oxygen associative detachment or O_2 ($^1\Delta_g$) dissociation or it can proceed on two different reaction sequences to ultimately produce NO_3^-. Note that atomic oxygen interrupts each of these sequences at two further points that can also lead back to detachment. It is clear that a good knowledge of the atomic oxygen concentration is necessary to calculate λ (n^-/n_e) and that any marked change in [O] with altitude will lead to a marked change in λ. The O_4^- path and the O_3^- path appear to be comparable in the daytime 60–80 km region, within the uncertainties of rate constants and O_3 concentration. An excellent review by Thomas (1971) gives representative time scales for the processes in Fig. 3 at 65 km both day and night. Better measurements on the O_4^- formation rate constant are needed, particularly at D-region temperatures. These will be fairly straightforward to obtain. Three-body reaction rate constants typically are quite sensitive to temperature, always decreasing with increasing temperature, while binary ion-neutral reactions are usually not very sensitive. A D-region value ranging from $\sim 10^{-30}$ cm^6 sec^{-1} at 200 K to $\sim 3 \times 10^{-31}$ cm^6 sec^{-1} at 300°K seems to be a reasonable estimate.

Several qualitative conclusions follow from Fig. 3 and the reaction rate constants. Since the concentration of CO_2 in the D-region is relatively high (3×10^{-4}) and the reactions of O_3^- and O_4^- with CO_2 have large rate constants, both about 4×10^{-10} cm^3 sec^{-1}, it follows that O_3^- and O_4^- concentrations will be low. We do not expect them to be observable. The relative concentration of NO on the other hand is much less

and the rate constants for CO_3^- and CO_4^- reactions with NO are also less, 9×10^{-12} and 4.7×10^{-11} cm^3 sec^{-1} respectively, so that much larger CO_3^- and CO_4^- ion concentrations must occur. The NO_3^- ion should certainly be a major D-region ion. Quantitative calculations giving the negative ion composition and λ as a function of altitude have been given by Reid (1970), using, however, a larger $O_2^- + O_2 \rightarrow O_4^-$ production rate than now seems reasonable.

One consideration not shown in Fig. 3 is the hydration of the ions. All stable D-region ions, positive and negative, can be expected to become hydrated. This is essentially a process due to charge-dipole interaction, which is very non-selective chemically. The question as to whether hydration can interrupt the reaction sequence is one which has not as yet been studied in the laboratory. We need to examine, for example, reactions such as:

$$CO_4^-(H_2O) + NO \rightarrow NO_3^- + CO_2 + H_2O \quad (4a)$$
$$\rightarrow NO_3^-(H_2O) + CO_2 \quad (4b)$$

to see if these occur. If hydration markedly lowers the reactivity of CO_3^-, CO_4^-, etc., then this will somewhat affect the negative ion composition. However, the probable rates of hydration of CO_3^- and CO_4^- are less than their reaction rates with NO, and less than the NO_2^- reaction rate with O_3, so that NO_3^- and its hydrates would still be expected to be the dominant ions.

One point to be made is that $O_2^-(H_2O)$ is not expected, since the reaction

$$O_2^-(H_2O) + CO_2 \rightarrow CO_4^- + H_2O \quad (5)$$

is very rapid, (Adams et al. 1970) $k_5 = 5.8 \times 10^{-10}$ cm^3 sec^{-1}.

Two groups have reported negative ion observations, Narcisi et al. (1971) from Air Force Cambridge Research Laboratories in Boston, and Arnold et al. (1971) from the Max-Planck Institute in Heidelberg. Narcisi et al. report the results of two nighttime flights with measurements between 73 and 117 km, obtained at Fort Churchill, Canada, under quiet conditions in August and October of 1969. One spectrometer had a scanning range of 12–79 amu and the other a range of 12–162 amu. Heavy ions with masses near 60, 62, 76, 78 (?), 80, 98, 116, 134, and 152 amu were measured between 73 and 90 km. Between 90 and 92 km the total negative ion concentration decreased by almost two orders of magnitude. Relatively small concentrations of ions with masses 16, 35/37, and 46 amu were observed above 90 km.

Table IV. AFCRL mass spectrometer negative ion observations (Narcisi et al. 1971)

Mass	Tentative identification
16	O^-
35/37	Cl^-
46	NO_2^-
60	CO_3^-
62	NO_3^-
76	CO_4^-
78 (?)	$CO_3^-(H_2O)$
80	$NO_3^-(H_2O)$
98	$NO_3^-(H_2O)_2$
116	$NO_3^-(H_2O)_3$
134	$NO_3^-(H_2O)_4$
152	$NO_3^-(H_2O)_5$

Table V. MPI mass spectrometer negative ion observations (Arnold et al. 1971)

Mass	Tentative identification	Max. no. of counts per mass peak
32	O_2^-	33
35	Cl^-, $OH^-(H_2O)$	210
37	Cl^-	64
60	CO_3^-	407
61	HCO_3^-	119
62	NO_3^-	77
68	$O_2^-(H_2O)_2$	16
76	CO_4^-	22
78	$CO_3^-(H_2O)$	18
93 ± 1	$CO_4^-(H_2O)$ $NO_2^-(HNO_2)$	73
111 ± 1	$CO_4^-(H_2O)_2$ $NO_2^-(H_2O)(HNO_2)$	70
$175 \pm$	$NO_3^-(HNO_3)$	50

These results are listed in Table IV with tentative ion identifications. The mass identifications have an uncertainty $\pm$ 0.015 M. The peak density at 88 km on one flight was estimated to exceed 200 ions cm^{-3}. The E-region negative ion densities were generally less than 10 ions cm^{-3}. Qualitatively, the Air Force Cambridge Research Laboratories' results seem reasonably compatible with expectations from the scheme of Fig. 3.

Arnold et al. also report a nighttime flight, in this case from Andoya, Norway, in March 1970 during a weak aurora. They found that the negative ion concentration was nearly 10^3 ions cm^{-3} from about 71 to 76 km. Table V summarizes their results. The ion composition differs substantially from the Narcisi et al. data and is in much poorer qualitative agreement with the scheme of Fig. 3. Whether this difference reflects the influence of the weak aurora or otherwise different atmospheric conditions, or is an artifact of one or the other of the experiments, cannot be determined until much more data becomes available.

The discussion above, and the usual discussions of ionospheric negative ion chemistry, are oriented toward explaining the dominant negative ions of the D-region. With the very sensitive detection used in the rocket experiments, in which a few ions cm^{-3} are detected, it is quite possible that some negative ions falling outside of the above scheme will be found. For example, a small but definite O^- concentration will be produced by radiative attachment (Branscomb 1964).

$$e + O \rightarrow O^- + h\nu, \tag{6}$$

with $k_6 = 1.3 \times 10^{-15}$ cm^3 sec^{-1}. The O^- signal is limited by (Fehsenfeld et al. 1967)

$$O^- + O \rightarrow O_2 + e, \tag{7}$$

with $k_7 = 1.9 \times 10^{-10}$ cm^3 sec^{-1}, and by

$$O^- + X^+ \rightarrow \text{neutrals}, \tag{8}$$

with $k_8 \sim 10^{-8}$ cm^3 sec^{-1} and in the daytime by photodetachment (Branscomb 1964)

$$O^- + h\nu \rightarrow O + e, \tag{9}$$

with $k_9 = 1.4$ sec^{-1}. Reaction (7) alone, which can be a dominating one, limits the O^- concentration to $[O^-]/n_e \leq 10^{-5}$. The O^- concentration (above the D-region) has recently been discussed by Hanson (1970) in connection with the tropical ultraviolet airglow. Radiative attachment is more likely to lead to a detectable effect in the E-region than in the D-region.

Dissociative attachment to ozone,

$$e + O_3 \rightarrow O^- + O_2 \tag{10}$$

with $k_{10} = 1.1 \times 10^{-11}$ cm^3 sec^{-1} at $300°K$ may be of importance in the D- and E-regions. The rate constant for k_{10} depends markedly on the electron energy, increasing to $\sim 3 \times 10^{-10}$ cm^3 sec^{-1} for an electron energy of ~ 0.3 eV (Phelps & Kasner 1969).

One of the possibly important reaction rate constants yet to be determined from laboratory studies concerns

$$NO_3^- + O \rightarrow NO_2^- + O_2 \tag{11a}$$
$$\rightarrow O_2^- + NO_2 \tag{11b}$$

Reaction (11) has been observed (Fehsenfeld et al. 1969) not to be fast, $k_{11} < 10^{-11}$ cm^3 sec^{-1}; however k_{11b} could be much slower than this and still be of importance, since it would lead to electron detachment from NO_3^-. Reaction (11b) is probably endothermic but this is not firmly established. Reaction (11a) is almost certainly exothermic but would be of no great consequence even if it should occur.

A further reaction to be investigated is

$$NO_3^- + H \rightarrow HNO_3 + e \qquad (12a)$$
$$\rightarrow OH^- + NO_2 \qquad (12b)$$
$$\rightarrow NO_2^- + OH \qquad (12c)$$

All of these channels are likely to be exothermic. Channel (12a) would be of the greatest significance, since it detaches the electron from NO_3^- and will be exothermic unless $EA(NO_3) > 4.4$ eV, which is a very large value, indeed larger than any known electron affinity.

One complication which I should briefly mention is that some negative ions are not uniquely specified by their mass, e.g. NO_2^- may be $[O-N-O]^-$ or $[N-O-O]^-$, depending on how it is produced. Similarly NO_3^- may be $\begin{bmatrix} O-N-O \\ O \end{bmatrix}^-$ or $[O-N-O-O]^-$. We have strong laboratory evidence (Adams et al. 1970) for two NO_3^- species, with quite different energies and reactivities, and some suggestive evidence in the case of NO_2^-. This is clearly a potential source of confusion and complexity. Specifically, we recently observed (Adams et al. 1970) the reaction

$$CO_3^- + NO \rightleftarrows NO_2^- + CO_2 \qquad (13)$$

to attain an equilibrium in the laboratory with an equilibrium constant of 11 at 300°K. With the large CO_2/NO ratio in the D-region the reverse reaction (13) could contribute to the CO_3^- production and interrupt the scheme of Fig. 3.

It is of interest to return to the negative ion results of Arnold et al. (1971) in Table V to see if they can be understood qualitatively. It appears that, with the exception of the signal at mass 61, they might be. The failure to observe NO_2^-, i.e. a small $[NO_2^-]/[CO_3^-]$ ratio, follows from the scheme of Fig. 3 and a large O_3/NO ratio at night. The steady state $[NO_2^-]/[CO_3^-]$ ratio would be approximately equal to the $[NO]/[O_3]$ ratio.

The HCO_3^- signal, which tracks the CO_3^- signal on both upleg and downleg, suggests that the reaction:

$$CO_3^- + H_2O \rightarrow HCO_3^- + OH \qquad (14)$$

may occur. However, the observation of $CO_3^- \cdot H_2O$ indicates that this reaction does not occur. If HCO_3^- were $OH^- \cdot CO_2$, an ion expected to be stable, then one would expect to see some OH^- just as both O_2^- and $O_2^- \cdot CO_2$ are observed.

Within the substantial uncertainties of unmeasured rate constants, neutral concentrations, etc., it seems at least plausible that CO_3^- and CO_4^- hydrates should form, i.e. the time scale for this is probably competitive with other CO_3^- and CO_4^- loss processes. One might have expected CO_4^- to be less hydrated than CO_3^-, since CO_4^- has a shorter lifetime due to reaction with NO (because of a larger rate constant). It might be pointed out that CO_4^- is a weakly bound cluster ion, $D(O_2^- - CO_2) = 0.8$ eV, whereas CO_3^- is much more stable, $D(O^- - CO_2) > 1.9$ eV, and thus CO_4^- may be broken up in the ion sampling, whereas CO_3^- would probably not be. This breakup would lower the apparent CO_4^- concentration and *lead to a spurious* O_2^- signal. Singly and doubly hydrated CO_4^- ions seem more likely for the 93 ± 1 and 111 ± 1 ion signals than the alternate HNO_2 clustered to NO_2^- and $NO_2^- (H_2O)$ suggestion.

Finally, it seems that a possibility of explaining the observed 125 ± 1 amu signal as $NO_3^- (HNO_3)$ may exist. Specifically the scheme

$$NO_3^- + H_2O + M \rightarrow NO_3^- \cdot H_2O + M, \qquad (15)$$

followed by

$$NO_3^- \cdot H_2O + HNO_3 \rightarrow NO_3^- \cdot HNO_3 + H_2O, (16)$$

would keep the $[NO_3^- \cdot H_2O]/[NO_3^-]$ ratio low (< 0.1) if $k_{15} \sim 10^{-27}$ cm^6 sec^{-1}, $k_{16} \sim 10^{-9}$ cm^6 sec^{-1}, and if $[HNO_3] \gtrsim 10^7$ cm^{-3}. The estimates of the rate constants are fairly reasonable, the estimate on $[HNO_3]$ is pure conjecture. Much of the ionization in the D-region leads to HNO_2 (nitrous acid) production by reaction (4) in Table II. This in turn is oxidized to nitric acid by reaction with ozone,

$$HNO_3 + O_3 \rightarrow HNO_3 + O_2 \qquad (17)$$

so that the HNO_3 production rate may be a significant fraction of the total ionization rate. If the daytime photodissociation rate of HNO_3 is not too great in the D-region, e.g. 10^{-6} sec^{-1} or so, then perhaps concentrations as large as 10^7 cm^{-3} can build up, particularly at night and particularly in disturbed conditions such as the Andoya flight (in contrast to the Fort Churchill flight).

One difficulty with this explanation is that by the same logic one would expect reactions such as

$$CO_3^- \cdot H_2O + HNO_3 \rightarrow$$
$$CO_3^- \cdot HNO_3 + H_2O \qquad (18)$$

to occur, and they apparently do not. It is possible that (16) is exothermic and (18) endothermic but this is merely speculation.

Such tentative schemes perhaps have only this to commend them, that they suggest a direction for further laboratory studies. This iteration of direct rocket observations and laboratory measurements slowly but surely increases our understanding. It is clear that a great deal still remains to be done, both in the laboratory and in the ionosphere itself, if we are ever to understand the ion chemistry.

Acknowledgement: This work has been supported in part by the Defence Atomic Support Agency.

REFERENCES

Adams, N. G., Bohme, D. K., Dunkin, D. B., Fehsenfeld, F. C. & Ferguson, E. E. 1970. *J. Chem. Phys. 52*, 3133.

Arnold, F., Kissel, J., Krankowsky, D., Wieder, H. & Zähringer, J. 1971. *J. Atm. Terr. Phys. 33*, 1169. Trans. Am. Geophys. Union 52, 304.

Branscomb, L. M. 1964. *Annales de Géophys. 20*, 49.

Dunkin, D. B., Fehsenfeld, F. C., Schmeltekopf, A. L. & Ferguson, E. E. 1971. *J. Chem. Phys. 54*, 3517.

Fehsenfeld, F. C., private communication.

Fehsenfeld, F. C. & Ferguson, E. E. 1968. *Planet. Space Sci. 16*, 701.

Fehsenfeld, F. C. & Ferguson, E. E. 1969. *J. Geophys. Res. 74*, 2217.

Fehsenfeld, F. C., Ferguson, E. E. & Bohme, D. K. 1969. *Planet. Space Sci. 17*, 1759.

Fehsenfeld, F. C., Mosesman, M. & Ferguson, E. E. 1971. *J. Chem. Phys. 55*, 2115, 2120.

Fehsenfeld, F. C., Schmeltekopf, A. L., & Schiff, H. I. & Ferguson, E. E. 1967. *Planet. Space Sci. 15*, 373.

Ferguson, E. E. in press. *ESRO/ESRIN Symposium*, Frascati, Italy, July 1970. Riedel Press.

Ferguson, E. E. & Fehsenfeld, F. C. 1969. *J. Geophys. Res. 74*, 5743. Also, *J. Chem. Phys. 55*, November 1971.

Good, A., Durden, D. A. & Kebarle, P. 1970. *J. Chem. Phys. 52*, 222.

Hanson, W. B. 1970. *J. Geophys. Res. 75*, 4343.

Howard, C. J., Rundle, H. W. & Kaufman, F. 1971. *Bull. Am. Phys. Soc. 16*, 213.

Huffman, R. E., Paulsen, E. E., Larrabee, J. C. & Cairns, R. B. 1971. *J. Geophys. Res. 76*, 1028.

Hunten, D. M. & McElroy, M. B. 1968. *J. Geophys. Res. 73*, 2421.

Leu, M. T., Biondi, M. H. & Johnson, R., private communication.

Narcisi, R. S. in preparation. International School of Atomic Physics, Erice, Sicily, June 1970.

Narcisi, R. S. & Bailey, A. D. 1965. *J. Geophys. Res. 70*, 3678.

Narcisi, R. S., Bailey, A. D., Della Lucca, L., Sherman, C. & Thomas, D. M. 1971. *J. Atm. Terr. Phys. 33*, 1147.

Phelps, A. V. & Kasner. W. H. 1969. Westinghouse Res. Labs. Report.

Puckett, L. J. & Teague, M. W. 1971. *J. Chem. Phys. 54*, 2564.

Reid, G. C. 1970. *J. Geophys. Res. 75*, 2551.

Reid, G. C. in press. *ESRO/ESRIN Symposium*, Frascati, Italy, July 1970. Riedel Press.

Thomas, L. 1971. *J. Atm. Terr. Phys. 33*, 157.

Recent Positive and Negative Ion Composition Measurements in the Lower Ionosphere by Means of Mass Spectrometers

D. KRANKOWSKY, F. ARNOLD, AND H. WIEDER

Max-Planck-Institut für Kernphysik, 69 Heidelberg, West Germany

Abstract: The results of three ion mass spectrometer rocket experiments in the lower ionosphere at high latitudes are reported. Two experiments were undertaken during disturbed conditions at nighttime and one experiment in the cold arctic summer mesopause. Positive molecular ions O_2^+, NO^+, and water cluster ions were observed in all cases. The data and characteristic differences between the three flights are discussed in terms of current reaction schemes. Negative ion data obtained during one flight are presented and compared with the results of a model computation.

1. INTRODUCTION

Within the last few years in situ mass spectrometric investigations have revealed the complexity of the D-region ion composition. After the first measurements of the hydrated ions $H^+(H_2O)$ and $H^+(H_2O)_2$ by Narcisi & Bailey (1965) the predominance of hydrated ions over O_2^+ and NO^+ below 80 km has been repeatedly demonstrated in many rocket flights for a variety of ionospheric conditions (e.g. Narcisi 1967, Narcisi et al. 1969a, Goldberg & Blumle 1970). Utilizing the results of laboratory studies Fehsenfeld & Ferguson (1969) proposed a reaction scheme that, starting from the molecular ionospheric ions O_2^+ and NO^+, leads to the production of $H^+(H_2O)_n$ clusters.

Negative ions in the D-region are believed to be formed by electron attachment to O_2 and by the reaction $e^- + O_3 \rightarrow O^- + O_2$ and subsequent reactions of O_2^- and O^- with neutral constituents. A substantial step forward in the understanding of the D-region negative ion chemistry came from laboratory measurements of negative ion-molecule reactions which suggested a reaction scheme involving O^-, O_2^-, O_3^-, O_4^-, CO_3^-, CO_4^-, NO_2^-, and NO_3^- (Fehsenfeld at al. 1967, Fehsenfeld & Ferguson 1968, Fehsenfeld et al. 1969). However, in contrast to the situation for positive ions, only very limited information on the actual negative ion composition in the ionosphere from direct measurements has been available until now (Arnold et al. 1971, Narcisi et al. 1971).

This paper presents the results of three mass spectrometer rocket flights at high latitudes. The first part deals with the positive ion results, the second part is concerned with the negative ion data obtained by Arnold et al. (1971).

2. EXPERIMENTAL TECHNIQUE

A summary of all data pertinent to the three rocket flights is given in Table I. Rockets F21 and F22 were launched in two joint sounding rocket campaigns with the Royal Norwegian Council for Scientific and Industrial Research from Andoya rocket range during disturbed ionospheric conditions at nighttime. C58/2 was launched in ESRO campaign CK22 from Kiruna during conditions of noctilucent clouds and sporadic E activity. In all three payloads the mass spectrometers were mounted in the rocket axis under the payload nose cone. Quadrupole mass spectrometers cryogenically pumped with liquid He were employed, using pulse counting technique with channeltron multipliers. The characteristic data of the three spectrometers are given in Table II. The instrument flown in F21 had a flat-plate sampling geometry (2.5 cm in diameter, entrance hole 1 mm in diameter), whereas in F22 and C58/2 a small cone with the sampling opening in its apex was added to the flat-plate. The spectrometers were programed to sweep alternately spectra of positive and negative ions. A small electron bombardment ion source mounted inside the ejectable protective cap supplied spectra of the residual gas from about 10 minutes prior to launching up to the moment when the spectrometer was exposed to

Table 1. Summary of the data pertinent to the rocket flights

Rocket Type and Code No.	Launch Site and Latitude	Launch Date	Launch Time (LT)	Sun Elevation (Degree)	Apogee (km)	Angle of attack at 80 km (Degree) Upleg	Downleg	Cap ejection at altitude (km)	Ionospheric Conditions and Riometer Absorption at 27 MHz (dB)
F21 Nike-Cajun	Andoya 69°17′N	26 Nov 1969	0138	− 38.8	107	~ 0°	88°	54	1.4
F22 Nike-Cajun	Andoya 69°17′N	23 March 1970	2358	− 19.6	102	4°	93°	60	0.2
C58/2 Centaure	Kiruna 67°54′N	10 Aug 1970	0039	− 5.5	114	13°	158°	59	Sporadic-E Noctilucent Clouds

Table 2. Mass spectrometer characteristics

Rocket	RF-Frequency (MHz)	Quadrupole Rods Length (mm)	Quadrupole Rods Diameter (mm)	Sweep Time (sec) Positive Ions	Negative Ions	Mass Range (amu) Positive Ions	Negative Ions	Draw-In Potential (Volts) Positive Ions	Negative Ions
F21	2	160	8	1	1	12– 85	12– 85	− 10	+ 5
F22	2	200	6	2	2	2–135	2–135	− 15	+ 15
C58/2	2	200	6	0.8	2.1	2– 91	2–160	− 15	+ 15

Table 3. Estimate of the relative importance of positive water cluster ion breakup in the shock layer under different conditions using the data of Kebarle et al. (1967)

Altitude (km)	Ambient temperature (°K)	Rocket maximum altitude (km)	Fraction of hydrated ions surviving travel through shock front 37+	55+	73+
85	200	106	1	1	0
80			1	0.1	0
75			1	0	1
85	150	106	1	1	0.8
80			1	1	0
75			0	0	0
85	200	140	0	0	0
80			0	0	0
75			0	0	0

the atmosphere. Thus a continuous monitoring of the instrument performance was achieved supplying in addition an inflight mass scale calibration which is of importance, particularly for the identification of peaks at large mass numbers and of negative ions.

3. POSITIVE IONS

Positive ion spectra were obtained on upleg and downleg in all flights. As can be seen from Table I the spectrometers were exposed to the atmosphere at relatively low altitudes. But generally the first spectra on upleg were recorded only some time after cap ejection. As a numerical analysis has shown, this must be attributed to a sudden increase of the pressure inside the spectrometer above the threshold where the instrument is operating. It takes a few seconds for the cryogenic pump to reduce this pressure as the ambient pressure drops. On the downleg portion of the flight ion spectra are recorded down to much lower altitudes. This is due to weaker shock conditions since the angle of attack is usually larger than on the upleg (Table I).

The following presentation of the data will be confined to NO^+, O_2^+, and hydrated ions. An account of the metal ions measured in the lower E- and D-regions will be given elsewhere.

The results of the three flights are shown in Figs. 1–5. Unsmoothed count rates in terms of counts per mass interval have been plotted for each mass peak. The data are corrected for mass discrimination inside the mass analyzer, as measured during the preflight laboratory calibrations of the instruments. Upleg and downleg data are plotted separately in order to allow for true spatial composition changes as may be expected under disturbed ionospheric conditions. As can be gathered from Table I the attitude of rocket C58/2 was unique on the downleg leading to ion sampling in the wake with a strong modulation of the data due to the large coning angle. The data are not readily comparable with the remainder of the results and need a further, more sophisticated, data analysis. Therefore they have been omitted in the present discussion.

A conversion of the measured count rate profiles into ambient ion number densities has deliberately been avoided for the following reasons:

a. There exists no quantitative description of the ion sampling at supersonic speeds in the transition region between continuum and molecular flow.

b. The composition of the hydrated ions may be altered by their decomposition in the sampling process, as will be discussed later on. A normalization of the measured total count rate to the ion density or electron density profiles as obtained by other experiments, will therefore give misleading results, in particular because the decomposition effect is probably different in upleg and downleg.

Fragmentation of weakly bounded hydrated ions as a possible effect of changing the ion composition from its true ambient value has been invoked before (Narcisi 1970, Narcisi & Roth 1970). This process can occur as collisional breakup in the electric fields of the draw-in electrode and ion optics or as thermodynamic breakup at increased temperatures in the shock layer. The relative importance of both effects is difficult to assess. However, from the laboratory work of Kebarle et al. (1967) estimates can be obtained of how the thermodynamic breakup process $H^+ (H_2O)_n + M \rightarrow H^+(H_2O)_{n-1} + H_2O + M$ can affect the water cluster ions under different conditions. Examples are given in Table III, where the fractions of hydrated ions surviving the shock layer crossing under zero angle of attack are estimated for stagnation point conditions at different altitudes and ambient temperatures. As may

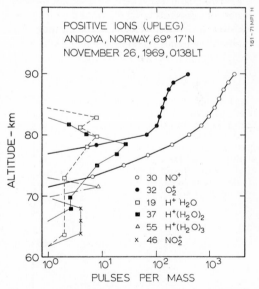

Fig. 1. Counts per mass versus altitude profiles for flight F21 obtained on the upleg. The unsmoothed data are only corrected for mass discrimination inside the analyzer. Total positive ion density at 80 km about 6×10^3 cm^{-3} (Folkestad, private communication).

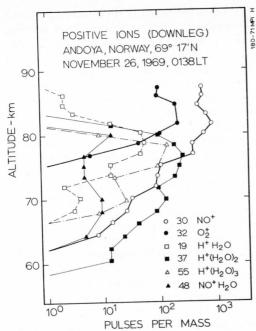

Fig. 2. Counts per mass versus altitude profiles for flight F21 obtained on the downleg. The unsmoothed data are corrected for mass discrimination inside the analyzer. Total positive ion density at 80 km about 1.5×10^4 cm^{-3} (Folkestad, private communication).

A common characteristic feature of all three flights is the steep drop in the hydrated ion profiles between 80 and 85 km. In the winter and spring shots from Andoya (Figs. 1–4) mass 19, 37, and 55 were seen on upleg and downleg, 37 being the dominant ion. In addition mass 48 the cluster ion $NO^+ \cdot H_2O$ was observed in relatively small abundances. The difference in the water cluster ion profiles between upleg and downleg is evident.

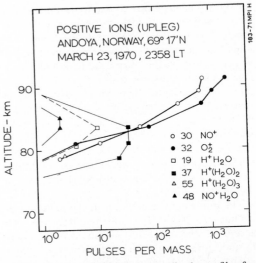

Fig. 3. Counts per mass versus altitude profiles for flight F22 obtained on the upleg. The unsmoothed data are corrected for mass discrimination inside the analyzer. Total positive ion density at 80 km about 1.2×10^3 cm^{-3} (Folkestad, private communication).

be gathered from Table III, the decomposition of cluster ions depends critically on the ambient gas temperature, rocket velocity, and altitude. The situation eventually changes within 10 km or less from a complete cluster destruction to negligible effects.

Fig. 4. Counts per mass versus altitude profiles for flight F22 obtained on the downleg. The unsmoothed data are corrected for mass discrimination inside the analyzer. Total positive ion density at 80 km about 4×10^3 cm^{-3} (Folkestad, private communication).

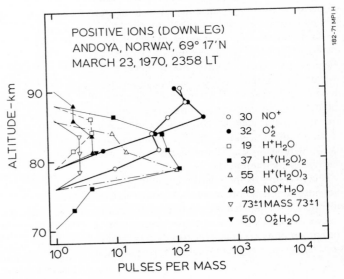

Both the relative abundances and the absolute values are different. The heavier hydrated ions are depleted on upleg. However, in both flights around 78 km mass 55 $H^+(H_2O)_3$ almost reaches mass 37 in abundance on the downleg. Furthermore in the March 23 flight very small peaks at mass number 73 ± 1 were recorded on the downleg in three spectra. They are attributed to the $H^+(H_2O)_4$ water cluster. Around 80 km the downleg data were measured under reduced shock conditions due to the large angle of attack (Table I), therefore cluster breakup is less effective.

The results of the August 10 flight from Kiruna seem to be unique in many respects, when compared with the just-discussed Andoya data. From Fig. 5, which is taken from Pollermann et al. (1971) it can be seen that even on the upleg mass 55 was measured in abundances comparable to those of mass 37 around 86 km. But in addition a mass 74 ± 1 identified as $H^+(H_2O)_4$ was detected in relatively high concentrations on the upleg. Furthermore mass 48 was observed in about the same abundances as masses 37 and 55 at 86 km. From thereon upwards it is the dominating cluster ion, reaching up to 96 km in measurable quantities. The process of thermodynamic cluster decomposition in the shock layer can be expected to be more severe for this flight than for the two Andoya shots, because of the higher velocity of C58/2. On the other hand, it is known that

the arctic mesopause undergoes pronounced seasonal temperature variations. During summer the temperature may be lower than during winter by as much as $70°K$ (e.g. Theon et al. 1969). Such a reduction of the ambient temperature largely reduces the cluster breakup.

Turning now to the NO^+ and O_2^+ profiles, it should be noted that in all three flights O_2^+ starts dropping fast at an altitude where the hydrated ions become important. The same is true for the NO^+ profile in flights F22 and C58/2, but in F21 NO^+ reaches down to lower altitudes in considerle ababundances. Between about 90 and 80 km rockets F21 and F22 were turning over due to aerodynamic drag. The fast-changing attitude caused the apparent scatter in the data above 80 km.

O_2^+ and NO^+ are intimately linked to the hydrated ions as they represent the starting points of the water cluster production chains. No attempt will be made to give a full account of the complete reaction schemes and rate constants as they are reviewed by Ferguson in these proceedings. However, the processes of importance to the following discussion will be repeated here.

In a sequence of fast reactions O_2^+ ions are converted into cluster ions of masses 19 and 37:

1. $O_2^+ + O_2 + M \rightarrow O_4^+ + O_2$
2. $O_4^+ + H_2O \rightarrow O_2^+(H_2O) + O_2$
3. $O_2^+(H_2O) + H_2O \rightarrow H^+(H_2O) \cdot OH + O_2$
$\rightarrow H^+(H_2O) + OH + O_2$
5. $H^+(H_2O) \cdot OH + H_2O \rightarrow H^+(H_2O)_2 + OH$

From then on further cluster buildup proceeds through relatively slow three-body attachment of water molecules. This scheme is interrupted in the presence of neutral atomic oxygen by the reaction:

6. $O_4^+ + O \rightarrow O_2^+ + O_3$

The reaction chain starting with NO^+ involves relatively slow three-body reactions:

7. $NO^+ + CO_2 + M \rightarrow NO^+ \cdot CO_2 + M$
8. $NO^+ \cdot CO_2 + H_2O \rightarrow NO^+ \cdot H_2O + CO_2$
9. $NO^+ \cdot H_2O + H_2O + M \rightarrow NO^+(H_2O)_2 + M$
10. $NO^+ \cdot (H_2O)_2 + H_2O + M \rightarrow NO^+(H_2O)_3 + M$
11. $NO^+ \cdot (H_2O)_3 + H_2O \rightarrow H^+(H_2O)_3 + HNO_2$

Thus the smallest water cluster produced in this scheme is mass 55. An efficient chain-breaking reaction which corresponds to reaction no. 6 is not known for this scheme.

Any attempt to compare rocket results with model computations suffers from the lack of

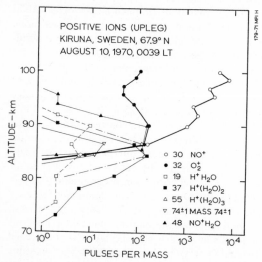

Fig. 5. Counts per mass versus altitude profiles for flight C58/2 obtained on the upleg. The unsmoothed data are corrected for mass discrimination inside the analyzer. Total positive ion density at 80 km about 10^2 cm^{-3} measured at 0150 LT (Pedersen, private communication).

knowledge of the true ambient cluster composition. Therefore, on the basis of the measured abundances it is difficult at present to decide upon the relative importance of both reaction schemes. The rapid appearance of cluster ions below an altitude between 80 and 90 km corresponds to a sudden decrease of the molecular ions O_2^+ and NO^+ in flights F22 and C58/2. This correlation has been observed in most of the mass spectrometer experiments flown so far (in eight out of ten cases; Narcisi 1967, Narcisi et al. 1969a, b). The relatively high NO^+ concentration measured in flight F21 below 75 km on downleg during moderately disturbed conditions must be considered as an exceptional case and will be discussed later on. The decrease of O_2^+ and NO^+ at the height where water clusters appear indicates their loss by clustering reactions. $H^+(H_2O)$ is produced only in the O_2^+ sequence, whereas $NO^+(H_2O)$ is characteristic for the NO^+ chain. The cluster $H^+(H_2O)_2$ is formed through the O_2^+ sequence, but in principle can also arise from the NO^+ chain by the reverse reaction $H^+(H_2O)_3 + M \to H^+(H_2O)_2 + H_2O + M$. The formation of cluster ions beyond $H^+(H_2O)_3$ proceeds through the same chain of reactions in the O_2^+ and the NO^+ branches.

For flights F21 and F22 when energetic particles were the dominant source of ionization during nighttime the O_2^+ production exceeds that of NO^+. Therefore the O_2^+ chain is expected to dominate clearly, because reaction no. 1 is more than a hundred times faster than reaction No. 7. As can be estimated from the O_2^+ data of F21 and F22 (Figs. 1–4), reaction no. 1 is more important than reaction no. 7 for the cluster formation. Therefore $H^+(H_2O)$ and $H^+(H_2O)_2$ are observed in relatively high abundance compared with $NO^+(H_2O)$. However, the question still remains what contribution to $H^+(H_2O)_2$ comes from a breakup of $H^+(H_2O)_3$ produced via the NO^+ chain. The breakup may occur during sampling in the shock layer even on the downleg. In addition ambient $H^+(H_2O)_2$ may be expected to be produced from reverse reactions involving cluster ions formed by the NO^+ sequence. The measured $H^+(H_2O)$ should not be affected by either of the two processes. For the summer flight C58/2 the large abundance of $NO^+(H_2O)$ compared to $H^+(H_2O)$ and $H^+(H_2O)_2$ leads to the conclusion that cluster formation through the NO^+ chain was relatively more important than in F21 and F22. Furthermore, no significant production of $H^+(H_2O)_2$ from $H^+(H_2O)_3$ either in the shock layer or through reverse reactions in the atmosphere will occur due to the low ambient temperature. Thus the high abundances of the $H^+(H_2O)$ and $H^+(H_2O)_2$ clusters indicate that clustering from O_2^+ is significant. As has been pointed out earlier, the temperature profile around the arctic summer mesopause with its pronounced minimum around 85 km and the steep gradients must be responsible for the unusual water cluster population found in this flight.

The outstanding result is the appearance of $H^+(H_2O)_3$ and $H^+(H_2O)_4$ above 80 km even on the upleg. This observation should probably be interpreted in terms of the low ambient temperature. The three body reactions leading to these ions are favored at low temperatures whereas the reverse reactions are slowed down. A lower ambient temperature also strongly reduces the effects of shock layer fragmentation of $H^+(H_2O)_3$ and $H^+(H_2O)_4$ ions. The altitude where these ions were measured in greatest abundance coincides with the location of the temperature minimum. Their steep decrease below 85 km possibly occurs because of increased cluster breakup due to the rapid increase of the ambient temperature towards lower heights. The decrease of $NO^+(H_2O)$ below 85 km cannot be explained as decomposition in the shock layer, otherwise the fragment NO^+ would have been observed. But instead the disappearance of $NO^+(H_2O)$ probably results from a rapid conversion into $H^+(H_2O)_3$ through reactions no. 10 and 11.

Finally two unusual phenomena observed in the data of the flight F21 will be discussed now. First the water cluster ledge and the corresponding O_2^+ ledge are located at 80 km. But in the majority of mass spectrometric D-region flights the water cluster ledge occurs around 85 km; only in two out of thirteen cases was the ledge found close to 80 km (F22, C58/2; Narcisi 1967, Narcisi et al. 1969a, b). In contrast to these flights F21 was flown into moderately disturbed conditions. As was pointed out before, under these conditions, due to the enhanced production of O_2^+, the cluster formation predominately occurs through the O_2^+ chain. The depression of both the cluster ledge and the O_2^+ ledge suggests that there is an active mechanism which interrupts this sequence in an early state before it has proceeded beyond $O_2^+(H_2O)$, thus giving back O_2^+. Possible processes are the chain-breaking reaction no. 6 with O or similar reactions of O_4^+ and $O_2^+(H_2O)$ with $O_2(^1\Delta_g)$ (Ferguson private communication). Little information on variations of minor neutral constituents, particularly under disturbed iono-

24

spheric conditions, is available, and it may be speculated whether O and/or $O_2(^1\Delta_g)$ were increased.

The second unusual phenomenon is the observation of NO^+ down to about 64 km. This increase of NO^+ could come from an increased NO^+ production. However, preliminary model computations have shown that unrealistically high NO concentrations are required. An NO^+ formation by the reaction $O_2^+ + N_2 \rightarrow NO^+ + NO$ cannot account for the observed NO^+ abundances either, even if the upper limit of 10^{-15} cm^3 sec^{-1} (Ferguson et al. 1965) is chosen for this rate coefficient. More likely the NO^+ clustering sequence which is the main loss process for NO^+ at these altitudes is interrupted. The break must occur before the chain has reached $H^+(H_2O)_3$ in order to regain NO^+. The relatively long-living $NO^+(H_2O)$ and $NO^+(H_2O)_2$ ions seem to be the best candidates. Furthermore $NO^+(H_2O)$ was observed down to 64 km, which indicates that the chain-breaking cannot occur at the beginning of the cluster sequence. Such a reaction has not been observed yet, but it may be argued that excited neutrals (e.g. $O_2(^1\Delta_g)$) may be responsible.

4. NEGATIVE IONS

Negative ion spectra were recorded only in flight F22. The results have been reported by Arnold et al. (1971). In a total of eight mass sweeps negative ions were found on upleg and downleg between 71 and 85 km. A notable feature has been the remarkable similarity of the upleg and downleg data. Both the relative count rates and their absolute values were almost the same, and it was therefore possible to combine upleg and downleg data in one altitude profile. Furthermore an attempt was made to convert the measured count rates into ambient densities by normalizing the profiles to a total negative ion density profile, taking advantage of the electron and total positive ion density profiles measured on the same payload by a Faraday rotation experiment and by electrostatic probes. The results for the most abundant masses are shown in Fig. 6. The dominating constituent up to about 79 km is an ion with mass 60 identified as CO_3^-. Next abundant is mass 35, which is attributed to Cl^- together with mass 37. This identification is made on the basis of the relative abundance of both masses, which is close to the chlorine isotope ratio except at the lowest

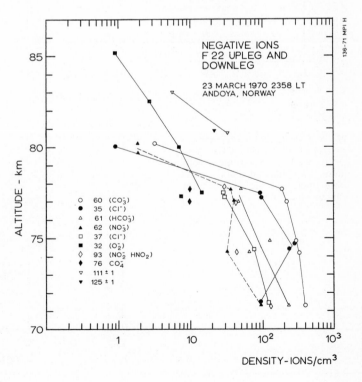

Fig. 6. Composite upleg and downleg negative ion densities obtained in flight F22.

NEGATIVE IONS
F 22 UPLEG AND
DOWNLEG

23 MARCH 1970 2358 LT
ANDOYA, NORWAY

136-71 MPI H

o	60	(CO_3^-)
●	35	(Cl^-)
△	61	(HCO_3^-)
▲	62	(NO_3^-)
□	37	(Cl^-)
■	32	(O_2^-)
◇	93	(NO_2^- HNO_2)
♦	76	CO_4^-
▽	111 ± 1	
▼	125 ± 1	

ALTITUDE – km

DENSITY–IONS/cm^3

altitudes where the low count rates introduce a high statistical error. Then masses 61, 93, 62, 32, and 76 follow, interpreted as HCO_3^-, NO_2^- · HNO_2 or $CO_4^-(H_2O)$, NO_3^-, O_2^-, and CO_4^-, respectively. Above 80 km the heavier masses 111 ± 1, 125 ± 1, and O_2^- are the dominant constituents. The rapid decrease of the negative ion concentration above 78 km and the predominance of heavy negative ions above that altitude together with a slowly decreasing O_2^- density are the main characteristic features of the negative ion profiles.

Laboratory work on negative ion reactions of atmospheric interest led Fehsenfeld et al. (1967) to propose a reaction scheme involving O^-, O_2^-, O_3^-, CO_3^-, NO_2^-, and NO_3^- ions. O_4^- and CO_4^- were included later (Fehsenfeld et al. 1969). It is not necessary to elaborate all the details of the negative ion reaction scheme, as it was reviewed by Ferguson at this meeting. Based on this scheme Reid (1970) carried out model computations for the daytime D-region. For the particular situation of flight F22 (i.e. nighttime and weakly disturbed conditions) a similar model calculation was performed and described in detail by Arnold & Krankowsky (1971). The results are shown in Figs. 7 and 8, where the measured data points are also included. A comparison of the computations with the mass spectrometer data naturally must be incomplete, because ion molecule reactions with hydrogen compounds were not included in the reaction scheme.

First it should be noted that all negative ion

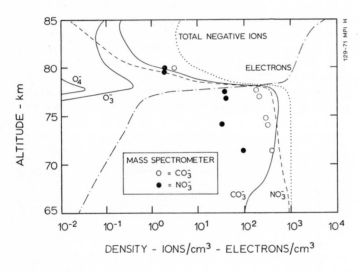

Fig. 7. Calculated number density profiles of electrons, NO_3^-, CO_3^-, O_3^-, and O_4^- (curves) for nighttime conditions. Experimental data points from flight F22 are included for comparison (dots).

Fig. 8. Calculated number density profiles of NO_2^-, O_2^-, CO_4^-, and O^- (curves) for nighttime conditions. Experimental data points from flight F22 are included for comparison (dots).

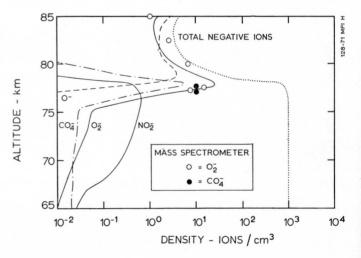

species included in the model with densities significantly exceeding several ions per cm^3 were observed in the flight. O$^-$ with a maximum density of several ions per cm^3 was not detected. Furthermore the overall behavior of the experimental CO_3^-, NO_3^-, CO_4^-, and O_2^- profiles, in particular the steep ledge of CO_3^- and NO_3^- and the slower decrease of O_2^-, is well reproduced by the model. Quantitatively a close agreement in the absolute number densities can be stated for CO_3^-, CO_4^-, and O_2^-. However, NO_3^- differs from its model densities by a factor of about 10 below 78 km.

It is obvious that the reaction scheme upon which the computations are based must be modified in order to account for the additional species observed. Arnold & Krankowsky (1971) have analyzed in a very qualitative manner the influence on the model if all the measured species are included with the identification given in Fig. 6. The net effect seems to be a decrease of the computed CO_3^-, NO_2^-, and NO_3^- concentrations by factors of 0.6, 0.3, and 0.2, respectively. They assumed that HCO_3^- is produced directly from CO_3^-, or from O$^-$ by the reactions $O^- + H_2O \rightarrow OH^- + OH$ and $OH^- + CO_2 + M \rightarrow HCO_3^- + M$. Furthermore Cl$^-$ was interpreted as an ambient constituent rather than contaminant and mass 93 ± 1 was identified as $NO_2^- \cdot HNO_2$.

The possibility that hydration of negative ions in the D-region may occur similar to the hydration of positive ions has been pointed out (Pack & Phelps 1966, Fehsenfeld et al. 1967, Fehsenfeld et al. 1969, Ferguson 1970). Unfortunately these reactions have not yet been studied in great detail in the laboratory. Consistent with the mass scale calibration of the spectrometer the masses 93 ± 1 and 111 ± 1 may be identified as $CO_4^-(H_2O)$ and $CO_4^-(H_2O)_2$ respectively. Additional evidence for negative water cluster ions comes from the presence of small mass peaks 68 and 78 attributed to $O_2^-(H_2O)_2$ and $CO_3^-(H_2O)$. As in the case of positive water clusters the question about the true ambient density of cluster ions arises. The breakup of clusters will be different on upleg and downleg. Accordingly such a process should manifest itself as a difference in the ion composition. From the limited amount of data available, however, no significant difference can be seen.

A major problem is to understand the large concentration of Cl$^-$ ions. As this ion is a well known contamination product often observed in laboratory studies such a source must be taken into account. In order to explain the Cl$^-$ concentrations as a contamination product from

charge exchange of chlorine compounds with ambient negative ions, about 10^{12} cm^{-3} molecules of neutral chlorine compounds are required in the payload vicinity. On the other hand, a concentration of less than 10^5 cm^{-3} is needed if the Cl$^-$ ions are ambient constituents produced by charge exchange of negative ions with the neutral chlorine compounds. A density of 10^5 cm^{-3} in the mesosphere appears to be possible. Chlorides have been measured (e.g. Junge 1963, Valach 1967) in relatively high tropospheric concentrations and may be transported into the mesosphere.

In summing up the negative ion results it can be stated that the data have shown a more complex negative ion composition than anticipated by the existing reaction scheme. All consituents of this scheme which exist in measurable concentrations have been found in the rocket flight. Their relative abundances are consistent with what is expected from the model with the exception of NO_3^-. This discrepancy seems to become smaller if the possible influence of the additional species on the scheme is considered. As in the model, the measured concentrations show a rapid decrease above 78 km.

5. SUMMARY

A rapid transition from O_2^+ and NO$^+$ to water cluster ions between 80 and 85 km is a common feature observed in all flights. Cluster formation proceeds mainly through the O_2^+ sequence during disturbed conditions whereas the NO$^+$ chain is relatively enhanced in the summer flight. The low temperature in the upper mesosphere prevailing during the artic summer causes an increased cluster buildup leading to more large cluster ions like $H^+(H_2O)_3$ and $H^+(H_2O)_4$. This observation can be understood by an increase of the foreward and a decrease of the reverse rate coefficient of the reaction $H^+(H_2O)_{n-1} + H_2O + M \rightleftarrows H^+(H_2O)_n + M$. In addition, and also due to the lower atmospheric temperature, cluster breakup during sampling, generally present in all flights, is evidently reduced.

Indications of the importance of chain-breaking reactions in the O_2^+ and NO$^+$ cluster sequences have been found under disturbed conditions. The simultaneous depression of the O_2^+ and water cluster ledge down to 80 km suggests an effective process reconverting O_4^+ and $O_2^+(H_2O)$ into O_2^+. The fact that NO$^+$ and NO$^+(H_2O)$ is observed down to 64 km also indicates the existence of a chain-breaking reaction for the NO$^+$ cluster sequence which recycles NO^+ before it can be converted into $H^+(H_2O)_3$. If this interpretation is correct, an enhanced occurrence of reactive neutral species like O and $O_2(^1\Delta_g)$ must be expected during disturbed conditions.

The observed negative species as well as their profiles are consistent with present ideas suggesting that the negative ion chemistry is mainly controlled by O_3 and O. Typical intermediates like O_2^- and CO_4^- and the so-called terminative ions CO_3^- and NO_3^- have actually been measured. However, unexpected ions like Cl^- and HCO_3^- and heavy cluster ions have been observed too. Only small amounts of hydrates were found besides the dominating atomic and molecular ions below 80 km. No indications of cluster breakup are evident from a comparison of upleg and downleg data. A model computation for a nighttime situation reproduces the sudden decrease in in the measured negative ion concentration. The relative abundance of CO_3^-, CO_4^-, and O_2^- is approximately confirmed in the model. However, about ten times less NO_3^- was measured than was computed in the model. It has been estimated that the inclusion of the effects on the reaction scheme introduced by those negative ions which were unexpectedly found will tend to reduce the computed NO_3^- densities. Finally, it should be mentioned that according to model and to the experimental data negative ions do not play a significant role in the E-region.

Acknowledgement: This research was supported in part through grant WRK 76 of the Bundesministerium für Bildung und Wissenschaft, Bonn.

REFERENCES

Arnold, F. & Krankowsky, D. 1971. *J. Atmos. Terr. Phys. 33*, 1693.

Arnold, F., Kissel, J., Krankowsky, D., Wieder, H. & Zähringer, J. 1971. *J. Atmos. Terr. Phys. 33*, 1169.

Fehsenfeld, F. C. & Ferguson, E. E. 1968. *Planet. Space Sci. 16*, 701.

Fehsenfeld, F. C. & Ferguson, E. E. 1969. *J. Geophys. Res. 74*, 2217.

Fehsenfeld, F. C., Ferguson, E. E. & Bohme, D. K. 1969. *Planet. Space Sci. 17*, 1759.

Fehsenfeld, F. C., Schmeltekopf, A. L., Schiff, H. I. & Ferguson, E. E. 1967. *Planet. Space Sci. 15*, 373.

Ferguson, E. E. 1970. Proceedings of ESRIN/ESLAB Symposium on Upper Atmospheric Models and Related Experiments. In press.

Ferguson, E. E., 1972. In Folkestad, (ed.) *Magnetosphere-Ionosphere Interactions*, Universitetsforlaget, Oslo.

Ferguson, E. E., Fehsenfeld, F. C., Golden, D. D. & Schmeltekopf, A. L. 1965. *J. Geophys. Res. 70*, 4323.

Goldberg, R. A. & Blumle, L. J. 1970. *J. Geophys. Res. 75*, 133.

Junge, C. E. 1963. *Air Chemistry and Radioactivity*, Academic Press, New York and London.

Kebarle, P., Searles, S. K., Zolla, A., Scarborough, J. & Arshadi, M. 1967. *J. Am. Chem. Soc. 89*, 6393.

Narcisi, R. S. 1967. *Space Research VII*, p. 186, North-Holland Publishing Company, Amsterdam.

Narcisi, R. S. 1970. *Trans. Am. Geophys. Union 51*, 366.

Narcisi, R. S. & Bailey, A. D. 1965. *J. Geophys. Res. 70*, 3687.

Narcisi, R. S. & Roth, W. 1970. *Advances in Electronics and Electron Physics 29*, 79. Academic Press, New York.

Narcisi, R. S., Bailey, A. D. & Della Luca, L. 1969a. In Sechrist, C. F., Jr. (ed.). *Aeronomy Report No. 32*, 450, University of Illinois, Urbana.

Narcisi, R. S., Bailey, A. D., Della Luca, L., Sherman, C. & Thomas, D. M. 1971. *J. Atmos. Terr. Phys.* In press.

Narcisi, R. S., Philbrick, C. R., Bailey, A. D. & Della Luca, L. 1969b. In Sechrist, C. F., Jr. (ed.) *Aeronomy Report No. 32*, 355. University of Illinois, Urbana.

Pack, J. L. & Phelps, A. V. 1966. *J. Chem. Phys. 45*, 4316.

Pollermann, B., Wieder, H. & Krankowsky, D. 1971. *Water Cluster Ions in the Cold Arctic Summer Mesosphere*. In preparation.

Reid, G. C. 1970. *J. Geophys. Res. 75*, 2551.

Theon, J. S., Nordberg, W. & Smith, W. S. 1969. In Sechrist, C. F., Jr. (ed.). *Aeronomy Report No. 32*, 18. University of Illinois, Urbana.

Thomas, L. 1970. *J. Atmos. Terr. Phys. 33*, 157.

Vallach, R. 1967. *Tellus 19*, 509.

On the Diurnal and Seasonal Variations of the D- and E-Regions above Kjeller

E. V. THRANE

Norwegian Defence Research Establishment, N-2007 Kjeller

Abstract: The paper discusses a preliminary model of the ion production and loss mechanisms in the E- and D-regions, with particular emphasis on a possible explanation of the diurnal and seasonal variation of ionospheric absorption as measured at Kjeller over the greater part of a sunspot cycle. It is demonstrated that the winter anomaly in ionospheric absorption can be quantitatively explained by a seasonal change in the height variation of the effective electron-ion recombination coefficient.

1. INTRODUCTION

The purpose of this paper is to discuss a preliminary model of the ion production and loss mechanisms in the E- and D-regions, with particular emphasis on a possible explanation of the diurnal and seasonal variations of ionospheric absorption as measured at Kjeller (60°N, 11°E) over the greater part of a sunspot cycle.

In the analysis the following simple approach has been adopted (Armstrong et al. 1970). First, the available information on the solar radiation ionizing in the E- and D-regions was collected from the literature and the total ion production $q(h, \chi)$ computed as a function of height h and solar zenith angle χ. Secondly a model of effective loss rate for summer and winter was adopted and combined with the ion production to yield electron density $N(h, \chi)$ as a function of height and zenith angle for both seasons. Thirdly, the absorption versus frequency in the range 1–6 MHz was computed for vertically incident waves, and the computations compared with the experimental values. These three steps are dealt with separately in sections 3, 4, and 5, and in the final section some of the implications of the results. First, however, some absorption measurements made at Kjeller will be presented, illustrating the diurnal, seasonal, and sunspot cycle variations of the lower ionosphere observed at this station.

2. ABSORPTION MEASUREMENTS AT KJELLER

Al absorption measurements, that is, measurements of the absorption of pulsed MF and HF radio waves vertically incident on the ionosphere, were made at Kjeller (60°N, 11°E) during the years 1951 through 1958. The observational programme included measurements for two or four hours every day near local noon as well as continuous measurements throughout the entire day and night at least once a week. The frequency range 1–6 MHz was used, and an absorption index D was derived from the data using the formula

$$D = L(f + f_L)^2, \qquad (1)$$

where L is the measured absorption in decibels, f the wave frequency, and f_L the longitudinal component of the gyrofrequency.

Care must be taken when absorption data are analysed in this way. As pointed out by Appleton & Piggott (1954), the index D is independent of frequency f for a radio wave passing through a Chapman-layer. In practice, however, L(f) may deviate appreciably from the $1/(f + f_L)^2$ law, depending upon the reflecting properties of the ionospheric layers. Fig. 1a and b shows examples of monthly median absorption near noon plotted versus frequency for January and July 1958. (1958 was a sunspot maximum year.)

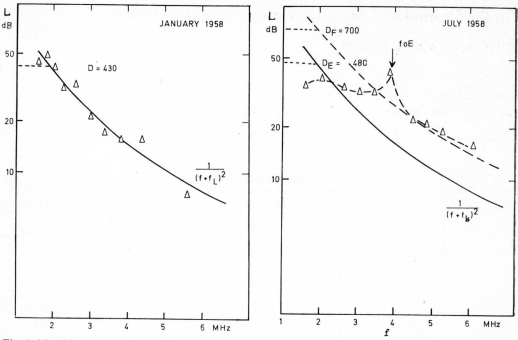

Fig. 1. Monthly median noon absorption versus frequency, a) January 1958, b) July 1958.

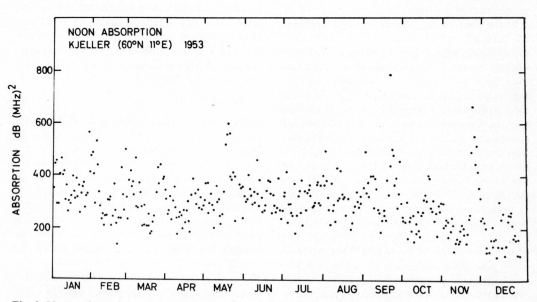

Fig. 2. Noon values of the absorption index D for sunspot minimum conditions.

30

The winter absorption clearly follows the 1/$(f + f_L)^2$ law, so that a meaningful value of D can be derived. In summer the frequency variation is very different, and no single value of D will describe the absorption measured for waves reflected from the E- and F-layers.

The problem mainly arises in summer for sunspot maximum years. In winter, at night, and near sunspot minimum, the index D is a useful parameter.

Fig. 2 shows the noon values of D for 1953 (sunspot minimum conditions). The Figure illu-

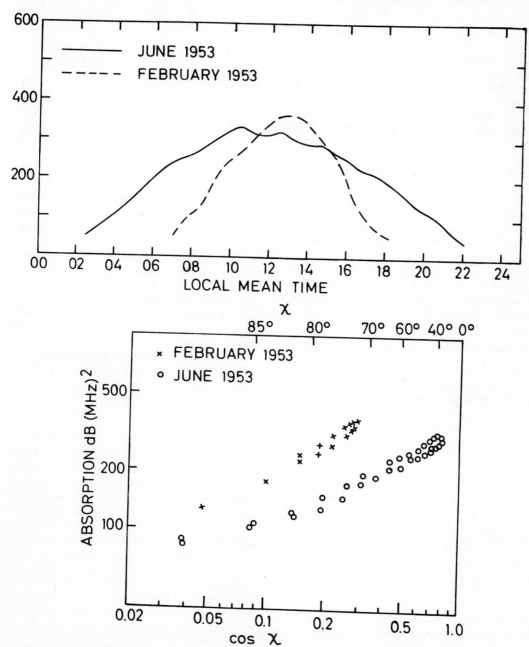

Fig. 3. Diurnal variation of absorption at Kjeller for summer and winter conditions. Monthly medians of half-hourly measurements plotted against a) local time b) solar zenith angle.

31

strates the day-to-day variability in the measured values, and also shows that there is very little seasonal change in the noon absorption, except for a small minimum in absorption in November-December.

Fig. 3a and b illustrates the diurnal variation of absorption for summer and winter. Monthly median values of absorption for every half hour throughout the day were plotted against local time and solar zenith angle. Note the apparent solar control for both seasons and the fact that the noon absorption is about the same in February and June despite the seasonal change in zenith angle ($\chi \approx 35°$ in summer and $\chi \approx 75°$ in winter).

The Figure clearly demonstrates that, at constant solar zenith angle χ, the absorption in decibels is on the average a factor of 2 greater in winter than in summer. This is the 'winter anomaly' in ionospheric absorption as observed at Kjeller for low and moderately low sunspot numbers. Near sunspot maximum the seasonal change in absorption at constant χ is about a factor of 2 for absorption measured on E-layer reflections, but somewhat smaller for waves reflected from the F-layer.

The sunspot cycle variation of absorption is shown in Fig. 4 for E-layer reflections. The increase in D from solar minimum to maximum is about a factor of 2.

3. THE ION PRODUCTION

Recent observations from rockets and satellites have mapped parts of the spectrum of solar electromagnetic radiation of importance for the ioni-

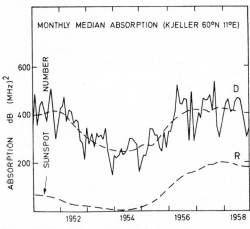

MONTHLY MEDIAN ABSORPTION (KJELLER 60°N 11°E)

Fig. 4. Monthly medians of noon absorption at Kjeller from 1951 through 1958.

Table I. Solar radiation intensities, height of unit optical depth and ionization efficiency for various wavelengths (Bordeau et al. 1966)

Wavelength λ (Ångstrøm)	Intensity outside the atmosphere Φ_∞ (photons cm^{-2}s^{-1})	Height of unit optical depth for overhead sun. h_0 (km)	Ionization efficiency η
2	1.0	68	165
4	$2 \cdot 10^2$	79.5	75
6	$1.2 \cdot 10^4$	86.5	45
8	$1.0 \cdot 10^5$	91.0	31
33.7	$7.63 \cdot 10^6$	95.9	7.8
40–75	$7.50 \cdot 10^7$	106.6	15.7
95	$2.50 \cdot 10^8$	116.0	3.5
140	$3.50 \cdot 10^8$	119.0	2.5
977	$3.00 \cdot 10^9$	109.0	0.5
1025	$3.50 \cdot 10^9$	103	0.7
1215	$2.70 \cdot 10^{11}$	75	

zation of the E- and D-region. The information is far from complete and not always accurate, for example the variation with solar activity and solar cycle of the ultraviolet radiation has not been established with certainty. The present model includes the best estimates available for the wavelengths of interest. Table I summarizes the data used for the intensities and optical depths of the ionizing radiation. It is based mainly on the data given by Bordeau et al. (1966) for sunspot minimum conditions.

With three exceptions the ion production was computed from these data using the formula

$$q = \frac{\eta \Phi_\infty}{eH} e^{1-z-e^{-z}} Ch(z, \chi), \qquad (2)$$

where $z = \dfrac{h - h_0}{H}$, χ is the solar zenith angle, and $Ch(z, \chi)$ is the Chapman function. The height variations of the scale height H were taken from the US Standard Atmosphere (Sissenwine et al. 1962). η is the ionization efficiency and Φ_∞ the intensity of the radiation outside the atmosphere.

The exceptions are a) the ionization by cosmic rays which is taken directly from Webber (1962), b) the ionization of $O_2(^1\Delta_g)$ by radiation in the band 1025–1118 Å where the recent estimates by Huffman et al. (1971) have been used, and c) the ionization of NO by Lyman-α radiation. Here the recently published NO profile measured by Meira (1971) has been used with the intensities given in Table I (see Fig. 5) and

$$\Phi = \Phi_\infty e^{-e^{-z}} Ch(z, \chi). \qquad (3)$$

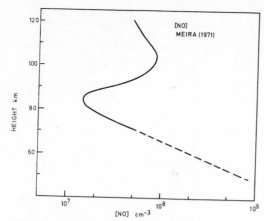

Fig. 5. Height variation of nitric oxide, NO, as measured by Meira (1971). The broken line shows an extrapolation of the measured curve below 70 km using the scale height of the neutral atmosphere.

Fig. 6 shows the resulting height variation of ion production for a zenith angle of $\chi = 50°$. It is clear that production by ultraviolet dominates at all heights but that X-rays make an important contribution above 85 km. Below this level H-Lyman-α dominates in a 20-km region. Fig. 7 shows the situation for $\chi = 85°$. Note that now Lyman-α ionization dominates right up to 105 km. The reason for this striking feature is the large NO densities measured by Meira at E-region heights, where the intensity of Lyman-α radiation is practically independent of zenith angle.

As mentioned earlier there is information available on the solar cycle variation of the intensities of the radiation, even though it is not complete. In particular, recent observations have given good indications of the variations of X-rays with solar cycle (Kreplin 1970, Pounds 1970). The nonflare X-ray spectrum becomes harder with increasing sunspot number, for example intensities in the 8–20 Å range increase by a factor of more than 200 from solar minimum to maximum, whereas intensities in the range 44–60 Å increase by about a factor of 20. Results given by Hall & Hinteregger (1970) indicate that the corresponding factor for ultraviolet is about 2.5. Using these factors the situation becomes as in Fig. 8. Note that X-rays now dominate the ion production in the E-region and in the upper D-region as low as 80 km.

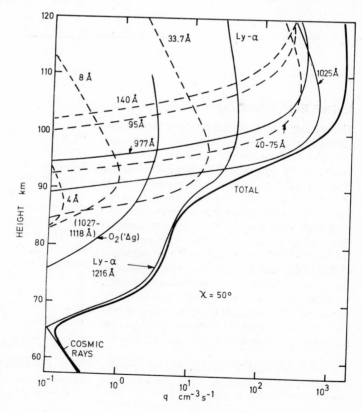

Fig. 6. Ion production versus height for sunspot minimum conditions and $\chi = 50°$. Broken lines show X-ray contributions, full lines UV ionization.

3

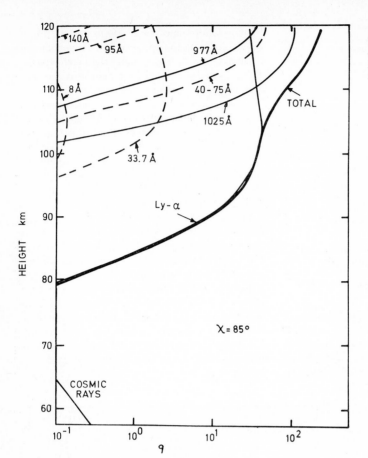

Fig. 7. Ion production versus height for sunspot minimum conditions and $\chi = 85°$. Broken lines show X-ray contributions, from UV radiation.

4. THE ELECTRON LOSS RATE

The primary ions produced by the radiation discussed in the previous section must be mainly O_2^+, N_2^+ produced by UV and X-rays, and NO^+ produced by hydrogen Lyman-α. Through a charge transfer N_2^+ will rapidly convert to O_2^+, so that O_2^+ and NO^+ are the primary ions we have to deal with. Laboratory measurements (Biondi 1969) show that the dissociative recombination coefficient α_D for electrons with these ions is about $5 \cdot 10^{-7}$ cm^3 s^{-1} at D-region temperatures (200–250°K), and perhaps somewhat smaller in the E-region where the temperature is higher. Electron attachment to neutral molecules with subsequent ion-ion neutralization is also a possible loss mechanism. The ion-ion neutralization rate coefficient α_i is about 10^{-7} cm^3 s^{-1} (Biondi 1969).

Considering these losses only, the electron-ion balance in steady state may be expressed as (see for example Nicolet & Aikin 1960):

$$q = (1 + \lambda)(\alpha_D + \lambda\alpha_i) N^2 = \alpha_{eff} N^2. \qquad (4)$$

Here $\lambda = N^-/N$, the ratio between the negative ion to electron density, and q is the ion production rate. Recent simultaneous measurements of electron and positive ion densities have made it possible to estimate λ (Folkestad 1971). During the day between 70 and 80 km, $\lambda \ll 1$, and (4) can then be used with the measured normal daytime electron densities at these heights (say 10^3 cm^{-3}) to estimate the production q from the laboratory values of α_D and α_i. This procedure yields values of q from two or three orders of magnitude smaller than the values given in the preceding section. Alternatively, using the recent estimates of q discussed in section 3 with the experimental values of N for summer conditions, $\alpha_{eff} = \dfrac{q}{N^2}$ turns out to be between 10^{-5} and 10^{-4} cm^3 s^{-1} (Reid 1970).

It is clear therefore that between 70 and 80 km

34

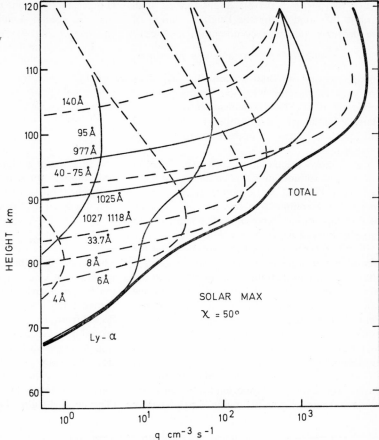

Fig. 8. Ion production versus height for sunspot maximum conditions and $\chi = 50°$. Broken lines show X-ray contributions, full lines contributions from UV radiation.

Figure labels: 140Å, 95Å, 977Å, 40–75Å, 1025Å, 1027 1118Å, 33.7Å, 8Å, 6Å, 4Å, Ly-α, TOTAL, SOLAR MAX, X = 50°. HEIGHT km axis, q cm⁻³ s⁻¹ axis.

there is a major discrepancy between the effective recombination coefficient $\alpha_{eff} = (1 + \lambda)(\alpha_D + \lambda\alpha_i)$, estimated from laboratory measurements for dissociative recombination of electrons with O_2^+ and NO^+, and the effective recombination coefficient $\alpha_{eff} = \dfrac{q}{N^2}$ derived from ionospheric measurements.

Results from ion mass spectrometers (Narcisi 1967, Krankowsky et al. 1972) show the presence below about 85 km of hydrated cluster ions of the type $H^+(H_2O)_n$, that must be formed from the primary ions O_2^+ and NO^+. Thus ions with masses 19^+, 37^+, 55^+, and 73^+ can be more numerous than the primary ions in the height range 70–85 km. The dissociative recombination coefficients of such ions have been measured in the laboratory (Biondi et al. 1971) to be between 10^{-6} and 10^{-5} cm³ s⁻¹ near 300°K. The recombination rate increases with increasing mass and decreasing temperature. Even though the measured recombination rates for the cluster ions are not very large, it seems possible that the presence of such ions can explain the very rapid electron loss rate observed in the D-region. It should be remembered that no laboratory measurements have been made at the very low temperatures found in the D-region, particularly near the high latitude summer mesopause (130–180°K). Furthermore the size of the cluster ions may be larger than the rocket observations indicate, since breakup of heavier clusters may occur in the shockfront near the rocket.

Haug & Landmark (1970) have proposed a model for the electron loss rate in an attempt to describe the complex situation. This model includes two types of positive ions, one with a small and one with a large recombination rate, the rate of production of the latter being proportional to the concentration of the first. The model can explain many of the observed features of the D-region (Landmark et al. 1970, Haug & Thrane 1970, Folkestad et al. 1971).

For the purposes of this discussion we shall assume two models for the height variation of the daytime effective recombination coefficient $\alpha_{eff} = \dfrac{q}{N^2}$, one for summer and one for winter conditions, and we shall assume that α_{eff} does not vary appreciably with ion production and with time of day. The refinements introduced by Haug & Landmark (1970) in their two-ion model will therefore be ignored in these preliminary calculations.

Fig. 9 shows the summer and winter model of α_{eff} (h). The summer model is based on estimates by Reid (1970) and, as he points out, the sharp decrease in recombination rate near 85 km may be due to a rapid decrease, with height, of the concentration of water cluster ions.

In the winter model we have assumed that the recombination rate is about $5 \cdot 10^{-7}$ cm^3 s^{-1} above 75 km and then increases rapidly with decreasing height. This is the type of variation one would expect if water cluster ions were absent. Below 75 km negative ions and ion-ion neutralization become important and $\alpha_{eff} = (1 + \lambda)(\alpha_D + \lambda\alpha_i)$ have been computed using Reid's (1970) estimate of $\lambda(h)$.

The idea that there is a seasonal variation in the electron loss rate is supported by experimental evidence from rocket launchings in North Norway

(Folkestad 1971) but must be regarded as tentative. No special significance should be attached to the particular summer and winter models for α_{eff} (h) shown in Fig. 9. They represent first attempts in modelling the seasonal variation of the D-region, and what is important is the concept of a seasonal change in the loss rate, not the exact values of α_{eff} used in the analysis.

The electron density profile

$$N\,(h, \chi) = \sqrt{q(h, \chi)/\alpha_{eff}} \qquad (5)$$

as a function of zenith angle and height may now be computed for summer and winter conditions using the models for the electron production and loss discussed in this and the preceding sections.

5. THE COMPUTATION OF ABSORPTION

The model described above specifies the height variation of electron density from the peak of the E-region and down to 60 km. In order to compute the absorption of HF-radio waves reflected from this model ionosphere, the following procedure was adopted:

a. A height variation of electron-neutral collision frequency $\nu_M = 8 \cdot 10^5$ p(h) s^{-1} was used, where p(h) is the atmospheric pressure in Newtons m^{-2} given in the US Standard Atmosphere (Thrane & Piggott 1966). In these preliminary

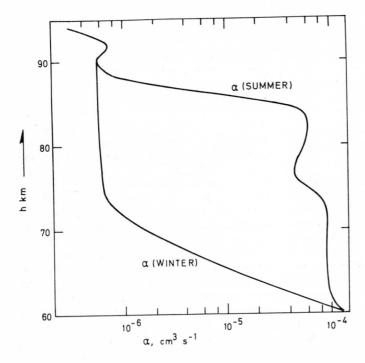

Fig. 9. Models of the height variation of the effective recombination coefficient for summer and winter.

calculations the seasonal changes in pressure and density were ignored, since the main effect of these changes would be a variation of the height of the lower ionosphere.

b. Using the collision frequency and electron density profiles, the total absorption for frequencies below f_0E was computed, using a modified version of a full wave computer programme developed by Pitteway (1965). This program accurately takes into account the absorption near the reflection level.

c. Above the peak of the E-layer the electron density was assumed to have a constant value equal to N_{max} up to an altitude of 140 km, and likewise the collision frequency was taken as $\nu_M = 4 \cdot 10^3 \ s^{-1}$ at all heights above 115 km. The absorption for waves with frequencies greater than f_0E was then computed from the formula

$$L = 2 \int_{h_0}^{h} \varkappa_0 \ dh, \qquad (6)$$

where $h_0 = 60$ km, $h = 140$ km, and $\varkappa_0(\nu_M, N, f)$ is the absorption coefficient for the ordinary wave as given by Sen & Wyller's generalized magneto-ionic theory (1960). Above 120 km the contribution to the integral (6) is small, and the error made when ignoring the deviative absorption in the F-region will also be small except for frequencies close to f_0F_1 og f_0F_2.

d. The computed values of absorption L were then plotted versus frequency f for each electron density profile, and a $1/(f + f_L)^2$ law was fitted to the results in the same way as was done with the experimental values (see Fig. 1) to yield a value of the absorption index D.

e. The computed values of D were then finally compared with the experimental results, and Fig. 10 shows the results for summer and winter, sunspot minimum conditions. The experimental points are the same as those given in Fig. 3b, and the full lines represent the results of the computations.

The agreement is very good.

6. DISCUSSION

The agreement in Fig. 10 between the absorption computed from the ionospheric model and the observations at sunspot minimum, demonstrates that it is possible to explain the diurnal and seasonal variations of absorption at Kjeller through a combination of an ion production controlled by solar elevation and a seasonal change in the effective electron loss rate. Of particular signif-

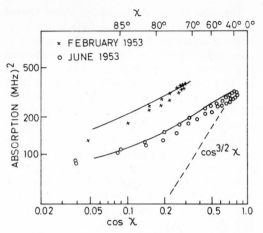

Fig. 10. Comparison of measured and computed diurnal variation of absorption for summer and winter conditions. Full lines represent computations from model, whereas broken line shows theoretical variation for Chapman-layer.

icance is the fact that the model reproduces the slope of the diurnal variation log D versus log $(\cos \chi)$ for both seasons. The dotted line in Fig. 10 shows the expected slope $D \propto \cos^{3/2} \chi$ for waves passing through a Chapman-layer. This theoretical prediction is indeed very far from the observed relation.

The accurate match between the actual values of absorption (as distinct from the match in slope) in Fig. 10 must be regarded as fortuitous since the level of absorption changes from month to month while the slope of the diurnal variation remains about the same. By reasonable adjustments of α_{eff} in the model, agreement can be obtained in most cases.

As mentioned above, the experimental values and the model computations both yield a slower diurnal variation of absorption than predicted from a Chapman-layer.

In the model calculation this slow change of absorption with solar zenith angle is caused by two factors. First the recent values of the nitric oxide concentration given by Meira (1971) (see Fig. 5) shows a maximum in the density of NO near 100 km. This maximum will provide a source of ionization that is turned on in the morning as soon as Lyman-α radiation illuminates this height region. Since Lyman-α radiation suffers little absorption above 100 km, this ionization source will not vary appreciably with solar elevation throughout the day and adds a constant term to the absorption.

37

The second factor that can cause a slow diurnal variation is that the increase of electron density in the E-region as the zenith angle decreases is compensated for by a lowering of the reflection level for waves with frequencies below f_0E. The use of E-layer reflections in the analysis both of the measured and the computed absorption will therefore tend to give a slower diurnal variation of the absorption index D than if only F-layer reflections are used. The effect will be most important near sunspot maximum when f_0E is large. For solar maximum only a few rough calculations of absorption have as yet been made, based on the ion production model in Fig. 8. However, the estimates show that the reported increases in X-ray and UV intensity with increasing solar activity can indeed explain the observed change of absorption through the solar cycle, provided the electron loss rate does not change appreciably.

7. CONCLUSION

In conclusion it should be stressed that the absorption data obtained at Kjeller show a solar control throughout the day for both summer and winter conditions, but with a very marked shift in the level of absorption at constant solar elevation. The evidence suggests an ion production controlled by the sun combined with a seasonal shift in the electron loss rate as a possible mechanism that can produce the observed effect, and the analysis described in this paper demonstrates that this is indeed possible.

There is some evidence to support the idea of a seasonally varying recombination rate, but as yet the suggestion must be regarded as tentative. The hypothetical seasonal change in electron loss rate could be caused by the observed increase in mesospheric temperatures in winter. High temperatures would inhibit the formation of water cluster ions and thus decrease the effective loss rate. A depletion of the mesospheric water vapour content in winter could possibly give the same result.

Acknowledgement: The author is grateful to Mr F. Lied for permission to use unpublished data.

REFERENCES

Appleton, E. V. & Piggott, W. R. 1954. *J. Atmos. Terr. Phys. 5*, 141.

Armstrong, R. F., Lied, F. & Thrane, E. V. 1970. *Phys. Norvegica 4*, 157.

Biondi, M. A. 1969. *Canad. J. Chem. 47*, 1713.

Biondi, M. A., Leu, M. T. & Johnson, R. 1971. Presented at Cospar Symposium on D- and E-Region Ion Chemistry, University of Illinois, July 6–9, 1971.

Bourdeau, R. E., Aikin, A. C. & Donley, J. L. 1966. *J. Geophys. Res. 71*, 727.

Folkestad, K. 1971. NDRE Report No. 59, Norwegian Defence Research Est. N-2007 Kjeller, Norway.

Folkestad, K., Landmark, B. & Thrane, E. V. 1972. *J. Atmos. Terr. Phys.* In preparation.

Hall, L. A. & Hinteregger, H. E. 1970. *J. Geophys. Res. 75*, 6959.

Haug, A. & Landmark, B. 1970. *J. Atmos. Terr. Phys. 32*, 405.

Haug, A. & Thrane, E. V. 1970. *J. Atmos. Terr. Phys. 32*, 1641.

Huffman, R. E., Paulsen, D. E., Larrabee, J. C. & Cairns, R. B. 1971. *J. Geophys. Res. 76*, 1028.

Krankowsky, D., Arnold, F. & Wieder, H. 1972. In Folkestad, Kr. (ed.). *Magnetosphere – Ionosphere Interactions,*, Universitetsforlaget, Oslo.

Kreplin, R. W. 1970. *Ann. Géophys. 26*, 567.

Landmark, B., Haug, A., Thrane, E. V., Hall, J. E., Willmore, A. P., Jespersen, M., Møller Pedersen, B., Anastassiades, M. & Tsagakis, E. 1970. *J. Atmos. Terr. Phys. 32*, 1873.

Meira, L. G. 1971. *J. Geophys. Res. 76*, 202.

Narcisi, R. S. 1967. *Space Research VII*, p. 186, North Holland Publ. Co., Amsterdam.

Nicolet, M. & Aikin, A. C. 1960. *J. Geophys. Res. 65*, 1469.

Pitteway, M. L. V. 1965. *Phil. Trans. Roy. Soc. 257*, 219.

Pounds, K. A. 1970. *Ann. Géophys. 26*, 555.

Reid, G. C. 1970. *J. Geophys. Res. 75*, 2551.

Sen, H. K. & Wyller, A. A. 1960. *J. Geophys. Res. 65*, 3931.

Sissenwine, N., Dubin, M. & Wexler, H. 1962. US Standard Atmosphere, US Government Printing Office, Washington, DC.

Thrane, E. V. & Piggott, W. R. 1966. *J. Atmos. Terr. Phys. 22*, 721.

Webber, W. 1962. *J. Geophys. Res. 67*, 5091.

The D-Region during PCA Conditions

G. C. REID

Aeronomy Laboratory, National Oceanic and Atmospheric Administration, Boulder, Colorado, U.S.A.

Abstract: The ion composition in the ionospheric D-region is likely to depend upon the intensity and the nature of the ionizing source. This paper describes model computations conducted to explore the changes in relative abundances of the species of the positive and negative ion populations during quiet and PCA conditions. A principal finding is that intense PCA events are associated with enhanced dissociative recombination and ion-ion neutralization, substantially favoring the earlier members in the ion-molecule reaction sequences.

1. INTRODUCTION

In recent years there have been major advances in our understanding of the sources of ionization in the D-region, and of the ambient ion composition of that complex region of the ionosphere. Though the outstanding problems are still far from being completely solved, it appears to be possible at this stage to predict some of the differences that might be expected between the quiet D-region, where the major sources of ionization above 70 km stem from the action of solar ultraviolet radiation, and the disturbed D-region during a polar-cap absorption event, when the ionization is due to energetic-proton irradiation. This paper employs model calculations to make such a comparison on the basis of the ion-molecule reaction rates that are presently thought to be of major importance.

2. THE MODEL

The chemical reaction scheme employed in the calculations is in most respects identical to that described in an earlier publication (Reid 1971), and will not be repeated in detail here. Some of the reaction rates have been modified in the light of more recent laboratory measurements, and two important reactions have been added to the scheme. The first of these is the reaction

$$O_4^+ + O \rightarrow O_2^+ + O_3,$$

which probably has a reaction rate of about 3×10^{-10} cm³ sec⁻¹ (Fehsenfeld & Ferguson 1971), and is of major importance in connection with the formation of water-cluster positive ions

in the D-region. The second added reaction is much more speculative and deserves some discussion.

It was pointed out (Reid 1971) that the long-standing problem of finding a sink for NO^+ in the D-region still remains, despite the major advances in our understanding of the ion chemistry. Briefly, current ideas suggest that NO^+ ought to be the dominant primary positive-ion species created in the quiet D-region, through direct ionization of NO by solar Lyman-alpha radiation. Mass-spectrometer observations (e.g. Narcisi & Bailey 1965) show that the dominant ambient species are water-derived clusters of the type $H_3O^+ \cdot (H_2O)_n$; these water-cluster ions form rapidly from O_2^+ (Fehsenfeld & Ferguson 1969), but form so slowly from NO^+ that their ambient concentration would be expected to be very small in an ionosphere derived from NO^+. The solution to this problem is not known, but one possibility is that NO^+ may undergo charge transfer with highly excited oxygen molecules whose ionization potential is less than that of NO. Quantitative examination of this possibility (Norton & Reid in press) shows that the observations can be accounted for if the concentration of such excited oxygen molecules is about 1% of the concentration of $O_2(^1\Delta_g)$ molecules, and the rate of the postulated charge-transfer reaction is about 3×10^{-10} cm³ sec⁻¹. In the calculations that have been carried out, this hypothetical reaction has been included with these numerical values. While it is obviously undesirable to include a totally unsubstantiated reaction such as this one, it has the definite advantage that it makes the quiet

D-region results agree reasonably well with observation, and is expected to have a much smaller influence on the PCA results, where the primary ions are O_2^+ and N_2^+, and the appearance of the water clusters is a more straightforward matter.

The model contains 16 species of positive ions and 8 of negative ions. The ion-ion mutual neutralization coefficient has been assumed to have an identical value of 10^{-7} cm^3 sec^{-1} for all possible combinations, but the dissociative-recombination coefficient has been assigned different values for the different species, including laboratory values where possible, but assuming high values of the order of 10^{-5} cm^3 sec^{-1} for the complex cluster ions. Published photodetachment rates have been used where possible for the negative ions, but photodetachment has been ignored if no evidence exists.

The calculations cover the altitude range between 70 and 90 km, and the Cira (1965) model atmosphere has been used for the major atmospheric constituents. The altitude profile of NO has been taken from the measurements of Meira (1971), and that of $O_2(^1\Delta_g)$ from Hunten & McElroy (1968); altitude profiles of O and O_3 were taken from model calculations by Hesstvedt (1971), and that of NO_2 from calculations by Shimazaki & Laird (1970). Carbon dioxide and water vapor were assumed to have constant number-density mixing ratios of 300 ppm and 3 ppm respectively.

In the case of the quiet D-region, a solar zenith angle of 60° was adopted, and the recent $O_2(^1\Delta_g)$ ionization rates computed by Huffman et al.(1971) were used, together with the rate of ionization of the [NO] concentrations of Meira (1971) by the solar Lyman-alpha flux measured by Smith et al.

(1965), the ionization rates by solar EUV and x-rays computed by Bourdeau et al. (1966), and the cosmic-ray ionization rate calculated by Webber (1962).

For the PCA case, three different models were adopted, and the rate of ion-pair production was calculated for each, assuming a pure proton flux isotropic over the upper hemisphere. The three cases were chosen as representing weak, moderate, and intense PCA events, and were selected from the list of solar-proton exponential-rigidity spectra published by Freier & Webber (1963). The proton energy range extended from 0.75 to 500 Mev, and the proton-flux characteristics are listed in Table I. The numerical techniques used in computing the rate of ion-pair production will be described in a future publication. For simplicity in this initial study, the contribution of alpha particles to the ionization was ignored, and the primary ions produced in the atmosphere were assumed to be simply N_2^+ and O_2^+, distributed in the same proportions as N_2 and O_2 in the neutral atmosphere.

Table I. Solar proton spectra for PCA model calculations. Solar-proton flux (protons cm^{-2} sec^{-1} $ster^{-1}$) for rigidity greater than P (Mv) is given by $J = J_0 \exp(-P/P_0)$, where J_0 is the total flux above zero rigidity and P_0 is the characteristic rigidity. Values of J_0 and P_0 below are taken from Freier & Webber (1963)

PCA model	Date and time of measurement	J_0	P_0
Intense	May 12, 1959, 0500 UT	30,000	65
Moderate	July 19, 1961, 2000 UT	210	100
Weak	April 20, 1960, 0300 UT	1.9	150

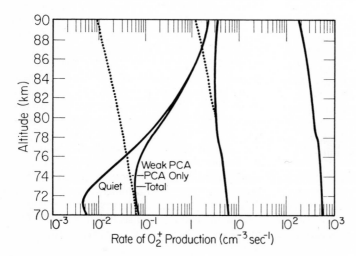

Fig. 1. Rate of production of O_2^+ during quiet conditions and during weak (left-hand curve), moderate (center curve), and intense (right-hand curve) PCA events. Dotted curves show production due to protons alone, and solid curves include the quiet-time production.

40

This implies that dissociation by the incident protons is being ignored, as is the presence of various minor neutral constituents, and that the ionization cross-sections of N_2 and O_2 for fast protons are identical. These assumptions are not likely to have an appreciable influence on the results, which can in any case only be regarded as semi-quantitative due to our lack of precise knowledge of many of the parameters involved in the computation.

The production rates of O_2^+ are shown in Fig. 1 for the three PCA cases and for quiet conditions. Similar profiles were obtained for N_2^+, but in the case of NO^+ only the quiet D-region production rate was used since NO^+ is not a primary species in the model (NO^+ is, however, rapidly produced as a secondary species in the PCA case through charge-exchange reactions). Note that throughout most of the altitude range the weak PCA production rate differs little from the quiet situation, and in what follows we shall consider only the moderate and intense PCA cases.

3. AMBIENT ION COMPOSITION

Having obtained profiles of ion-pair production rate for the different cases, we can now solve the reaction-rate equations under the assumption of steady-state conditions to obtain the ambient distribution of free electrons and of the various ion species. An iterative procedure was used, in which an initially assumed value for the electron concentration was used to compute the various positive-ion concentrations; these were then used

to compute the negative-ion concentrations, and hence the ratio of the concentrations of negative ions and electrons (Λ). The charge-neutrality condition was then used to find a new value for the electron concentration, and the whole procedure was iterated until adequate convergence was reached. In practice, convergence was found to be rapid, and a relatively small number of iterations was required. The principal results will be described below.

4. POSITIVE IONS

Fig. 2 shows the altitude profiles obtained for the water-cluster positive ions of the type $H_3O^+ \cdot (H_2O)_n$ ($n = 0$ to 3) for the quiet and intense PCA cases. The following points are noteworthy:

a. There is a sharp decrease in the concentration of these ions above about 83 km in quiet conditions, and above about 80 km in intense PCA conditions. This is in general accord with observations, and is due to the reaction

$$O_4^+ + O \rightarrow O_2^+ + O_3 \qquad (1)$$

which, as was first pointed out by Ferguson (1971), effectively breaks the chain of reactions leading from O_2^+ to the water-cluster sequence. The competition between (1) and

$$O_4^+ + H_2O \rightarrow O_2^+ \cdot H_2O + O_2 \qquad (2)$$

rapidly swings over in favor of (1) above 80 km, as [O] increases sharply with increasing altitude and [H_2O] continues to decrease with the neutral-atmosphere density.

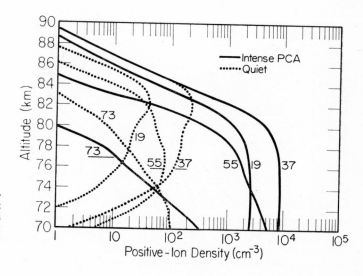

Fig. 2. Altitude profiles for water-cluster positive ions during quiet and intense PCA conditions. Labels are in the ion masses: $19 = H_3O^+$, $37 = H_3O^+ \cdot H_2O$, $55 = H_3O^+ \cdot (H_2O)_2$, $73 = H_3O^+ \cdot (H_2O)_3$.

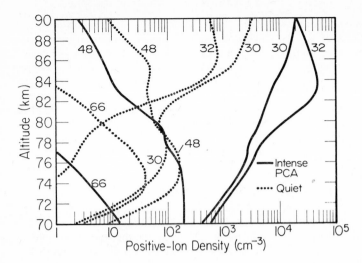

Fig. 3. Altitude profiles for molecular positive ions and hydrates during quiet and intense PCA conditions. Mass identifications are: $30 = NO^+$, $32 = O_2^+$, $48 = NO^+ \cdot H_2O$, $66 = NO^+ \cdot (H_2O)_2$.

b. The dominant water-cluster species throughout most of the altitude range in both cases is $H_2O^+ \cdot H_2O$ (mass 37), again in accord with observations (e.g. Narcisi & Bailey 1965). The dominance of this species is largely due to the high recombination rates of the complex clusters, which inhibits the formation of the larger clusters. During PCA conditions this effect is enhanced, due to the large concentrations of free electrons, and mass 37 remains dominant below 74 km, where the heavier clusters tend to dominate in quiet conditions.

c. As a consequence of this, it is worth noting that the concentration of mass 73 is actually lower during intense PCA conditions than during quiet conditions above 73 km; this is also true for mass 55 above 83 km. At the highest altitudes, the concentrations of mass 19 and mass 37 are nearly identical during quiet and PCA conditions, indicating that their distribution is determined by the neutral-atmosphere model (primarily by the [O] profile) rather than by recombination.

The concentration of the molecular positive-ion species (NO^+ — mass 30; O_2^+ — mass 32), and of the first two hydrates of NO^+ (mass 48 and mass 66) is shown in Fig. 3. The following points should be noted:

a. In quiet conditions there is a steep increase in O_2^+ concentration above 80 km, as reaction (1) above assumes increasing importance, but this is partially accompanied by an increase in NO^+ concentration, and NO^+ remains dominant among these ions down to 78 km, below which hydration becomes important and mass 48 becomes domi_ nant. During PCA conditions O_2^+ remains domi-

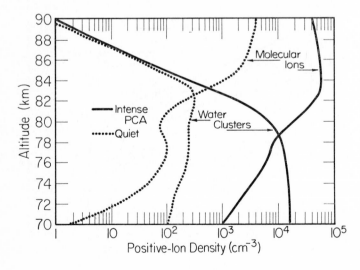

Fig. 4. Altitude profiles for the total ion concentrations of Fig. 2 (water clusters/ and Fig. 3 (molecular ions).

nant throughout, reflecting the greatly increased primary production rate of this ion.

b. The second hydrate of NO^+ (mass 66) is greatly depleted during intense PCA conditions, and the same is true of mass 48 above 80 km. This is again a consequence of the enhanced recombination rates during PCA, and effectively rules out NO^+ as a direct source of water-cluster ions, since the reaction chain proceeds through the first three hydrates of NO^+ (Fehsenfeld & Ferguson 1969).

The positive-ion situation is summarized in Fig. 4, which shows profiles of the sum of the curves of Figs. 2 and 3. The major point to note is the downward extension of the region in which molecular ions predominate during PCA conditions; the cross-over between molecular and water-cluster regimes occurs at about 83 km during quiet conditions and 79 km during intense PCA conditions. This change is once again due to the enhanced efficiency of recombination as a competitive factor in the formation of more complex ions during PCA, and it has an important influence on electron concentrations and on the concept of an 'effective loss coefficient' in the D-region, as we shall discuss later.

5. NEGATIVE IONS

Since the concentrations of negative ions are relatively small and sharply decreasing with increasing altitude in the range considered here, percentage composition is presented rather than absolute concentrations. Fig. 5 shows the percentage com-

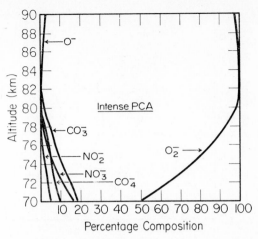

Fig. 6. Percentage composition of negative ions during intense PCA conditions. Only those ions exceeding 1 % of the total are shown.

position obtained for quiet conditions, and shows a rather sharp transition between a region dominated by NO_3^- below 77 km and a region dominated by O_2^- above this altitude. This is in agreement with earlier calculations (Reid 1970), and reflects the importance of the $[O]/[O_3]$ ratio in the reactions leading to the formation of the heavier negative ions. Small quantities of CO_3^- and NO_2^- are present at the lower altitudes and of O^- (resulting from dissociative attachment to O_3) at the higher levels, but the other negative-ion species individually form less than 1 % of the total. It should be noted that hydrogen reactions, particularly hydration, have been omitted entirely from the negative-ion reaction scheme, and in reality substantial concentrations of hydrated ions would be expected.

The situation during intense PCA conditions is shown in Fig. 6, and the major change is obviously the increased dominance of O_2^-. As we shall see, however, the actual concentrations of negative ions in relation to electrons is considerably less during PCA conditions. Just as enhanced dissociative recombination during PCA favors earlier members of the positive-ion sequence, so enhanced ion-ion mutual neutralization due to the large concentrations of positive ions favors earlier members of the negative-ion sequence. This is also illustrated for the heavier negative ions by the fact that CO_3^- dominates NO_3^-, and appreciable quantities of CO_4^- have appeared. It is worth noting that O_2^- is now dominant down to altitudes that give a large contribution to radiowave absorption, and this leads us to expect a

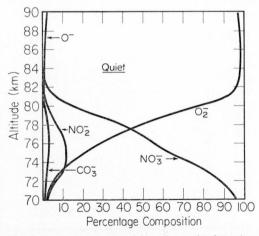

Fig. 5. Percentage composition of negative ions during quiet conditions. Only those ions exceeding 1 % of the total are shown.

43

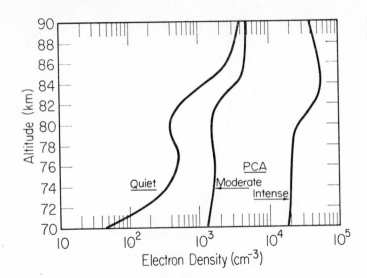

Fig. 7. Electron concentration during quiet conditions and during moderate and intense PCA conditions.

small visible-light photodetachment effect to occur during intense PCA events, since O_2^- has a substantial photodetachment cross-section in the visible spectrum.

6. ELECTRONS

Profiles of electron concentration are shown in Fig. 7 for quiet conditions and for moderate and intense PCA events. The most notable feature is the sharp increase in the 84-km region in quiet conditions, due to the change from cluster-ion dominance below to molecular-ion dominance above (Reid 1970), and the fact that this steep increase appears to move down in altitude during intense PCA events, reflecting the downward shift

in the molecular-ion regime shown in Fig. 4. The quantity Λ, the ratio of the total negative-ion concentration to the electron concentration, is shown in Fig. 8. During quiet conditions this quantity is 1 at about 70 km, but as the PCA intensifies the height at which $\Lambda = 1$ moves down markedly. The basic reason for this, as mentioned above, is the increased importance of ion-ion mutual neutralization during PCA events, when positive-ion concentrations are large. Λ also falls steeply with increasing altitude, particularly during quiet conditions, due to the sharp increase in the ratio of [O] to [O_3], so that the region in which O_2^- is the dominant species always contains relatively few negative ions in relation to the electron concentration.

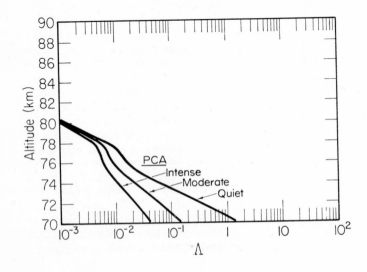

Fig. 8. Altitude profiles of the ratio of the total negative-ion concentration to the electron concentration (Λ).

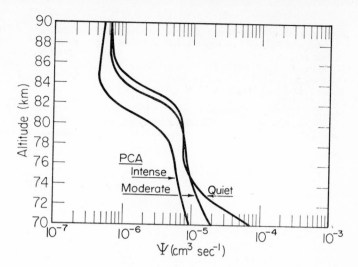

Fig. 9. Altitude profiles of the effective electron loss coefficient (Ψ).

Finally, Fig. 9 shows the 'effective loss rate' that has often been used in the calculation of electron-density profiles from known electron production rates. This quantity is $\Sigma q/n_e^2$, where Σq is the total production rate and n_e is the electron concentration. In the altitude range considered here, there is little difference between quiet conditions and moderate PCA conditions, but the profile for intense PCA conditions is substantially different. At 82 km the loss rate during intense PCA is nearly an order of magnitude lower than that during quiet conditions, since this particular level is in the cluster-ion regime during quiet conditions, and in the molecular-ion regime during PCA conditions. At higher levels, the PCA profile is appreciably lower than the quiet profile, reflecting the increased dominance of O_2^+ over NO^+ during PCA and the fact that their dissociative-recombination coefficients differ by about a factor of 2. These profiles illustrate the kind of changes that might be expected to occur in the effective loss rate from event to event, and indicate that caution must be used in attempting to draw conclusions about a particular event from a loss coefficient determined during another event.

7. CONCLUSIONS

The principal conclusion is that the D-region is likely to be substantially different in both positive- and negative-ion composition during quiet and during PCA conditions. The basic reasons for the differences as they appear in this particular model are (1) the different nature of the primary positive ions produced in the ionization process, and (2) the increased effectiveness of recombination dur-

ing PCA events as a competitor with ion reactions. In practice, there is likely to be a third source of differences between the two situations, in that differences in neutral composition due to dissociation effects will enter the picture. Any estimate of the magnitude of these effects, however, is beyond the scope of this initial study.

Many of the parameters entering this model calculation are highly uncertain, and some of them are completely unknown. The results can therefore only be taken as a rather qualitative indication of the kind of effects to be expected, rather than as precise numerical predictions. Hopefully many of the outstanding problems can be solved by combining actual observations with computations of this kind, which can only be regarded as indicators of the situation that might be expected.

Acknowledgement: This work was partially supported by the Defense Atomic Support Agency.

REFERENCES

Bourdeau, R. E., Aikin, A. C. & Donley, J. L. 1966. *J. Geophys. Res. 71*, 727.
CIRA (COSPAR International Reference Atmosphere) 1965. Compiled by COSPAR Working Group IV, North-Holland, Amsterdam.
Fehsenfeld, F. C. & Ferguson, E. E. 1969. *J. Geophys. Res. 74*, 2217.
Fehsenfeld, F. C. & Ferguson, E. E. 1971. Paper presented at COSPAR Symposium on D- and E-Region Ion Chemistry, University of Illinois, Urbana, July 1971.
Ferguson, E. E. 1971. In Fiocco, G. (ed.). *Mesospheric Models and Related Experiments*, Reidel Publishing Company. In Press.
Freier, P. S. & Webber, W. R. 1963. *J. Geophys. Res. 68*, 1605.

Hesstvedt, E. 1971 In Fiocco, G. (ed.). *Mesospheric Models and Related Experiments*, Reidel Publishing Company. In press.

Huffman, R. E., Paulsen, D. E., Larrabee, J. C. & Cairns, R. B. 1971. *J. Geophys. Res. 76*, 1028.

Hunten, D. M. & McElroy, M. B. 1968. *J. Geophys. Res. 73*, 2421.

Meira, L. G. 1971. *J. Geophys. Res. 76*, 202.

Narcisi, R. S. & Bailey, A. D. 1965. *J. Geophys. Res. 70*, 3687.

Reid, G. C. 1970. *J. Geophys. Res. 75*, 2551.

Reid, G. C. 1971. In Fiocco, G. (ed.). *Mesospheric Models and Related Experiments*, Reidel Publishing Company. In press.

Shimazaki, T. & Laird, A. R. 1970. *J. Geophys. Res. 75*, 3221.

Smith, L. G., Accardo, C. A., Weeks, L. H. & McKinnon, P. J. 1965. *J. Atmos. Terr. Phys. 27*, 803.

Webber, W. 1962. *J. Geophys. Res. 67*, 5091.

Theoretical Investigation of Nitric Oxide and Its Role in D-Region Ionization

I. ISAKSEN

Institute of Geophysics, University of Oslo, Norway

Abstract: A model of the distribution of nitric oxide in the height region 65–110 km has been calculated. Photochemical reactions above 90 km and turbulent diffusion determine the height profile. The primary source of NO, as well as of other odd nitrogen species, is expected to be X-ray ionisation of N_2 followed by the reaction $N_2^+ + O \rightarrow N + NO^+$. O_2^+ is taken into the reaction scheme, being important through the reaction $O_2^+ + NO \rightarrow O_2 + NO^+$. It is found that the efficiency of the reaction $NO^+ + e \rightarrow N + O$ in producing excited state atomic nitrogen must be about 0.6–0.7 in order to match NO concentrations with observations.

1. INTRODUCTION

It should be well established that nitric oxide is a major source in D-region ionisation. The importance of NO is due to low ionisation potential, allowing ionisation by the strong Lyman-α radiation.

There is, however, still some uncertainty as to how abundant NO is below approximately 100 km, and how important different photochemical reactions are in the destruction and formation of it, compared with turbulent diffusion.

It is not only in the E-region where NO makes NO^+ one of the major ion species by charge exchange from O_2^+ to NO^+, or in the D-region where it dominates by direct ionisation, but also in the far more complex ion chemistry in the region below 80 km that it plays a significant role. It is probably an important source of water cluster ions (Ferguson 1971), and it is also involved in the complex chain leading to the terminal negative ion in the lower ionosphere (Mohnen 1970, Reid 1970).

It is therefore the aim of this paper to investigate the influence of different photochemical reactions, and to examine the effect of NO on ionic species like NO^+ and O_2^+.

Measurements of NO have been performed on various occasions (Pearce 1969, Meira 1970). The No measurements by Pearce seem to be in error, giving too high concentrations. Meira's measurements are presumed to be more correct. The calculations will therefore be compared with the latter's results.

2. THE MODEL

A model of the five components NO, $N(^4S)$, $N(^2D)$, O_2^+, and NO^+ in the height region 65–110 km will be described below. Photochemical reactions between the five species are given in the scheme. Only the reactions that are expected to have any influence on the calculations are included.

Ionic reactions are expected to influence the NO profile above 80 km; below this height, turbulent diffusion is expected to dominate. Thus the ionic scheme can be simplified to NO^+ and O_2^+, since these two are by far the dominating ions above 80 km.

Atomic nitrogen in the ground state ($N(^4S)$) and excited state ($N(^2D)$) are both considered. Different efficiencies in producing excited state nitrogen will be considered, since the efficiency will be crucial to the NO production.

Any effect of NO_2 on the system is neglected. Below 70 km, NO is converted to NO_2 during the night, but at sunrise the conversion back to NO is rapid through the reaction

$$NO_2 + O \rightarrow NO + O_2.$$

Oxygen components involved in the reactions are taken from a model similar to that given by Hesstvedt (1971).

$O_2(^1\Delta_g)$ is added to the reaction scheme with the reactions:

$$O_3 + h\nu \rightarrow O_2(^1\Delta_g) + O \qquad \lambda < 3100\,\text{Å}$$
$$O_3 + O \rightarrow O_2(^1\Delta_g) + O_2(^1\Delta_g) \qquad k = 1.8 \times 10^{-11}$$
$$\exp(-4.0/RT)$$

$$O_2(^1\Delta_g) \rightarrow O_2(^3\Sigma_g^-) + h\nu \qquad A = 2.8 \times 10^{-4}$$
$$O_2(^1\Delta_g) + M \rightarrow O_2(^3\Sigma_g^-) + M \quad k = 2 \times 10^{-19}.$$

Two of the components in our scheme have relatively long chemical lifetimes, $N(^4S)$ in the upper part of the height region and NO in the whole region. The two components are therefore expected to be influenced by transport processes, and turbulent diffusion is included in the calculations of NO and $N(^4S)$.

The time-dependent differential equation, with diffusion included, is given by

$$\frac{\partial n_i}{\partial t} = -\frac{\partial}{\partial z}\left(K_z M \cdot \frac{\partial\left(\dfrac{n_i}{M}\right)}{\partial z}\right) - Q_p \cdot n_i + P_p,$$

where K_z is the diffusion coefficient and M is the total number density. Q_p and P_p are photochemical loss and production terms. The diffusion term is solved by finite differences (Hesstvedt 1969), giving similar production and loss terms, as for photochemistry.

As initial conditions, a direct implicit method (see Isaksen, in preparation) is used with $\dfrac{\partial n_i}{\partial t} = 0$.

$N(^2D)$, O_2^+, and NO^+ all have short photochemical lifetimes, and diffusion can be neglected.

$$\frac{\partial n_i}{\partial t} = -Q_p \cdot n_i + P_p.$$

Initial conditions are arrived at by setting $\dfrac{\partial n_i}{\partial t} = O$. The time variation of the species is given by solving the differential equations:

$$n_i = n_e + (n_0 - n_e) \cdot \exp\left(-Q \cdot \Delta t\right),$$

where $n_e = \dfrac{P}{Q}$ are equilibrium values, and n_0 is the starting value. P and Q are the total production and loss terms. We are not especially interested in values near sunrise and sunset, when rapid changes in some of the components take place, while the two components NO and $N(^4S)$ have small variations during the day. The calculations are therefore carried out for time steps of 10–30 min, and are continued for several days until there is no change in the 24-hour cycle from one day to the next.

The diffusion equation is of second order; it is therefore necessary to specify upper and lower boundary conditions. At 65 km the calculations give NO concentrations around 10^8, depending on the model chosen, and a mixing ratio [NO]/[air] that differs little from the mixing ratio in the troposphere. An assumption of constant mixing ratio with height is taken as a lower boundary condition, giving zero downward flux.

Ground state atomic nitrogen is rapidly broken down by chemical reactions. Photochemical equilibrium is therefore used for this component at the lower boundary. At the upper boundary the conditions are more complicated. As a result of the present calculations it turns out that photochemical reactions dominate over transport processes for $N(^4S)$, and that both photochemical processes and diffusion affect NO, photochemical processes being the most important. A boundary condition including turbulent diffusion is therefore used. The flux through the upper boundary is given in finite differences by a flux in the layer above 110 km equal to the flux in the layer below 110 km. A constant flux is chosen because we expect the ionisation and the neutral species involved in the odd nitrogen production to vary little around 110 km.

This gives a transport of odd nitrogen into the region. The nitrogen budget is balanced by photochemical conversion of odd to molecular nitrogen within the region, followed by an upward transport of N_2. The decrease in the N_2 mixing ratio with height, necessary to match the (N + NO) transport, is negligible, since the ratio of $[N_2]$/[odd nitrogen] is 10^5 or more. Consequently a constant N_2 mixing ratio is used.

3. DATA

In the height region 65–110 km considerable ionisation of N_2, O_2, $O_2(^1\Delta_g)$, and NO takes place.

N_2 and O_2 have ionisation thresholds at 796 Å and 1028 Å respectively. At $\lambda < 1028$ Å solar radiation is effectively absorbed at heights below 100 km. Above 100 km there is an important ionisation of O_2 by Lyman-β radiation at 1025.7 Å, just short of the ionisation threshold. Absorption and ionisation cross sections are taken from Huffman (1968) with the values 1.58×10^{-18} cm^2 and 0.98×10^{-18} cm^2. For X-ray radiation, $\lambda < 100$ Å, absorption cross sections decrease. The ionisation takes place mainly below 110 km. Absorption cross sections for the interval 2–100 Å are taken from Friedman (1960). O_2 and N_2 are expected to be equally ionised, with an energy loss of 35 eV for each ion pair formed. $O_2(^1\Delta_g)$ has its ionisation threshold at 1118 Å. In the region between ionisation of ground state O_2 and of $O_2(^1\Delta_g)$, there are several important 'windows' in the absorption of solar radiation by O_2; the cross sections are given by Watanabe (1958). Recently ionisation cross sections of $O_2(^1\Delta_g)$ have been measured by Clark & Wayne (1970) and their values are used in the calculations. The importance of this source for D-region ionisation is strongly reduced when the absorption by CO_2 at $\lambda < 1118$ Å is included, as proposed by Huffman et al. (1971).

Finally the ionisation of NO is calculated. NO has a low ionisation potential (9.4 eV), and is ionised for $\lambda < 1350$ Å. The ionisation results mainly from Lyman-α radiation at 1215.7 Å.

Solar fluxes are taken from Hall & Hinteregger (1970) for the extreme ultraviolet, and from Bourdeau et al. (1966) for X-ray fluxes at solar minimum. During a solar cycle there are marked variations in the X-ray fluxes. At solar maximum X-ray fluxes at short wavelengths are strongly enhanced (Craig 1965). Calculations will therefore also be carried out for solar maximum conditions, with values taken from Friedman (1964).

Flux enhancement in the extreme ultraviolet is by a factor of 2 from solar maximum to solar minimum. X-ray enhancements are given by a factor of 7 at 44–60 Å and by a factor of 45 at wavelengths 10–20 Å. At solar minimum, total X-ray fluxes are 0.1–0.2 ergs cm^{-2} sec^{-1}.

Cosmic ray ionisation has an effect that has no importance during the day, while at night it determines the ion profile in the lower region.

Other nighttime sources are Lyman-α radiation, which is taken to be 1 % of its daytime value, and Lyman-β radiation, 0.3 % of its daytime value.

Dissociation of NO, whereby N(^{4}S) is produced, is also included in the reaction scheme. Values for NO dissociation are taken from Watanabe (1958), and for O_2 absorption in the S–R bands from Huffman (1968). All calculations are done for 45° summer.

4. PHOTOCHEMICAL REACTIONS

The results of the calculations depend strongly upon the reaction rates used in the model. A more detailed description of the reaction scheme will therefore be given before the results of the calculations are presented.

Ionisation of N_2, O_2, $O_2(^1\Delta_g)$, and NO are given by the first four reactions. It should be noticed that the three first species do not depend on what model we use, and that ionisation of these species is independent of NO. Lyman-α ionisation, on the other hand, is proportional to NO.

The reactions

$$\text{(5a) } N_2^+ + O \rightarrow NO^+ + N(^4S)$$
$$\text{(5b) } N_2^+ + O \rightarrow NO^+ + N(^2D) \quad k_5$$

are extremely important, since they are the main sources of odd nitrogen production. Reactions (5a) and (5b) compete with reaction

$$\text{(6) } N_2^+ + O_2 \rightarrow N_2 + O_2^+ \quad k_6$$

in removing the N_2^+ ion. These reactions are the main loss processes of N_2^+. The expression of odd nitrogen production can be set up as

$$P_{\text{odd nitrogen}} = 2 \cdot k_5 \cdot [N_2^+] \cdot [O] \; \alpha \cdot Q_{N_2^+}$$

where α is the efficiency of reactions (5a) and (5b) in deactivating N_2^+ given by:

$$\alpha = \frac{k_5 \cdot [O]}{k_5 \cdot [O] + k_6 \cdot [O_2]}.$$

Below approximately 90 km, where atomic oxygen concentrations decrease rapidly (Hesstvedt 1968), production of odd nitrogen can be neglected.

At the upper boundary the ratio $[O]/[O_2]$ is 0.6. With a value of 2.5 (Ferguson, 1967) for the ratio k_5/k_6, reactions (5a) and (5b) will dominate over reaction (6). One reaction that has aroused some interest is

$$\text{(8) } N_2 + O_2^+ \rightarrow NO^+ + NO \quad k_8$$

as the possible source of odd nitrogen. The rate coefficient is probably small. A value of 10^{-18} has been adopted; this makes it unimportant in comparison with other reactions. Except for reaction (15), all the other reactions in the scheme are involved in an internal chain between the species NO, N(^{4}S), N(^{2}D), NO^+, and O_2^+.

It should be noted that O_2^+ is involved in this chain through the reaction

$$\text{(7) } O_2^+ + NO \rightarrow O_2 + NO^+ \quad k_7.$$

The reaction proceeds rapidly with a rate coefficient $k_7 = 8 \times 10^{-10}$. NO may therefore very well determine whether O_2^+ or NO^+ should be the dominating ion in the lower E-region and in the D-region.

The only loss process for odd nitrogen is the reaction

$$\text{(15) } N(^4S) + NO \rightarrow N_2 + O \quad k_{15}.$$

The loss by reaction (15) is equal to the production by reaction (5) in the height region plus the downward transported NO and N(^{4}S) through the upper boundary.

The only efficient production of NO is through the reaction

(1)	$O_2, N_2 + h\upsilon \rightarrow O^+_2, N^+_2 + e$	$2\,\text{Å} < \lambda < 100\,\text{Å}$ (X-rays)
(2)	$O_2 + h\upsilon \rightarrow O_2^+ + e$	$\lambda = 1025.7\,\text{Å}$ (Lyman-β)
(3)	$O_2(^1\Delta_g) + h\upsilon \rightarrow O_2^+ e$	$\lambda < 1118\,\text{Å}$
(4)	$NO + h\upsilon \rightarrow NO^+ + e$	$\lambda = 1215.7\,\text{Å}$ (Lyman-α)
(5a) (5b)	$N_2^+ + O \rightarrow \begin{cases} NO^+ + N(^4S)\ (1-\beta) \\ NO^+ + N(^2D) \quad \beta \end{cases}$	$k = 2.5 \times 10^{-10}$
(6)	$N_2^+ + O_2 \rightarrow N_2 + O_2^+$	$k = 1.0 \times 10^{-10}$
(7)	$O_2^+ + NO \rightarrow O_2 + NO^+$	$k = 8 \times 10^{-10}$
(8)	$O_2^+ + N_2 \rightarrow NO^+ + NO$	$k = 1 \times 10^{-18}$
(9)	$O_2^+ + e \rightarrow O + O$	$k = 2.0 \times 10^{-7} \cdot \left(\dfrac{300}{T}\right)$
(10a) (10b)	$NO^+ + e \rightarrow \begin{cases} N(^4S) + O\ (1-\gamma) \\ N(^2D) + O \quad \gamma \end{cases}$	$5.0 \times 10^{-7} \cdot \left(\dfrac{300}{T}\right)$
(11)	$NO + h\upsilon \rightarrow N(^4S) + O$	($\lambda < 1910\,\text{Å}$)
(12)	$N(^2D) + O_2 \rightarrow NO + O$	$k = 5.0 \times 10^{-12}$
(13)	$N(^4S) + O \rightarrow NO + h\upsilon$	$k = 2 \times 10^{-17}$
(14)	$N(^4S) + O_2 \rightarrow NO + O$	$k = 1.2 \times 10^{-11} \cdot \exp(-3530/T)$
(15)	$N(^4S) + NO \rightarrow N_2 + O$	$k = 2.2 \times 10^{-11}$

Units are cm^3s^{-1} for 2-body reactions, and s^{-1} for solar dissociation rates.

12 $N(^2D) + O_2 \rightarrow NO + O$ k_{12}.

NO production is therefore critically dependent on the efficiencies of reactions (5) and

(10a) $NO^+ + e \rightarrow N(^4S) + O$

(10b) $NO^+ + e \rightarrow N(^2D) + O$

in producing excited nitrogen.

The efficiency of reaction (5) is given by β and of reaction (6) by γ.

Production of NO by the reaction

(14) $N(^4S) + O_2 \rightarrow NO + O$ k_{14}

is rather small since the rate coefficient is strongly temperature-dependent, $k_{14} = 1.4 \times 10^{-11}$ exp $(-3,530/T)$ (Schiff 1968). At lower altitudes, with higher O_2 concentrations and higher temperatures, reaction (14) effectively reduces the $N(^4S)$ concentrations.

Through reaction (15) atomic nitrogen will act to break down NO. The consequence of this is that the production of odd nitrogen, reaction (5), must to a large extent be into the excited state ^2D, reaction (5b). If not, $N(^4S)$ will play a dominating role over NO at heights of 100–110 km. β is given the value 0.8.

The efficiency of the conversion into the same state by reaction (10) determines the NO profile in the whole region, and in order to examine this effect four models with different γ values are calculated.

Reaction coefficients for ionic reactions are taken from Ferguson (1967), recombination rates for O_2^+ and NO^+ from Biondi (1968), and from Schiff (1968), Schofield (1967), Nicolet (1970),

Norton & Barth (1970), and Strobel et al. (1970) for the other reactions.

5. DISCUSSION

A discussion of the ionisation in the height region 65–110 km can be divided into two parts. Above 90 km X-ray ionisation of N_2 and O_2 and Lyman-β ionisation of O_2 will dominate during solar minimum. Below that height, Lyman-α ionisation of NO is the main source (Fig. 1).

X-rays and Lyman-β are about equally important down to about 95 km. Below 95 km X-rays have somewhat higher rates. Maximum ionisation is between 100–105 km with 2000 ion-pairs cm^{-3} sec^{-1}. Below 90 km where NO is the ion source, production rate will strongly depend on the γ value chosen. For $\gamma = 0.8$, ionisation rates of about 20 cm^{-3} sec^{-1} are obtained, while $\gamma = 0.5$ gives rates of about 2 cm^{-3} sec^{-1} at 80 km.

It should be noted that ionisation of $O_2(^1\Delta_g)$ gives a contribution to the ion production which is less than that of the other sources at all heights and which has hardly any noticeable effect.

By solar maximum, ionisation rates have changed. The strongly enhanced X-ray fluxes (a factor of 7 or more), make X-rays the dominant ion source. The rise in production is especially noticeable between 80 and 90 km. If we choose $\gamma = 0.6$, X-ray ionisation will dominate down to about 85 km.

Total rates of ionisation are raised by a factor of 4, and the ionisation has its maximum between 100 km and 105 km, with ionisation rates of about

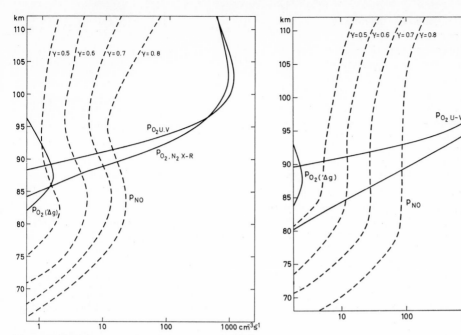

Fig. 1. Ionisation rates of N_2, O_2, NO, and $O(^1\Delta_g)$ at noon for solar minimum. $P_{O_2, N_2 X-r}$: X-ray ionisation of O_2 and N_2. $P_{O_2 u-v}$: ultraviolet ionisation of O_2 (Lyman-β). P_{NO}: Lyman α ionisation of NO for different γ values. $P_{O_2(^1\Delta_g)}$: ionisation of $O_2(^1\Delta_g)$ at $\lambda < 1118$ A.

Fig. 2. Same as Fig. 1 for solar maximum.

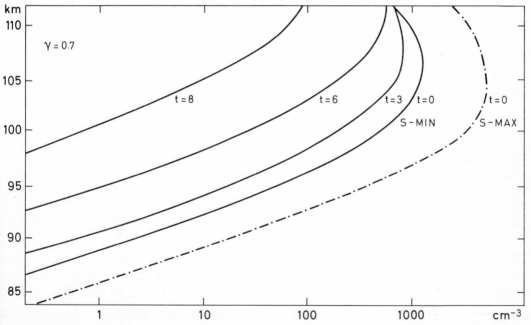

Fig. 3. Odd nitrogen production through reaction $N_2^+ + O \rightarrow NO^+ + N$ for solar maximum (s-max), and solar minimum (s-min).

$8000 \text{ cm}^{-3} \text{ sec}^{-1}$. At 80 km the rates, for $\gamma = 0.6$, are about $10 \text{ cm}^{-3} \text{ sec}^{-1}$.

We have already pointed out reactions (5a) and (5b) as the only effective sources of odd nitrogen. Since N_2 is ionised by X-rays, this means that the main sources of NO and $N(^4S)$ are the highly variable X-ray fluxes.

Odd nitrogen species should therefore vary with solar cycle variations. Production rates at solar maximum are given in Fig. 3. Variations during the day can be seen from the solar minimum curve. The production of odd nitrogen takes place almost entirely above 85 km; below this height the ratio $[O]/[O_2]$, which determines the production of odd nitrogen, decreases rapidly. The presence of NO below 85 km must therefore be due to the downward transport by turbulent diffusion.

The role of NO in controlling ion species is given by reaction (7). How important this reaction is will to some extent be determined by the choice of γ value. If we take $\gamma = 0.7$, reaction (7) will be the dominating loss term for O_2^+ below 98 km at high solar elevation (Fig. 4). For greater zenith distances, nitric oxide will dominate in the whole height region, since the loss from reaction (9) varies strongly over the day (see Fig. 4, curve qe). The effect of reaction (8) can safely be neglected

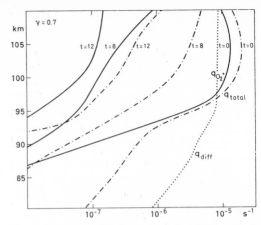

Fig. 5. Loss rates of NO. $q_{O_2^+}$: $O_2^+ + NO \rightarrow O_2 + NO^+$ q_{total}: total loss rate of NO.

(curve q_{N_2}). Similar curves for NO are given in Fig. 5. Reaction (7) is the dominating loss process for NO down to about 92 km at high solar elevation ($t = 0$, curve $q_{O_2^+}$).

At low solar elevation and at night ($t = 8$, $t = 12$), reaction (7) is only responsible for a fraction of the total loss (Fig. 5). Curve $q_{O_2^+}$ is given by calculating the fractional part of reaction (7) going into ground state of atomic nitrogen:

$$k_7 \cdot [O_2^+] \cdot [NO] \cdot (1 - \gamma)$$

The production of excited nitrogen gives NO through the sequence

(7) $NO + O_2^+ \rightarrow NO^+ + O_2$
(10b) $NO^+ + e \rightarrow N(^2D) + O$
(12) $N(^2D) + O_2 \rightarrow NO + O$

A high γ value will therefore make the feedback of NO efficient, and reduce the effect of reaction (7) as a loss term for NO.

The loss processes for O_2^+ (Fig. 4) and NO (Fig. 5) clearly show that the two species influence each/other in the height region 90–100 km. It should also be noticed for NO (Fig. 5), that photochemical processes (q_{total}), dominate for high solar elevation, and are negligible for low solar elevation ($t = 8$), and at night ($t = 12$), compared with the turbulent loss term (q_{diff}).

NO^+ is a terminal ion, and the only loss is by dissociative recombination:

(10a) $NO^+ + e \rightarrow N(^4S) + O$
(10b) $NO^+ + e \rightarrow N(^2D) + O.$

Photochemical lifetimes given by these reactions are shown in Fig. 6 (curve q_{NO^+}). In the region in which we are primarily interested, 80 km or

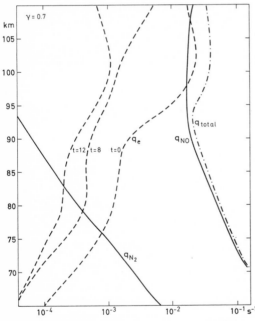

Fig. 4. Loss rates for O_2^+. q_{NO} from reaction $O_2^+ + NO \rightarrow O_2 + NO^+$, q_e: $O_2^+ + e \rightarrow O + O$, q_{N_2}: $O_2^+ + N_2 \rightarrow NO^+ + NO$. Total loss rate is given by the line of dofs and dashes (q + total).

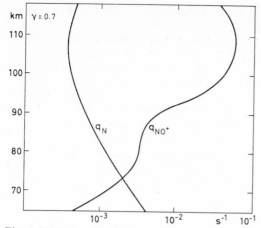

Fig. 6. Lifetimes of N(^{4}S) (q_N) and NO$^+$ (q_{NO}).

above, the lifetimes are minutes or less. Lifetimes of N(^{4}S) are also included in Fig. 6 (curve q_N). The loss term is

(15) $\quad N(^4S) + NO \rightarrow N_2 + O$.

The lifetime decreases from one hour at 100 km to about five minutes at 65 km. Both species are dominated by photochemical processes, and the introduction of turbulent diffusion in the N(^{4}S) calculations has very little effect. The curves are for $\gamma = 0.7$. $\gamma = 0.6$ and 0.5 will lower the photo-chemical lifetimes for N(^{4}S) due to the lower NO concentrations. In these cases turbulent diffusion will have some effects. Reaction (7) breaks down O_2^+, and produces NO$^+$ as a result of this. Different γ values change the NO$^+$ and the O_2^+ con-

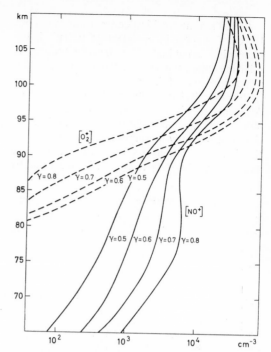

Fig. 7. Concentrations of NO$^+$ (unbroken lines), and O_2^+ (dashed lines) at noon for different γ values and at solar minimum.

centrations. NO$^+$ increases with increasing γ value, while O_2^+ decreases. The dependence on γ is especially marked around 80 km, where NO$^+$ is proportional to NO. $\gamma = 0.8$ gives NO$^+$ con-centrations 6×10^3 cm^{-3} at 80 km, while $\gamma = 0.6$ gives only 1000 cm^{-3}.

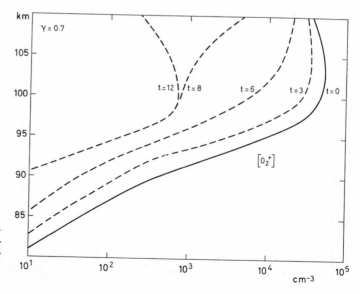

Fig. 8. Diurnal variation of O_2^+ concentrations for $\gamma = 0.7$ and for solar minimum. t gives hours after noon.

53

At 100 km the total ion concentration is about 10^5 cm^{-3}, almost independent of γ. This is for solar minimum at high solar elevation (noon). At solar maximum, the concentrations are raised by a factor of about 1.5.

O_2^+ and NO$^+$ have strong diurnal variations. After sunset, nighttime values of scattered Lyman-α and Lyman-β radiation are sources in addition to cosmic ray ionisation. The diurnal variation in concentrations is shown in Fig. 8 for O_2^+, and in Fig. 9 for NO$^+$. O_2^+ varies from day to night by a factor of almost 100. From a maximum daytime value of about 6×10^4 cm^{-3} around 100 km, it decreases at midnight to a value of about 7×10^2 cm^{-3}. NO$^+$ has a less marked variation, a factor of about 10 around 100 km, and less below.

A maximum daytime concentration of about 4×10^4 cm^{-3} at 100 km, decreasing to about 4×10^3 at night, is obtained for NO$^+$.

The difference in diurnal variations of O_2^+ and NO$^+$ is clearly demonstrated in Fig. 10. The ratio [NO$^+$]/[O_2^+] has its lowest value at noon, about 0.8 at 110 km, decreasing to 0.5 at 100 km, and

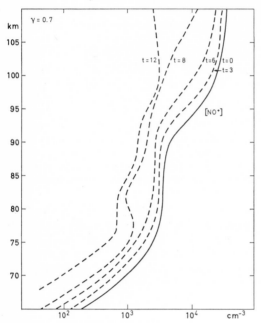

Fig. 9. Same as Fig. 8 for NO$^+$.

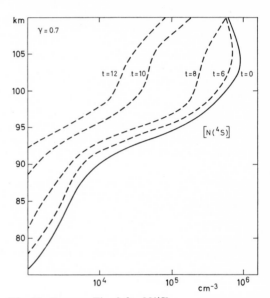

Fig. 11. Same as Fig. 8 for N(^{4}S).

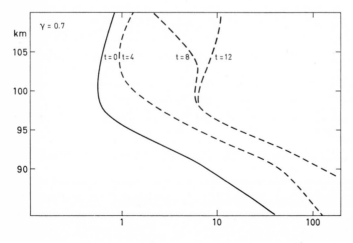

Fig. 10. The diurnal variation of the ration [NO$^+$]/ [O_2^+] for $\gamma =$ 0.7 and for solar minimum. t gives hours after noon.

54

increases to about 10 at 90 km, and 50 at 85 km. At night the values are 10 at 110 km, 7 at 100 km, and 100 at 90 km.

Odd nitrogen production has a marked diurnal variation, and since the components in the loss process (reaction (15)) are photochemically controlled above 95 km (Figs. 5 and 6), we must expect a diurnal variation, at least in one of the two components, NO and $N(^4S)$. Variations of $N(^4S)$ are given in Fig. 11. The decrease from maximum at noon to minimum at night is a factor of 10 or more at all heights. The peak concentration is found between 100 km and 105 km with a value of 10^6 cm^{-3}. $N(^4S)$ varies inversly as NO and will therefore have its lowest concentrations for high γ values. NO has a diurnal variation that is much less pronounced than the variation of $N(^4S)$. Below 100 km it is negligible, above 100 km we have a decrease of about 10% from day to night.

This might be surprising since the production of odd nitrogen is extremely variable during the day (Fig. 3). The almost constant concentrations of NO can be explained by the loss reaction (15). For $\gamma = 0.7$, NO concentrations are a factor of

more than 10 higher than those of $N(^4S)$, and since both components are involved in the loss reaction (15), the less abundant component, $N(^4S)$, will almost entirely disappear before any changes can be detected in the NO concentrations.

NO concentrations for the different γ values at solar minimum and maximum are given in Fig. 12.

As one may expect, the height profile of NO is strongly dependent on the γ value. The differences are strongest in the region below 95 km, with an increase in NO concentrations of about a factor of 30 for an increase from 0.5 to 0.8 in γ.

A low γ value (0.5) gives a profile of NO that is controlled by photochemical processes down to 85 km. Below 85 km, turbulent diffusion will dominate. If the γ values are increased the diffusion-controlled regime is extended upwards.

For $\gamma = 0.8$, turbulent diffusion dominates up to almost 100 km. High γ values will also give a less pronounced minimum.

A comparison of the theoretical NO profiles and observed values seems to give reasonable values in the 90 to 100 km region (Meira 1970).

If we take $\gamma = 0.7$, we get NO concentrations of $2-3 \times 10^7$ cm^{-3} at 100 km and above, a minimum around 90–95 km of 1.5×10^7 cm^{-3}, and a constant mixing ratio below, with 5×10^7 cm^{-3} at 80 km and 2×10^8 cm^{-3} at 65 km. These values are for solar minimum. At solar maximum, concentrations are raised by a factor of 2–3 at all heights.

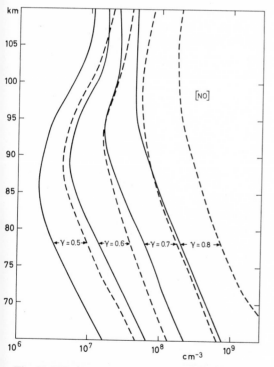

Fig. 12. NO concentrations for solar minimum (unbroken lines), and solar maximum (dashed lines) for different γ values.

6. CONCLUSION

From the calculations we can conclude that the concentrations of NO are independent of photochemical processes below 80 km. The only important process is turbulent diffusion. It should therefore be safe to use the simple ionic scheme adopted in this model.

It is evident from the calculations that a strong link exists between NO^+, O_2^+, and NO through reaction (7) in the photochemically active region between 90 and 110 km. Changes in one of the species will automatically lead to changes in the other two.

The influence of NO on the ion chemistry of the lower ionosphere is manifold.

First we have the direct ionisation of NO by Lyman-α radiation. This will, as we have shown (Fig. 7), strongly depend on the γ value used in the calculations. A value of 0.6 to 0.7 is favoured.

Next the NO is involved in the formation of water cluster ions. It is an important source of the water cluster ion $H_3O^+(H_2O)_2$ (Ferguson 1971) through the equation

$$NO^+ + H_2O + M \rightarrow NO^+ \cdot (H_2O) + M$$

leading to

$$NO^+(H_2O)_3 + H_2O \rightarrow H_3O^+(H_2O)_2 + HNO_2.$$

A variation in NO concentrations will affect the production of water cluster ions.

NO is further involved in the negative ion scheme (Ferguson 1967), through reactions like

$$CO_3^- + NO \rightarrow NO_2^- + CO_2$$
$$O_3^- + NO \rightarrow NO_3^- + O.$$

NO seems to influence the whole ion chemistry of the lower ionosphere. A proper investigation of ionic species is therefore largely determined by a reliable NO model.

These calculations are part of a model of the complete ion chemistry of the D-region, which is being constructed.

REFERENCES

Biondi, M. A. 1968. Symposium on laboratory measurements of aeronomic interest, York University, Toronto.

Bourdeau, R. E., Aikin, A. C. & Donley, J. L. 1966. *J. Geophys. Res. 71*, 727.

Clark, I. D. & Wayne, R. P. 1970. *J. Geophys. Res. 75*, 699.

Craig, R. C. 1965. *The Upper Atmosphere, Meteorology and Physics*, Academic Press, New York and London.

Fehsenfeld, F. C., Mosesman, M. & Ferguson, E. E. 1971. *J. Chem. Phys.* In press.

Ferguson, E. E. 1967. *Rev. Geophys. 5*, 305.

Ferguson, E. E. 1971. *J. Chem. Phys.* In press.

Friedman, H. 1960. *Physics of the Upper Atmosphere*, Academic Press, New York and London.

Friedman, H. 1964. *Research in Geophysics, 1. Sun, Upper Atmosphere and Space*, MIT Press, Cambridge, Mass.

Hall, L. A. & Hinteregger, H. E. 1970. *J. Geophys. Res. 75*, 6959.

Hesstvedt, E. 1968. *Geofys. Pubkl. 27*, No. 4.

Hesstvedt, E. 1969. Private communication.

Hesstvedt, E. 1971. Proceedings ESRIN symposium on Upper atmospheric models and related experiments, Frascati, Italy. In press.

Huffman, R. E. 1968. Symposium on laboratory measurements of aeronomic interest, York University, Toronto.

Huffman, R. E., Paulsen, D. E., Larabee, J. C. & Cairns, R. B. 1971. *J. Geophys. Res. 76*, 1028.

Isaksen, I. To be published.

Meira, L. C. 1970. Ph.D. thesis. University of Colorado, Boulder.

Mohnen, V. A. 1970. *J. Geophys. Res. 75*, 1717.

Nicolet, M. 1970. *Planet. Space Sci. 18*, 1111.

Norton, R. B. & Barth, C. A. 1970. *J. Geophys. Res. 75*, 3903.

Pearce, J. B. 1969. *J. Geophys. Res. 74*, 853.

Reid, G. C. 1970. *J. Geophys. Res. 75*, 2551.

Schiff, H. I. 1968. Symposium on laboratory measurements of aeronomic interest, York University, Toronto.

Schofield, K. 1967. *Planet. Space Sci. 15*, 643.

Strobel, D. F., Hunten, D. M. & McElroy, M. B. 1970. *J. Geophys. Res. 75*, 1717.

Watanabe, K. 1958. *Advances in Geophysics*, Academic Press, New York and London.

A Theory for Energetic Electron Lifetimes within the Plasmasphere

L. R. LYONS

Department of Meteorology, University of California, Los Angeles

Abstract: The removal of radiation belt electrons through pitch-angle scattering by the observed obliquely propagating plasmaspheric whistler wave band is investigated. Electron lifetimes are calculated as a function of L and energy. The effects of high latitude interactions and of oblique wave propagation with the resulting diffusion at all cyclotron harmonics are quantitatively incorporated into the calculations. The inclusion of these effects appears to extend the role of whistler-driven electron pitch-angle diffusion to provide an explanation of the positioning of the quiet time radiation belt electron slot and the electron losses within the slot region.

Pitch-angle diffusion by electromagnetic wave turbulence is now known to be an important factor in driving charged particles into the loss cone of the Earth's radiation belts (Dragt 1961, Dungey 1963, Andronov & Trakhtengerts 1964, Cornwall 1964, 1966, Kennel & Petschek 1966a, Tverskoy 1967, Roberts 1968, Kennel 1969, Russell & Thorne 1970). Here, we calculate pitch-angle diffusion rates for electrons in cyclotron resonance with a spectrum of whistler-mode wave turbulence modeled after the average properties of the hiss band observed throughout the plasmasphere. The effects of interactions occurring away from the geomagnetic equator and of wave progation obliquely to the geomagnetic field direction are quantitatively evaluated. While it has been suggested that these effects may be important, they have not previously been systematically studied. From the calculated diffusion rates, we are able to predict the lifetimes of electrons of all radiation belt energies as a function of L-value within the plasmasphere. Finally, we compare our results with electron lifetimes observed in the radiation belts.

Kennel & Petschek (1966a) predicted that whenever the radiation belt electron fluxes exceed a critical value J*, a whistler wave instability is set up in the radiation belts and the resonant electrons are lost. This theory predicts that electron losses will only occur within a limited energy range inside the plasmasphere, since J* is independent of energy within the plasmasphere and electron fluxes generally decrease with increasing energy. J* is proportional to L^{-4}, and radiation belt fluxes at all energies fall well below J* for L $\lesssim$ 4. Thus the Kennel & Petschek theory, taken literally, does not predict any electron losses at these lower L-values.

However, a process by which electrons can be lost for all radiation belt energies at L-values of less than 4 is necessary to explain the quiet time morphology of the radiation belts. During quiet times, the radiation belt electrons are distributed in two zones. Fluxes peak near L = 1.5 but decrease below the level of detectability near L = 2 to L = 3.5. (The exact positions are functions of electron energy.) The fluxes increase again near the plasmapause and form the outer zone. The region between the two zones, which is devoid of electrons, is known as the electron slot. During magnetic storms, the slot can be filled by electrons of all energies; however, the amount of filling decreases with increasing electron energy. Following a storm, the fluxes decay, presumably by precipitation, and the slot is reformed (Pfitzer et al. 1966, Russell & Thorne 1970). Recent in situ observations of plasmaspheric whistler-mode waves suggest the need to include the effects of oblique wave propagation and off-equatorial interactions. By including these effects we can extend the role of whistler-driven pitch-angle diffusion to provide an explanation of the electron losses in the slot regions. Kennel & Petschek (1966b), Kennel (1967), Tverskoy (1964), and Roberts (1968) have pointed out the possible importance of these effects. Here we quantitatively incorporate them into the theory of electron pitch-angle diffusion.

Plasmaspheric whistler-mode waves are now known to extend to low L-values and high latitudes (Russell et al. 1969) and to propagate with a wide distribution of wave normal angles relative to the geomagnetic field, B_0 (Thorne et al. 1970). A possible explanation of why waves are seen at low L-values, even though the electron fluxes are too low to generate them by the Kennel & Petschek mechanism, is that the waves are typically below the lower hybrid frequency. Thus waves generated near the plasmapause by the Kennel & Petschek mechanism can easily propagate across field lines (Lyons and Thorne 1970) to lower L-values.

Allowing oblique wave propagation vastly increases the range of electron energies that can interact with a given whistler wave band. Waves propagating parallel to B_0 cause diffusion at only the principal, -1, cyclotron harmonic. Obliquely propagating waves, on the other hand, cause diffusion at all cyclotron harmonics. Thus not only can electrons in first-order resonance be driven into the atmospheric loss cone, but so can *all* higher energy electrons. Fig. 1 schematically illustrates the regions in electron momentum-space where cyclotron resonance occurs with a given wave band. Interaction occurs over a band of $P_{\parallel}$'s for each order resonance ($P_{\parallel}$ is the component of particle momentum parallel to B_0). Generally the bands for different resonances overlap somewhat; however, for clarity the overlap is not shown in

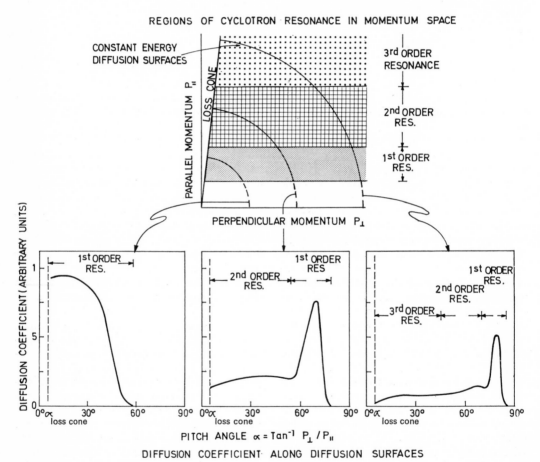

REGIONS OF CYCLOTRON RESONANCE IN MOMENTUM SPACE

DIFFUSION COEFFICIENT ALONG DIFFUSION SURFACES

Fig. 1. Schematic illustration of pitch-angle diffusion. In the upper part of the Figure, the regions in the $(P_{\perp}, P_{\parallel})$-plane where first-, second-, and third- order diffusion occurs are illustrated by different shadings. Also shown are three of the circular surfaces along which particle diffusion occurs. The inner diffusion surface corresponds to a particle energy for which first-order resonance controls the diffusion into the loss cone. The higher particle energies corresponding to the outer diffusion surfaces require higher harmonic diffusion to reach the loss cone. Calculated pitch-angle diffusion coefficients for electron energies corresponding to the three diffusion surfaces are sketched as a function of pitch-angle in the lower part of the Figure.

58

the Figure. At low values of $P_\parallel$ there is no inter-action. As $P_\parallel$ is increased, first-order resonance is encountered, and as $P_\parallel$ is increased further, successively higher-order resonances are encountered.

Plasmaspheric wave frequencies are well below the electron gyrofrequency (Dunkel & Helliwell 1969, Russell et al. 1969, Thorne et al. 1970). In this limit, wave-particle interactions cause primarily particle pitch-angle diffusion (Engel 1965, Kennel 1966, Kennel & Englemann 1966), and the particles diffuse along constant energy surfaces. Three such circular surfaces are shown in Fig. 2. Lower energy electrons are subject solely to first-order diffusion except at high pitch-angles where no cyclotron interaction occurs. Bounce resonance can probably account for high pitch-angle radiation belt particle diffusion (Roberts & Schulz 1968). Higher energy electrons undergo first-order diffusion over a limited range of moderately high pitch-angles. They, however, encounter successively higher order resonances as they diffuse towards small pitch-angles, and they can be driven into the loss cone by these higher harmonic interactions.

Using relativistic quasi-linear diffusion theory, we have obtained expressions for the pitch-angle diffusion coefficients resulting from a specified band of wave turbulence. The expressions give the pitch-angle diffusion rates at one point in space for all cyclotron harmonics as a function of particle energy and pitch-angle. Pitch-angle diffusion coefficients plotted as a function of pitch-angle are shown in the lower part of Fig. 1 for electron energies corresponding to the above three diffusion surfaces. A wave distribution with energy distributed over a wide range of wave normal angles was used in performing the calculations, and we have added together the effects of all cyclotron harmonic resonances. The diffusion rates at the edge of the loss cone are non-zero for all three energies. However, since high harmonic diffusion rates are small at small pitch-angles, the rates decrease significantly with increasing electron energy.

On the basis of these results, one might expect plasmaspheric electron loss rates to decrease rapidly with increasing electron energy. However, as has been pointed out by Roberts (1968), the pitch-angle diffusion coefficients must be averaged over a complete electron bounce orbit. Since the observations of Thorne et al. (1970) show that the plasmaspheric wave intensity is not a strong function of latitude, interactions occurring off the

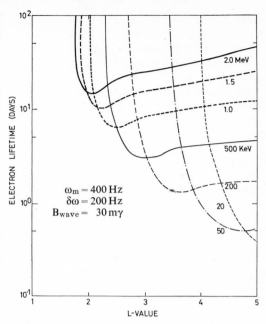

Fig. 2. Electron lifetimes calculated as a function of L for various radiation belt energies. The results are valid only for weak diffusion within the plasmasphere. The sharp inner boundary predicts the position of the inner edge of the electron slot at each electron energy. The lifetimes for electrons of a given energy are fairly constant outside this boundary.

geomagnetic equator are important. As an electron travels away from the equator, the increasing geomagnetic field intensity causes both the electron's pitch-angle and the parallel momentum required for first-order resonance to increase. All high energy electrons therefore undergo first-order resonance somewhere along their bounce orbit. This implies that off-equatorial interactions will significantly increase the high energy electron diffusion rates at the edge of the loss cone.

Using the pitch-angle diffusion equation, and performing the bounce orbit averaging of the diffusion coefficients as a function of equatorial pitch-angle, allows electron lifetimes to be calculated as a function of L-value and electron energy. This calculation involves obtaining the electron pitch-angle distribution function, since the lifetimes are inversely proportional to the slope of the distribution function evaluated at the edge of the loss cone. Since the pitch-angle diffusion coefficients become zero at high pitch angles, we have assumed the pitch-angle distribution is constant at high pitch-angles. This assumption is compatible with observations of a flattening in the pitch-angle distribution near $\alpha = \pi/2$ (Pfitzer

59

1968). Fortunately, the slope of the distribution function at the edge of the loss cone, and thus the calculated lifetimes, are not strongly affected by the details of the high pitchangle part of the distribution.

The results of the lifetime calculations are shown in Fig. 2. A Gaussian distribution of wave energy with frequency, peaked at 400 Hz with a half-width of 200 Hz, and a total wave amplitude of 30 mγ, were used in obtaining these lifetimes. Also, the wave energy was taken to be distributed over a wide range of wave normal angles. The lifetimes are inversely proportional to the square of the wave amplitude. Thus changing the wave amplitude alters the magnitude of the lifetimes accordingly. The chosen wave parameters represent average observed plasmaspheric values, and they have been taken to be constant over the entire plasmasphere. Since the electron lifetimes are of the order of days to months, ignoring short-term variations of the wave parameters is reasonable.

At any L-value, there is a minimum energy required for interaction. Above this minimum energy all electrons have finite lifetimes, though the lifetimes generally increase with increasing electron energy. As the L-value is decreased, the minimum

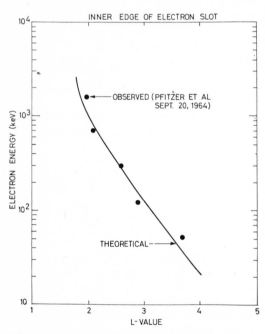

Fig. 3. Comparison of the theoretically predicted position of the inner edge of the electron slot as a function of energy with the observations of Pfitzer et al. (1966).

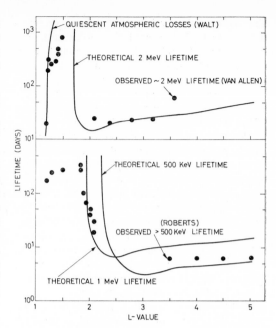

Fig. 4. Comparison of the electron lifetimes calculated as a function of L with observations. The ~ 2 MeV electron lifetimes observed by Van Allen (1964) support the predicted 2 MeV lifetimes of ~ 1 month in the slot region. The predicted lifetimes for 500 keV and 1 MeV electrons surround the ~ 1 week slot region lifetimes observed by Roberts (1968) for electrons of all energies > 500 keV. The rapid increase in the lifetimes near $L = 2$ is also supported by Roberts' data.

interaction energy increases. For all electron energies, there is a sharp boundary separating the region of no interaction at lower L-values from the region of precipitation losses. Beyond this boundary, the lifetimes remain fairly constant (increasing slightly) until the plasmapause is encountered. Assuming the electron slot lies between the inner boundary of diffusion and the plasmapause, the L-value where the sharp lifetime boundary is located should predict the inner edge of the slot for any electron energy. Fig. 3 shows the L-value where the lifetime falls to 20 days as a function of electron energy. Also shown are the quiet time locations of the inner edge of the slot as observed by Pfitzer et al. (1966), and it can be seen that the theoretical curve predicts the position of the inner edge of the slot quite accurately. Increasing or decreasing the frequency of peak wave intensity, taken here to be 400 Hz, would shift the theoretical curve to lower or higher L-values respectively.

Fig. 4 compares the electron lifetimes calculated

as a function of L with observations. The upper plot shows data obtained by Van Allen (1964) for ~ 2 MeV electrons, and the lower plot shows lifetimes obtained by Roberts (1968) for electrons of energy > 500 keV. Both sets of observations support the magnitude and the variation with L-value of the calculated lifetimes. The decrease in the lifetimes at very low L-values is probably due to atmospheric coulomb scattering (Walt 1964).

The inclusion of high latitude interactions and of oblique wave propagation and the resulting diffusion at all cyclotron harmonics are all necessary to obtain the lifetimes shown in Fig. 2. The neglect of any of these effects would significantly alter the magnitudes of the lifetimes, and it would result in a far more rapid increase of the lifetimes at L-values outside the inner edge of the electron slot. Including these effects appears to greatly extend the role of whistler-driven electron pitch-angle diffusion in the radiation belts.

Acknowledgements: This research was done in collaboration with Charles F. Kennel and Richard M. Thorne and benefited from fruitful conversations with F. V. Coroniti. The work was supported in part by NSF, GA-28045; NASA, NGR-05-007-190; and an NSF Traineeship.

REFERENCES

Adronov, A. A. & Trakhtengerts, V. Y. 1964. *Geomagn. and Aeronomy 4*, 181.

Cornwall, J. M. 1964. *J. Geophys. Res. 69*, 1251.

Cornwall, J. M. 1966. *J. Geophys. Res. 71*, 2185.

Dragt, A. J. 1961. *J. Geophys. Res. 66*, 1641.

Dunckel, N. & Helliwell, R. A. 1969. *J. Geophys. Res. 74*, 6371.

Dungey, J. W. 1963. *Planet, Space Sci. 11*, 591.

Engel, R. D. 1965. *Phys. Fluids 8*, 939.

Kennel, C. F. 1966. *Phys. Fluids 9*, 2190.

Kennel, C. F. 1967. abstract, *Trans. Am. Geophys. Union, 48*, 180.

Kennel, C. F. 1969. In Williams, D. & Mead, G. (eds.). *Magnetospheric Physics*, p. 379. American Geophysical Union, Washington.

Kennel, C. F. & Englemann, F. 1966. *Phys. Fluids 9*, 2377.

Kennel, C. F. & Petschek, H. E. 1966a. *J. Geophys. Res. 71*, 1.

Kennel, C. F. & Petschek, H. E. 1966b. Avco Everett Research Laboratory, Research Report 259.

Lyons, L. R. & Thorne, R. M. 1970. *Planet. Space Sci. 18*, 1753.

Pfitzer, K. A. 1968. Ph. D. Thesis, School of Physics and Astronomy, University of Minnesota.

Pfitzer, K. A., Kane, S. & Winkler, J. R. 1966. *Space Res. 6*, 702.

Roberts, C. S. 1968. In McCormac, B. M. (ed.). *Earth's Particles and Fields*, p. 317, Reinhold, New York.

Roberts, C. S. & Schultz, M. 1968. *J. Geophys. Res. 73*, 7361.

Russell, C. T., Holzer, R. E. & Smith, F. J. 1969. *J. Geophys. Res. 74*, 755.

Russell, C. T. & Thorne, R. M. 1970. *Cosmic Electrodynamics 1*, 67.

Thorne, R. M., Burton, R. K., Holzer, R. E. & Smith, F. J. 1970. abstract, *Trans. Am. Geophys. Union 51*, 803.

Tverskoy, B. A. 1967. *Geomagn. and Aeronomy 7*, 177.

Van Allen, J. A. 1964. *Nature 203*, 1006.

Walt, M. 1964. *J. Geophys. Res. 69*, 3947.

Mid-Latitude D-Region Ionization Associated with the 'Slot' in Radiation Belt Electrons

R. M. THORNE

Department of Meteorology, University of California, Los Angeles

Abstract: High energy electrons are continuously removed from the radiation belts through resonant pitch-angle scattering by ELF electromagnetic whistler mode waves. Within the plasmasphere the naturally occurring ELF turbulence shows no definite polarization and is confined to a relatively narrow band centered on a few hundred Hz. Parasitic cyclotron resonance of relativistic electrons with this wave turbulence readily accounts for the electron lifetimes and the spatial location of the 'slot'. Resulting precipitation fluxes indicate that this process must be considered as an important ionization source for the nocturnal D-regions of the ionosphere. This precipitation source appears to be related to storm after-effects.

The concept that radiation belt particle precipitation should be considered as a significant ionizing agent for the lower ionosphere is by no means novel. It has been well established that particle precipitation is of the utmost importance at high latitudes and we were treated to a magnificent display of such particle influx during our first night at Dalseter. Precipitation fluxes at middle latitudes, however, are considerably less than those in the auroral zone. Nevertheless, there is a general consensus of opinion that precipitating energetic electron fluxes are sufficient to explain the enhanced D-region ionization observed following magnetic storms (Lauter & Knuth 1967, Belrose & Thomas 1968). Furthermore, it has been suggested that precipitating electrons are at least partially responsible for the winter anomaly (Maehlum 1967, Manson & Merry 1970) and that they compete favorably with other nocturnal ionization sources (Potemra & Zmuda 1970).

In a previous paper at this symposium Lyons presented a theoretical description of the loss of energetic electrons from the region of radiation belts within the plasmapause. In his model the electrons are scattered in pitch angle by resonant interactions with ambient whistler-mode turbulence and are thus precipitated into the upper atmosphere. Using observed characteristics of the plasmaspheric hiss band (Thorne et al. 1970), he finds excellent agreement with the average electron lifetimes measured throughout the plasmasphere. In what follows I will discuss the impor-

tance of such electron precipitation as a D-region ionization source. My remarks will of necessity be somewhat qualitative since the work is still in the early stages of development.

The major difference between the approach that I will adopt and those already published in the literature is in the way the precipitation flux is evaluated. Previous treatments have arbitrarily assumed some average energy spectrum for the precipitation flux. Lyons's model, however, precisely specifies the loss rate and hence the precipitation flux as a function of energy. At each invariant latitude the calculations predict the energy of electrons which have the strongest interaction with the ambient plasmaspheric hiss band and hence are most rapidly removed from the radiation belts. As an example, referring to Fig. 2 of the paper by Lyons, it is clear that at L = 3 (or $\Lambda \simeq 55°$), electrons with an energy of about 300 keV are lost most rapidly with a typical lifetime of a few days. Higher and lower energy electrons have considerably longer lifetimes. It is apparent that the spectrum of the precipitating particles depends very critically on invariant latitude and will not in general be a monotonically decreasing function of energy (as has been generally used in previous theoretical studies). In fact at each L-value there is a minimum energy which can interact with the waves and thus be removed. This lower cut off in the precipitation spectrum moves to higher energies as Λ is decreased.

The unidirectional precipitation flux J_P (aver-

63

aged over the loss cone) can be obtained in terms of the average unidirectional trapped flux J_T from the expression developed by Coroniti & Kennel (1970)

$$\frac{J_P}{J_T} = \frac{\tau_{min}}{\tau_{loss}}. \tag{1}$$

Here τ_{loss} is the precipitation loss time (to be obtained from Fig. 2 of Lyons) and

$$\tau_{min} = \frac{2\tau_B}{\alpha_0^2} \tag{2}$$

is the minimum lifetime for particles subject to strong pitch-angle diffusion (Kennel 1969); τ_B is the quarter bounce period along the geomagnetic field, and α_0 is the pitch-angle of the atmospheric loss cone. Notice that on strong pitch-angle diffusion J_P approaches J_T; in other words the pitch-angle distribution becomes isotropic. For the high energy particles between $L = 2$ and 4 we estimate τ_B to be about 10 secs. This is clearly much less than the predicted lifetimes (~ 1 day) indicating that the electrons are removed from the 'slot' by weak pitch-angle scattering.

Following a magnetic storm the slot between the inner and outer radiation belts (say $2 < L < 4$) is repopulated with energetic electrons. Fluxes generally increase by several orders of magnitude and typically attain values of order 10^4 electrons cm^{-2} sec^{-1} sterad^{-1} keV^{-1} for energies of a few 100 keV (Pfitzer et al. 1966). Using (1) and the lifetime estimates of Lyons, we thus obtain precipitation fluxes J_P (300 keV) ~ 1 electron cm^{-2} sec^{-1} sterad^{-1} keV^{-1} at $L = 3$. Rees (1964) estimates that the energy of such precipitating electrons is deposited over a range of altitude 20 km deep centered near 75 km. Assuming that on an average one requires roughly 30 eV to produce an ion pair implies that each 300 keV electron will produce 10^4 ion pairs over this altitude range. The predicted precipitation flux is thus equivalent to an average production rate $Q \approx 1$ ion pair cm^{-3} sec^{-1}. On the assumption that the density of negative ions greatly exceeds that of electrons over the altitude range of interest we follow Potemra & Zmuda (1970) and use an ion-ion recombination coefficient of between (10^{-8} and 10^{-7}) cm^3 sec^{-1} to obtain equilibrium ion densities of (3×10^3 to 10^4) ions cm^{-3} which

agree favorably with recent measurements. Corresponding electron densities will of course be considerably less. One important feature of the present model which differs from earlier work is that the selective precipitation of only the high energy components of the radiation belt implies that only the lower layers of the ionosphere will be affected. Furthermore, the altitude range over which energy is deposited will be lower at lower invariant latitudes due to the increase in the energy of precipitating particles.

In summary, it appears that under certain conditions the precipitation of energetic electrons in cyclotron resonance with the observed whistler-mode band of wave turbulence is an important ionization source for the ionospheric D-region. This offers the possibility of building self-consistent models for the radiation belts which both account for the observations of particles and waves in the magnetosphere and make firm predictions of the transfer of radiation belt energy to the ionosphere. In particular the model presented here will be further developed in an attempt to account for observed ionization enhancements following magnetic storms (storm after-effects) and certain properties of the nocturnal D-region.

Acknowledgments: This work was supported in part by NSF Grant GA-28045 and by Air Force Cambridge Research Laboratory contract F 19628–71–C–0075.

REFERENCES

Belrose, J. S. & Thomas, L. 1968. *J. Atmos. Terr. Phys. 30*, 1397.
Coroniti, F. V. & Kennel, C. F. 1970. *J. Geophys. Res. 75*, 1279.
Kennel, C. F. 1969. *Rev. Geophys. 7*, 379.
Lauter, E. A. & Knuth, R. 1967. *J. Atmos. Terr. Phys. 29*, 411.
Maehlum, B. N. 1967. *J. Geophys. Res. 72*, 2287.
Manson, A. H. & Merry, M. W. J. 1970. *J. Atmos. Terr. Phys. 32*, 1169.
Pfitzer, K. A., Kane, S. & Winckler, J. R. 1966. *Space Res. 6*, 702.
Potemra, T. A. & J. Zmuda, A. J. 1970. *J. Geophys. Res. 75*, 7161.
Rees, M. H. 1964. *Planet. Space Sci. 12*, 722.
Thorne, R. M., Burton, R. K., Holzer, R. E. & Smith, E. J. 1970. *Trans. Am. Geophys. Union 51*, 803.

The High Latitude Ionosphere above the E-Layer

B. HULTQVIST AND L. LISZKA
Kiruna Geophysical Observatory, S–981 01 Kiruna 1, Sweden

Abstract: After a brief summary of the morphology of the upper polar ionosphere, the physical processes believed to be responsible for the morphology are discussed, namely the effects on the F-layer and above of energetic particle precipitation, winds, magnetic field aligned currents, and electrostatic fields.

1. BRIEF SUMMARY OF THE MORPHOLOGY

The polar F-region shows a very variable and complex behaviour with several more or less irregularly occurring maxima and minima. It is mainly in the last half a dozen years that some regularities have become recognized and that an understanding of some of the behaviour in terms of physical processes has begun to develop.

The high-latitude upper ionosphere is characterized by the following phenomena:

a. The polar peak (neutral point peak) around magnetic noon at ~ 75° invariant latitude.

b. The auroral peak (auroral cliff) in the auroral zone at night.

c. The troughs at subauroral latitudes at night as well as occasionally at higher latitudes.

d. The UT-control of the polar cap F-layer.

e. The occasional existence of an extremely thin ionosphere above 1000 km.

f. The high degree of irregularity poleward of the trough.

Fig. 1 illustrates in a schematic way the existence in the upper ionosphere of the polar peak on the opposite side, with the trough just equatorward of it.

Fig. 2 shows observations by Hagg (1967) of electron densities below 30 el/cm3 at altitudes between about 1500 and 3000 km. According to Timleck & Nelms (1969) electron densities below

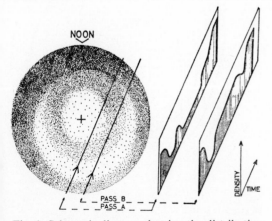

Fig. 1. Schematic diagram showing the distribution of electrons in the altitude range 300–1000 km above the winter polar region. The electron density is greater where the density of the dots is greater. The polar cavity, the trough, the plasma torus and the most poleward part of the plasmasphere are shown. The sketch on the right shows two possible distributions observed along satellite tracks (after Thomas & Andrews 1969).

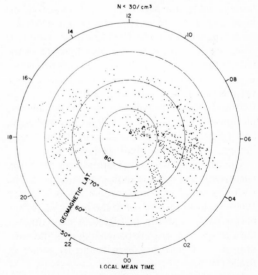

Fig. 2. Points of observation on board Alouette II, in the altitude range 1500–3000 km, of electron densities below 30/cm3 (after Hagg 1967).

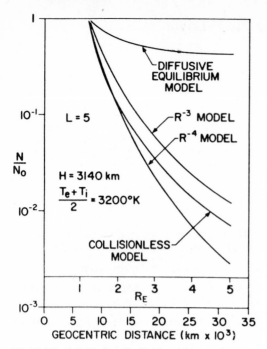

Fig. 3. Plasma density distribution along a magnetic field line, whose apex in the equatorial plane is at $L = 5R_e$, is shown for a diffusive equilibrium, a collisionless model, and R^{-3} and R^{-4} power law models indicated by whistler observations (after Bauer 1969).

100 cm^{-3} were observed in 12% of all measurements by Alouette II north of 60° invariant latitude in the winter period analysed. Observations indicate that O$^+$ is dominating even at 3000 km under these conditions. The electron density falls off much more rapidly with altitude north of the trough than south of it. This is also illustrated by Fig. 3. Thus, although within the plasmasphere the ionosphere is produced by solar XUV radiation and is in diffusive equilibrium, outside the plasmasphere it is not in diffusive equilibrium, and energetic particle production plays a very important role, as we shall see later.

The trough is two to five latitude degrees wide, narrower in the evening than in the morning. The width is inversely proportional to K_p (Sharp 1966). Its location relative to the projection of the plasmapause is shown in Fig. 4. A maximum of the electron temperature coinciding with the position of the trough has been found by Miller & Brace (1969).

Ionospheric storms produce large electron density changes on a global scale. The onset of the storm is generally difficult to determine, and the

general characteristics during its initial phase have not been well established. In the polar region an foF2 enhancement can be seen some 12 hours before the SC of the associated magnetic storm (see Fig. 5). A simplified generalization of the electron density variation in the entire F-layer is shown in Fig. 6.

At high latitudes the electron density varies a good deal in both space and time and it is therefore difficult to generalize. The overall storm effect seems, however, to be a decrease of electron density, but near the auroral oval there is generally an increase. One of the most ambitious investigations of the relative variation of the electron density at different altitudes has been carried out by Sato & Chan (1969) on the basis of Alouette measurements. Some results are shown in Fig. 7. This Figure does not show a polar peak enhancement, so the schematic Figs. 1 and 6 on the one hand and Fig. 7 on the other are obviously different in this respect. The electron density and the electron temperature have also been found to be much enhanced over regions with active auroras

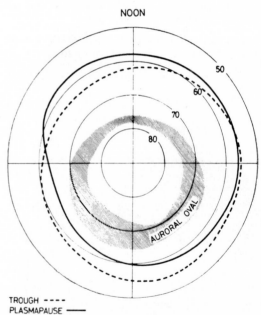

Fig. 4. The relative positions in invariant latitude of the trough boundary and the plasmapause projected along a field line to the ionosphere. The positions given are those expected for moderate magnetic activity ($K_p \simeq 3$). The position of the trough is extended over the dayside, where a real trough is not observed, on the basis of observations of a sudden drop (step) in the latitudinal distribution of electron density (after Thomas & Andrews 1968).

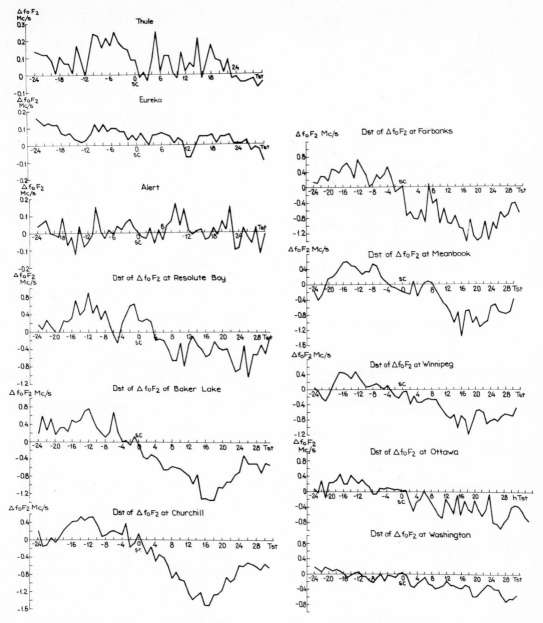

Fig. 5. In high latitudes an enhancement of foF2 is generally seen some 12 hours before the sudden commencement of the geomagnetic storm associated with the ionospheric storm (after Ondoh 1966).

by other workers (e.g. Nishida 1967, Norton & Findlay 1969). An example of electron density distribution is shown in Fig. 8. Thus it seems that the information is somewhat contradictory. The F2 peak height is in general increased during storms in all seasons and for all latitudes (Matsushita 1963). The slab thickness is also increased

(see e.g. Taylor & Earnshaw 1969, Liszka & Olsson 1971).

The ionospheric electron *content* over the polar caps increases during the first hours of a storm, after which it decreases (Bratteng 1971). At sub-auroral latitudes a decrease of electron content is seen to be accompanied by an expansion of the

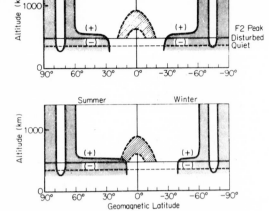

Fig. 6. The schematic distribution of electron density variations in the upper ionosphere on the dayside during the main phase of a geomagnetic storm (after Obayashi & Matuura 1970).

layer during the first day of a storm. This is illustrated in Fig. 9.

2. PHYSICAL PROCESSES OF IMPORTANCE FOR THE PRODUCTION OF THE POLAR F-LAYER CHARACTERISTICS

The continuity equation for the electrons is generally written

$$\partial N_e/\partial t = Q - L - \text{div} (N_eV). \tag{1}$$

The streaming velocity $V = V_d + V_N + V_E$ (cf. e.g. Obayashi & Matuura 1970), where V_D is the velocity of ambipolar diffusion, V_N is the velocity due to air drag, and V_E is the velocity due to electric or electromagnetic drift.

Q is influenced by energetic particle precipitation (and, of course, by solar XUV radiation).

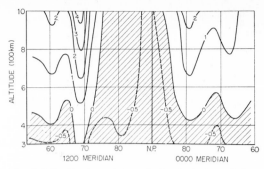

Fig. 8. Distribution of the relative deviation of electron density during a storm from average values. The K_p value was 9–. In the shaded area the electron density is reduced (after Nishida 1967).

L is influenced by plasma density, composition, and temperature.

Div (N_eV) depends on pressure and temperature gradients (in neutral air as well as in electrons and ions), on neutral air density, on the Coriolis force, kimematic viscosity, electric and magnetic fields, and electrical currents.

We are still far from being able to determine all the parameters needed for evaluation of the whole picture. In the last few years we have gained a new understanding of the roles of a number of processes. These may be listed as follows:

– particle precipitation
– winds
– electric currents
– electrostatic fields

Particle precipitation may influence all three terms on the right-hand side of (1).

Winds may have an effect on L and div (N_eV) and this is true also for the electric current and electrostatic fields. The latter may also influence Q.

Among the winds the 'polar wind' is an interesting case, thought to drive the light ions out of the

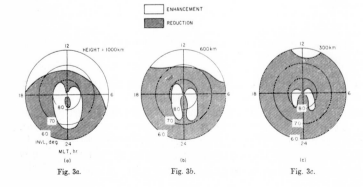

Fig. 7. Storm-time electron density variations at 1000 km (a), 600 km (b), and 300 km (c) against invariant latitude and magnetic local time. In shaded areas the electron density is reduced; in white areas it is enhanced (after Sato & Chan 1969).

68

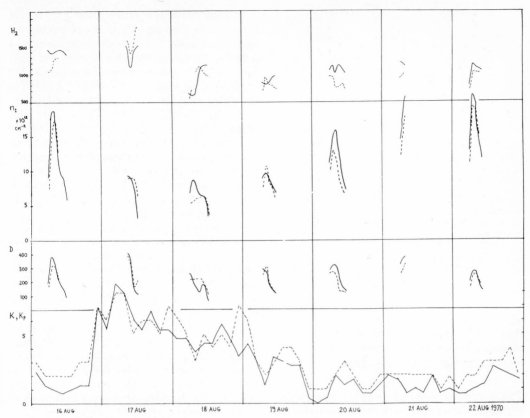

Fig. 9. The Figure shows, from the top, H_2: the altitude where the electron density has the value $10^4/cm^3$; n_t: the total electron content (per cm^2 column); D: the slab thickness; K: Kiruna (dashed curve); and K_p: solid curve. The satellite was visible only during limited periods of each day. The Figure illustrates the decrease of the electron content at subauroral latitudes during the storm (after Liszka & Olsson 1971).

polar ionosphere into the magnetosphere at supersonic speeds. It is the subject of another paper presented at this conference and it will therefore not be dealt with here.

In the remainder of this paper the properties of the polar F-layer which are thought to have to do with the four basic phenomena listed above are discussed.

3. EFFECTS OF PARTICLE PRECIPITATION

a. *Production of ionization.* Firstly, the energetic particles ionize the atmosphere. The polar peak and the auroral peak are due to precipitation of particles of energies around 1 keV or below. A 'plasma torus' is produced approximately along the auroral oval with a 'polar cavity' inside it (see Fig. 1).

b. *Heating of the ionosphere.* The precipitating energetic particles do not only ionize the atmosphere, they also heat it. It is known that the thermospheric temperature (Roemer 1969) as well as the electron and ion temperatures (Dyson & Zmuda 1970) in high latitudes increase during geomagnetic disturbances. This gives rise to:

i. Thermal expansion: the elevation of the F2-layer peak and the increased slab thickness are certainly due partly to thermal expansion (Garriott & Rishbeth 1963), but this effect alone is not sufficient to explain the observed descrease of NmF2 (Thomas 1966).

ii. Change of loss processes: the reaction rates for $O^+ + N_2 \rightarrow NO^+ + N$ and $O^+ + O_2 \rightarrow O_2^+ + O$ decrease slightly with increasing temperature for temperatures below some $600°$ K (Ferguson 1969). However, if N_2 is vibrationally excited,

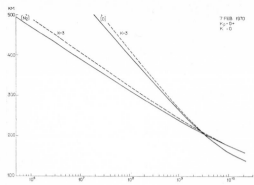

Fig. 10. The Figure illustrates the effect of increased local disturbance on the ratio between the densities of atomic oxygen and molecular nitrogen. The solid curves are for $K_p = O^+$, $K = O$. The dotted curves are for $K_p = O^+$, $K = 3$. The densities of both O and N_2 increase significantly in practically the entire altitude range shown, but the increase in the N_2 density is about twice as great as that of the O density.

which it may possibly be in regions with high electron temperature, then the rate coefficient will increase very rapidly with temperature above approximately 1200° K (Thomas 1968).

iii. Change of composition: relative N_2 concentration increases with increasing temperature (see Fig. 10). Relative increase of the concentration of molecular components will enhance the loss rate of electrons in the F-region and hence reduce the electron density. Conversely, relative increase of O will increase the electron density.

c. *Universal time control of the polar cap F-layer.* The shape of the polar cavity is not very regular, and has been found to vary with universal time. The average minimum size was about 20° near 20.00 UT during June/July 1967 and the maximum size was some 35° near 07.00 UT (Maehlum 1968). The time variation in the size of the cavity results in significant variations in electron fluxes between about 70° and 85° invariant latitude. Particle observations fit with electron density measurements concerning UT dependence (Maehlum 1969).

4. EFFECTS OF WINDS

Particle precipitation contributes, by heating the atmosphere, to the creation of winds. Other additional heat sources during disturbed conditions may be electric currents, MHD waves, gravity waves, and heat conduction from the magnetosphere.

a. *Regular global wind system above 120 km.* The normal solar heating of the upper atmosphere also sets up winds. It creates a high pressure centre a little to the east of the subsolar point and a low pressure centre approximately at its antipode. The resulting wind system is shown in Fig. 11. The calculated wind system there is based on Jacchia's atmosphere model. At the F-layer peak the wind speed is 50–100 m/s on the day side and 200–300 m/s in the night when the ion drag is much lower. The direction is poleward around noon, equatorward at midnight, westward in the morning and eastward in the evening, which latter directions are opposite to the drift directions of the ionized constituents and aurora.

The horizontal wind system also produces a vertical drift of a velocity of about 1 m/s (Kohl 1970), which transports about the same amount of energy as is absorbed in the entire thermosphere above 150 km from solar radiation. This wind system is also thought to be responsible for the diurnal temperature maximum being at about 1400 LT instead of shortly before sunset, as expected if solar XUV radiation is the dominant energy source and there are no winds. It also reduces the variation of the exospheric temperature from night to day to 1.3–1.5 from the value of about 2.5 expected when solar heating alone (without winds) is taken into account.

The above-mentioned influences on the F-layer ionization are thus very important and have many additional effects.

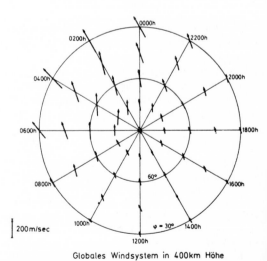

Globales Windsystem in 400km Höhe

Fig. 11. Calculated wind velocities at 400 km altitude for maximum conditions (after Kohl 1970).

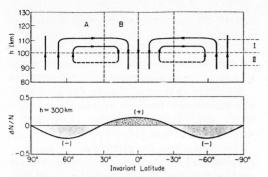

Fig. 12. Atmospheric meridional circulation caused by heating of the polar upper atmosphere and associated global changes of the ionospheric electron density (after Obayashi & Matuura 1970).

b. *Global meridional wind system associated with ionospheric storms.* Enhancement of thermospheric temperature accompanying magnetic disturbances is observed primarily at high latitudes. Therefore, one expects a large-scale atmospheric motion towards the equator to be set up (Obayashi & Matuura 1970). The neutral air drags the ions with it in the deeper layers of the ionosphere. In doing so the ionization may be driven upwards along the magnetic field lines, and this may decrease the loss rate and increase NmF2. So the existence of an equatorward wind may not be sufficient as an explanation of the storm effect decrease of foF2 in high latitudes.

Obayashi & Matuura (1970) have proposed a meridional circulation system (see Fig. 12) which changes the composition in such a way that the observed decrease of the F-layer electron density in high latitudes and the increase in the winter middle latitudes and at the equator can be understood. The circulation takes place around the turbopause. The forces driving equatorwards are the pressure gradient produced by particle precipitation and the Lorenz force ($J \times B$). The air moves up at higher latitudes increasing the N_2 concentration and moves down in the middle and low latitudes increasing the atomic oxygen concentration in lower layers. The circulation thus leads to an increase of the atomic oxygen concentration in middle latitude winter F-region, which may be the main cause of the winter anomaly.

There are also fairly local wind systems produced by auroral particle precipitation. Such a wind system probably plays an important role in the production of the main trough.

c. *Production of the trough.* The trough is not simply a result of the superposition of photon-produced and particle-produced ionization latitude profiles. A strong depletion of electron density is seen in the entire F2-layer and above. The F-layer trough is probably not caused mainly by escape of ionization along open field lines for the following reasons:

– In the F-layer the troughs (there are sometimes several of them) have a fairly small extension in latitude whereas in the height range 1500–3000 km almost the entire polar cap seems to be depleted. In any case one does not see the same structure there as in the F-layer. It therefore seems highly improbable that the structure in the F-layer should be due to varying rates of escape into the outer magnetosphere. Local effects in the F-layer have to be sought for. The escape effect (polar wind) may of course be important in the uppermost ionosphere.

– Troughs occur in a height range of high production, whereas nearly all ionization near the plasmapause in the equatorial plane must have been produced elsewhere and transported there over large distances, which takes considerable time. Significant phase shifts are therefore expected between the temporal behaviour of the trough and the projection of the plasmapause along the magnetic field lines.

– There are some new direct observations which show that the poleward boundary of the main trough follows in great detail the movement of the equatorial boundary of precipitation of 1 keV auroral particles. This has been found by Liszka & Turunen (1971) using ESRO 1 measurements and data from the net of ionospheric sounders in northern Scandinavia.

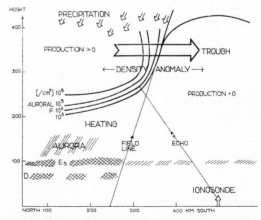

Fig. 13. Schematic situation in the ionosphere at the equatorward boundary of the particle precipitation zone (after Liszka & Turunen 1971).

The trough in the F-layer is therefore probably caused mainly by the following mechanism.

In the particle precipitation zone there is a strong additional ionization and also an increase of temperature, and thus density, in the F-region. This creates a high-pressure region from which winds blow away, i.e. equatorward on the equatorward side of the precipitation zone. Ionization cannot follow in the F-region because it is stuck to the magnetic field lines. Thus only the heated neutral atmosphere is blown away and the atmosphere is heated just outside the precipitation region without any additional ionization being introduced there. A schematic illustration of the situation is shown in Fig. 13. Increased temperature means increased loss rate due to (a) increased density, (b) increased relative concentration of N_2, and (c) increased electron temperature.

The driving of the ionization upwards by the wind counteracts this, but the upward wind may increase the relative N_2 concentration in the F-layer sufficiently to compensate for it. The escape rate from higher altitudes may also increase because of the increased temperature. There are direct observations of an increased density at the F-layer heights in the particle precipitation zone on Explorer 32 reported by Newton (1970). For the 300–550 km height range the density was about twice that of the Jacchia model, for the 550–700 km range it was three times that of the model. There are also direct observations in support of an increased relative concentration of molecular nitrogen in high latitudes. Hedin et al. (1970) found from OGO–6 measurements that at 70° geomagnetic latitude the N_2 density varied by a factor of 4, with maximum near midnight.

A relative increase of the N_2 density follows also immediately from an increase of the exospheric temperature in Jacchia's model and is shown in Figs. 10 and 14.

This mechanism for production of the main trough in the F-layer can also explain the observed fact that the width of the trough is inversely proportional to K_p (Liszka & Turunen 1971). Jacchia's exospheric temperature may be corrected with a term $\Delta T_a = 150 \cdot \exp\{-(\lambda_{sb} - \lambda)/5\}$ where λ_{sb} is the invariant latitude of the southern boundary of the precipitation zone and 150° K is taken to obtain agreement with Newton's density measurements. One then finds that the driving force of the wind decreases with increasing K_p (see Fig. 15). This also means that the loss coefficient, $\beta = \gamma [N_2]$, decreases (see Fig. 16).

d. *Universal time control of the polar cap F-layer.* Maehlum (1969) expressed the view that the observed UT control of the polar F-layer can only be understood in terms of particle precipitation. Recently, however, Challinor (1970) and King et al. (1970) have shown that the UT control in the Antarctic can be explained by the lifting of the F-layer and the consequently reduced loss rate,

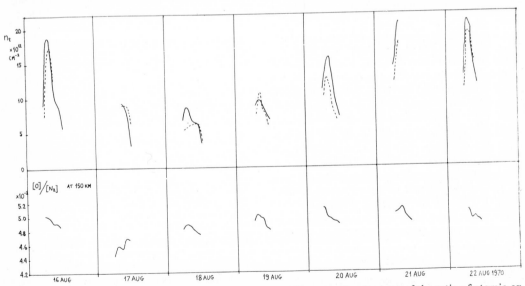

Fig. 14. For the same storm as shown in Fig. 9, this Figure illustrates the decrease of the ratio of atomic oxygen to molecular nitrogen densities during ionospheric storms (after Liszka & Olsson 1971).

72

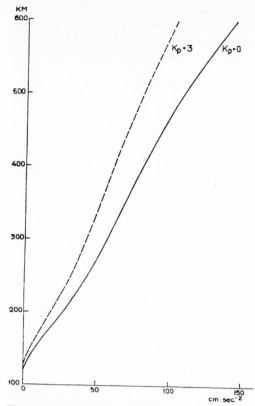

Fig. 15. The driving force for the neutral gas motion, $-(1/\varrho) \cdot dp/dx$ calculated at a distance of one latitude degree from the precipitation region as a function of altitude. The Jacchia model atmosphere for winter and low solar activity has been used. The solid line represents $K_p = 0$ and local $K = 0$, and the broken curve $K_p = 3$ and local $K = 0$ (after Liszka & Turunen 1971).

which has its maximum when the horizontal wind blows along the horizontal projection of the geomagnetic field lines. In the Antarctic this happens within a few hours of 06.00 UT for nearly all stations. In the Arctic the corresponding maximum of the F-layer electron density occurs at different UT for the different stations according to Challinor (1970), and good agreement is found between observations and theory. There is thus no real UT dependence in the Arctic, which detracts from Maehlum's theory and supports the wind explanation.

5. EFFECTS OF FIELD-ALIGNED CURRENTS

Block & Fälthammar (1968) have pointed out that due to the fact that the plasma is collision-dominated in the E-layer and practically collis-

sionless at the top of the ionosphere, one may expect that the relative contributions from electrons and positive ions to the magnetic-field-aligned current may be quite different in the upper and lower ionospheres, causing significant changes in the ionosphere. They have made model computations and have shown that quite appreciable effects on the plasma density in the upper F-layer may be produced by this process (see Fig. 17), if the currents can flow for sufficiently long time intervals (of several hours). The current intensities needed are well within the limits indicated by observations (corresponding to 10^9 ions/cm^{2}s or 10^{-6} amp/m^2). This effect may contribute to the observed depletion of the upper polar ionosphere.

6. ELECTROSTATIC FIELDS

Another basic phenomenon which may influence the plasma density in the uppermost ionosphere

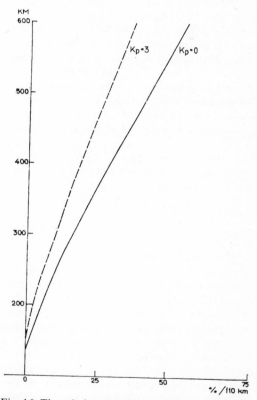

Fig. 16. The relative variation of the loss coefficient, β, along one latitude degree as a function of altitude. The calculations have been made for the same model as used in Fig. 15. The solid line corresponds to $K_p = 0$ and local $K = 0$, and the broken line to $K_p = 3$ and local $K = 0$ (after Liszka & Turunen 1971).

73

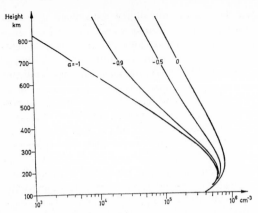

Fig. 17. Electron density distributions calculated for the following values of ion current density 3.7 μamp/cm^2 ($\alpha = -1$), 3.3 μamp/m^2 ($\alpha = -0.9$), 1.8 μamp/m^2 ($\alpha = -0.5$), and O μamp/m^2 ($\alpha = O$) (after Block & Fälthammar 1968).

is the fairly frequent existence of magnetic-field-aligned electric potential differences in the kV range over the polar caps. The existence of such potential differences is concluded from observations on board ESRO 1 satellites of ion pitch-angle distributions strongly peaked along the magnetic field lines. These electrostatic fields are thought to be produced by the interaction of the hot magnetospheric plasma and the cold ionosphere (Hultqvist 1970, 1971). This type of field is a stationary state type of phenomenon and may extend sometimes over large fractions of the polar cap. The lower boundary of the field region is located in, or fairly close to, the ionosphere and the field is directed downwards.

The existence in the uppermost ionosphere for a period of some hours of such electrostatic fields will, of course, have a profound influence on the plasma. The electric field will draw current out of the plasma until the field region is more or less empty of plasma. A stationary state is reached when the rate of diffusion of plasma into the field region from outside equals the rate of elimination of charged particles by the field. Below the layer there will be some increase of ion density. The electrons and ions inside the field region will sometimes be accelerated to keV energies, which will constitute a very special part of the energetic particle population, but which will not be discussed here. Finally, it is obvious that when these strong electric fields exist the polar wind cannot blow.

Acknowledgement: The research on which this paper is based has been supported in part by the Swedish Natural Science Research Council and the Swedish Board of Technical Development.

REFERENCES

Bauer, S. J. 1969. *Proc. IEEE 57*, 1114.
Block, L. P. & Fälthammar, C.-G. 1968. *J. Geophys. Res. 73*, 4807.
Bratteng, O. 1971. Personal communication.
Challinor, R. A. 1970. *J. Atmos. Terr. Phys. 32*, 1959.
Dyson, P. L. & Zmuda, A. J. 1970. *J. Geoph. Res. 75*, 1893.
Ferguson, E. E. 1969. *Ann. Geophys. 25*, 819.
Garriott, O. K. & Rishbeth, H. 1963. *Planet. Space Sci. 11*, 587.
Hagg, E. L. 1967. *Can. J. Phys. 45*, 27.
Hedin, A. E., Reber, C. A. & Horowitz, R. 1970. Paper presented at 1970 National Fall Meeting, San Fransisco, December 1970.
Hultqvist, B. 1970. Proceedings of the Solar-Terrestrial Physics Symposium in Leningrad, May 1970.
Hultqvist, B. 1971. *Planet. Space Sci*. In press.
King, J. W., Eccles, D. & Kohl, H. 1970. Personal communication to Challinor.
Kohl, H. 1970. *Space Research X, 550*, North-Holland Publ. Co., Amsterdam.
Liszka, L. & Olsson, S. 1971. KGO Report 712.
Liszka, L. & Turunen, T. 1971. KGO Preprint No. 71:306.
Maehlum, B. N. 1968. *J. Geophys. Res. 73*, 3459.
Maehlum, B. N. 1969. *J. Atmosph. Terr. Phys. 31*, 531.
Matsushita, S. 1963. Proceedings. International Conference on the Ionosphere, London, The Institute of Physics and the Physical Society, p. 120.
Miller, N. J. & Brace, L. H. 1969. *J. Geophys. Res. 74*, 5752.
Newton, G. P. 1970. *J. Geophys. Res. 75*, 5510.
Nishida, A. 1967. *J. Geophys. Res. 72*, 6051.
Norton, R. B. & Findlay, J. A. *Planet. Space Sci. 17*, 1867.
Obayashi, T. & Matuura, N. 1970. Proceedings of the Solar-Terrestrial Physics Symposium, Leningrad, May 1970.
Ondoh, T. 1966. *Rept. Ionosphere and Space Res. Japan 20*, 79.
Roemer, M. 1969. *Ann. Geophys. 25*, 765.
Sato, T. & Chan, K. L. 1969. *J. Geophys. Res. 74*, 2208.
Sharp, G. W. 1966. *J. Geophys. Res. 71*, 1345.
Taylor, G. N. & Earnshaw, R. D. 1969. *J. Atmos. Terr. Phys. 31*, 211.
Thomas, G. R. 1968. *J. Atmos. Terr. Phys. 30*, 1429.
Thomas, J. O. & Andrews, M. K. 1968. *J. Geophys. Res. 73*, 7407.
Thomas, J. O. & Andrews, M. K. 1969. *Planet. Space Sci. 17*, 433
Timleck, P. L. & Nelms, G. L. 1969. *Proc. IEEE 57*, 1164.

74

High Latitude Variations of F-Region Electron Temperature

W. J. RAITT AND A. P. WILLMORE

Mullard Space Science Laboratory, University College, London

Abstract: Results of electron temperature measurements made on the satellite ESRO–IA over the N polar region are described. It is shown that during geomagnetically disturbed periods, and also during a particle event when 'field-aligned' low energy protons were observed, a broad zone of high temperatures develops with maximum temperatures at about 70° magnitude latitude. This shows little local time dependence and is well correlated with the presence of energetic electrons. During the main phase of the storm, a second zone develops in the midnight sector at latitudes near the trace in the ionosphere of the plasmapause. No energetic particles are associated with this zone, in which the highest temperatures are observed. In the first zone, the electron density is enhanced relative to the value extrapolated from lower latitudes, while in the second it is diminished. Possible heating mechanisms in the two zones are discussed.

1. INTRODUCTION

Extensive measurements of electron temperature over a period of 10 years have been made in the mid-latitude F-region by means of satellites and incoherent scatter observatories (see Willmore 1970 for a review). It is thus known that in this region the day temperature is largely governed by the balance between heat input by solar EUV radiation and loss by a variety of collision processes, while during the night heat which has been stored in the magnetosphere during the day is brought down into the ionosphere by thermal conduction along the geomagnetic field lines. At latitudes above 50° the importance of solar radiation as a heat source rapidly diminishes, yet observations show that the electron temperature may even exceed the values normally encountered at lower latitudes. Heating mechanisms which have been explored theoretically by Walker & Rees (1968a), Walker & Rees (1968b), and Rees & Walker (1968) include secondary electrons produced by the interaction with the atmosphere of precipitated energetic particles, electric field heating by field components transverse to the geomagnetic field, and thermal conduction from hot regions of the magnetosphere.

The observations to be described here were made from Langmuir probes carried on the satellite ESRO–IA. The probes were mounted on booms and were operated in an AC mode. The satellite was launched on 3 October 1968 into a near-polar orbit with apogee 1550 km and perigee 260 km. It was magnetically stabilised and the plane probes were so mounted that the surface of one was approximately parallel to and of the other approximately normal to the geomagnetic field direction. All the results given here were obtained from the probe mounted normal to the geomagnetic field. Detailed descriptions of the AC technique can be found in Bowen et al. (1964), Wrenn (1969), and Raitt (1970), and of the spacecraft and the probe installations in Page (1970).

2. OBSERVATIONS

Quiet orbit behaviour. – Orbit 281 on 23 October 1968 (Fig. 1) is a good example of the temperature distribution in a magnetically quiet period. This Figure, as with all the observations reported in this paper, refers to the N polar region. On the nightside, at about 23^h 30^m LST, the electron temperature is constant at 1100°K. There is a small rise over the polar cap to about 1300°K on the dayside. These temperatures are somewhat higher than the neutral atmosphere temperatures at lower latitudes, presumably because of heat conducted down from the magnetosphere. Raitt (1970) has given similar data for another quiet period.

Storm of 12–13 October 1968. – Fig. 2a shows data assembled from 15 consecutive N-bound passes over the polar region above 40°N. Since the orbit plane precesses only slowly relative to the Sun, this Figure does not show the polar cap at a fixed universal and varying local time, but rather at a fixed local time (which is approximately 24^h) and varying universal times. It is impossible

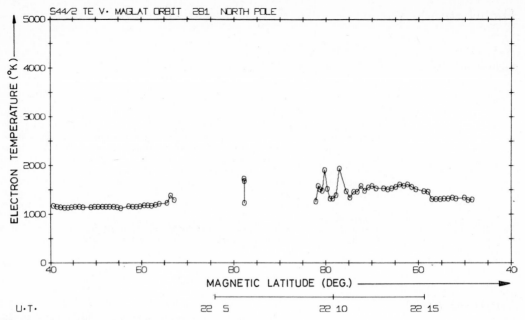

Fig. 1. Polar temperature distribution during magnetically quiet period.

in principle to distinguish variations which arise from changes in universal time or from the changes in the longitude of the orbit which also occur, but from a comparison with the results of sections 2c and 2e, which show similar results for a longitude 90° further west, it appears that storm time is the relevant variable.

A sudden commencement occurred at $06^h 18^m$ on 12 October, i.e. about six hours before the start of the data shown in Fig. 2, which thus refers to the main and recovery phases of the storm. It can be seen that temperatures up to 3000°K were recorded over a broad zone centred at about 60° magnetic latitude. During the early hours of 13 October a high temperature zone, with temperatures exceeding 4000°K, developed at rather lower latitudes, persisting to the end of the period of observation, i.e. for at least nine hours.

The average position of the plasmapause deduced from a relation given by Chappell et al. (1970) based on OGO–V observations is also given on Fig. 2a. Results obtained from another experiment on this satellite (Norman, private communication) tend generally to place the plasmapause closer to the Earth in disturbed periods, as does the empirical formula due to Binsack (1967). It is clear that the high temperature zone correlates well with the trace in the ionosphere of

the plasmapause, but because of these uncertainties in the precise position of the latter, it is not clear whether the zone is just on the equatorward side as shown or approximately centred on it. We shall see in section 2c that the high temperature zone can be identified with the 'mid-latitude trough' in the ionosphere discovered from topside sounder observations. Rycroft & Thomas (1970) have shown statistically that the trough and the plasmapause approximately coincide, whilst Rycroft & Burnell (1970) showed on one particular occasion that the plasmapause lay just inside the poleward boundary of the trough.

Fig. 2b shows the corresponding results on the dayside at a local solar time of 12^h, obtained from the S-bound passes over the N polar cap. The temperatures here are lower and confined to higher latitudes. The poleward shift of the temperature maximum is about 10°, of a similar magnitude to the diurnal movement of the auroral oval. Again the temperature falls to a minimum over the polar cap. The most striking feature is the absence of the high temperature zone observed in the night hours.

Storm of 19 October 1968. – Two other storms which occurred under approximately similar circumstances of local time and altitude to that described in the last section were studied and

76

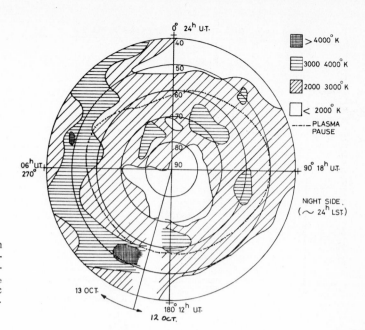

Fig. 2. a. Contour plots of T_e in magnetic latitude-geographic longitude plane, local time approximately 24ʰ. b. Contour plots of T_e in magnetic latitude-geographic longitude plane, local time approximately 12ʰ.

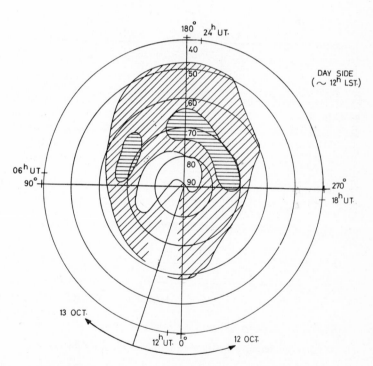

found to give similar results. One of these will be described, since additional relevent observations are available. The data refers to the recovery phase of a moderate disturbance, with Kp values around 4 during the period covered by the electron temperature observations, which are shown for two consecutive passes in Fig. 3. The local time when the satellite approaches the polar cap is approximately 24ʰ; as it leaves it is 12ʰ. The arrows give the plasmapause position according to the empirical relation of Chappell et al. (1970).

The high temperature zone associated with the

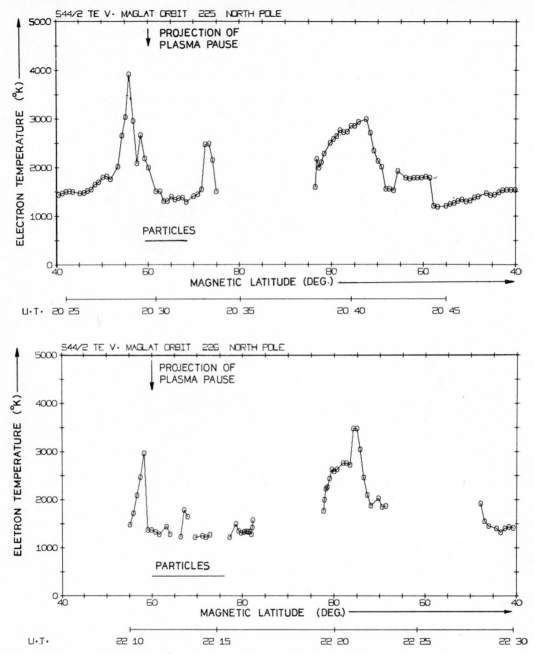

Fig. 3. Polar temperature distribution during moderately disturbed period.

plasmapause on the nightside is clearly seen, together with the high-latitude zone of rather lower temperature which is especially clear on the dayside in this case. Comparison of the two orbits shows a general decrease of electron temperature to be taking place. Also marked is the portion of the orbit over the Tromso telemetry station where electrons of energy greater than 1.4 keV were detected by an energetic particle experiment on the satellite (Hultqvist, private communication, data exchanged in ESRO–I joint study); data are not available on the dayside, which was out of

78

range of the station. It will be seen that the poleward boundary of the high temperature zone coincides with the equatorward boundary of the energetic particles, a feature of every pass for which both observations are available. Another quite common feature which can be seen in orbit 226 (and also in Fig. 5) is the remarkable sharpness of the N edge of the hot zone. Within the region of particle precipitation, the nightside temperatures are 1300–1400°K, i.e. they are enhanced by only 200–300°K above the quiet day values.

The electron density data for these orbits show that a substantial reduction occurs in the high temperature zone on the nightside. This is similar to, though less marked than, that which can be seen in Fig. 5. The density falls at the temperature peak to a value which is lower by a factor of 2–3 than that estimated by extrapolation from lower latitudes. The recovery in density is very sharp on the N side. From its relationship to the plasmapause we can thus deduce that the high temperature zone is identical with the well-known 'midlatitude trough' in the ionosphere, as noted in section 2b. We should note, however, that the temperature in the mid-latitude trough is enhanced, leading to the formation of the high temperature zone, only in the midnight sector.

Solar Proton Event of 25 February 1969. – The solar proton event of 25 February 1969 coincided with a prolonged interval of magnetic disturbance

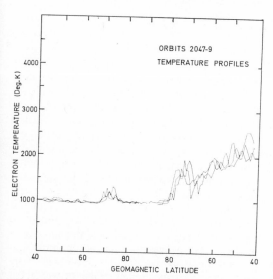

Fig. 4. Polar temperature distributions during moderately disturbed period coinciding with the solar proton event of 25 February 1969.

of moderate intensity during which data for a number of orbits have been analysed. Fig. 4 shows typical results for some of these. The LST was 07ʰ approaching and 19ʰ when leaving the polar cap. Also marked are times when energetic electrons were encountered (Riedler 1970). It will be seen that the temperature rise is always small (about 500°K), that it coincides with the region of precipitation, and that it occurs in regions of enhanced electron density. No evidence exists throughout the period for the high temperature zone, which is thus observed to occur only in the midnight sector. All these remarks are equally applicable to the other orbits analysed in this period.

Event of 30 November 1968. – Of the events for which data have so far been analysed, the most intense electron temperature enhancements occurred in that of 30 November 1968. The temperature and density profiles for two selected orbits on this day are shown in Fig. 5, together with the positions of the plasmapause and the regions where electrons with energies near 1.4 keV were found. The energetic particle data is available only for the nighttime section of the orbit. This is the approach to the polar cap where the local time is approximately 22ʰ; correspondingly the local time on leaving the cap is 10ʰ.

Apart from the remarkably high temperatures, all the features associated in the previous sections with geomagnetic disturbance can be seen. It will be convenient to summarise them. The temperature is elevated in a broad, high latitude zone on both the day- and nightsides. This zone coincides with the region where 1.4 keV electrons are encountered and in it the ambient electron density is enhanced. On the nightside only a second zone of yet higher temperature exists approximately coincident with the trace in the ionosphere of the plasmapause, the poleward boundary of this zone coinciding accurately with the equatorward boundary of the energetic electrons. This zone has a very sharp boundary on the poleward side and in it the electron density is very much reduced relative to the extrapolated value from lower latitudes.

The remarkable feature is that this very strong event did not occur during a period of geomagnetic disturbance, Kp ranging only from 0_0 to $1+$ on this day. The day was originally one of those selected for cooperative studies by the ESRO–I experimenters at the instance of the particle experimenters, because on this day anistropic fluxes

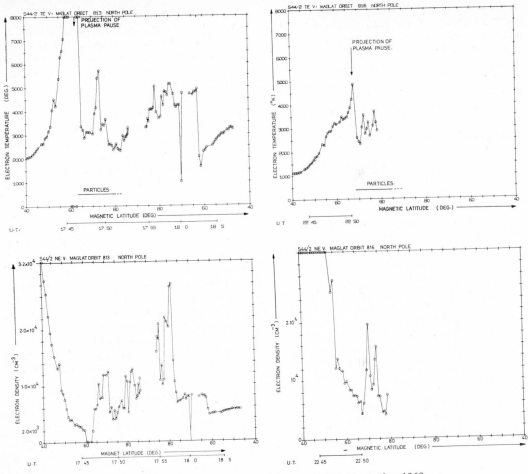

Fig. 5. Electron temperatures and density profiles for the event of 30 November 1968.

6 keV protons were observed, the pitch-angle distribution being peaked along the field line (Hultqvist, private communication). The electron fluxes were not unusually large, being about the same as during the geomagnetically disturbed days previously discussed.

3. DISCUSSION

From the observations described in section 2, we can see that in general the electron temperature in polar regions in magnetically quiet conditions is but moderately enhanced above the neutral gas value. At times of magnetic disturbance, enhanced temperatures of several thousand degrees K occur. These are associated with electron density changes and with energetic particles, the relationship having been summarised in section 2e. In

addition, on one occasion, very large electron temperature increases have been observed during a magnetically quiet period when a sequence of events closely resembling a magnetic storm appears to have occurred without an associated magnetic disturbance. The interpretation of the observations is very much complicated by this event, since it is not clear whether or not it must be accounted for in the same way as a magnetic storm, or if the resemblances are merely coincidental. It is also not clear how common a phenomenon it is. Here we shall be content to discuss the magnetic disturbance phenomena in the light of past theoretical studies, pointing out the difficulties in the interpretation which are raised if it must be applied to the 30 November 1969 event without modification.

From the different behaviour of electron density, the different temporal variations, and the different relation to the energetic particles, it appears that different heating mechanisms must operate in what have here been distinguished as the high-latitude and the high-temperature zones.

The high-latitude zone may be accounted for in terms of heating due to secondary electrons produced in the interaction of energetic precipitated electrons with the atmosphere. This conclusion would be justified on the following grounds.

a. The temperature enhancement occurs where electrons of energies near 1.4 keV are observed to be present. The correlation is excellent wherever both sets of data are present, except that the temperature enhancement persists to higher latitudes, indeed, to some degree, across the polar cap, and that there is not a detailed agreement in shape between the 1.4 keV flux and the temperature enhancement. But 1.4 keV electrons when precipitated will produce their maximum ionospheric effects well below the F-region peak and softer electrons may be primarily responsible for the effects observed at satellite heights. Thus the correlation with 1.4 keV electrons assumes that the spectrum extends to lower energies. Since the spectrum is certainly very variable, a detailed correlation is not to be expected. The persistence of enhanced temperatures across the polar cap implies that very soft electrons are commonly precipitated there. This is in agreement with the general tendency for fluxes of soft electrons to persist at generally higher latitudes.

b. The electron density is also enhanced in this region. This would be expected from the additional ionisation resulting from the precipitation of very soft electrons.

c. The magnitude of the temperature enhancement – 200–500°K – is consistent with the calculations of Walker & Rees (1968a) and Rees & Walker (1968).

The principal doubt arises if this explanation is also to be applied to the high-latitude zone of the event on 30 November 1968. Walker & Rees (1968a) showed that the temperature rise was insensitive to the magnitude of the particle flux since if the flux is large, the collision cooling rate rises due to the additional ionisation produced at much the same rate as the energy input, leaving the temperature rising only slowly. It would not be possible to account for the high temperatures of

6000°K by this mechanism. Thus, either the high-latitude zone of this event, or the high-latitude zone in general, must be accounted for by some other mechanism. Since some heating by precipitated and trapped particles cannot be avoided, it seems most likely that the extreme heating in this event resulted from an additional process which is either weak or absent in a normal magnetic disturbance. There is no evidence to suggest what this process may be; it is obviously desirable to identify and study other events of this type.

The low-latitude high-temperature zone is certainly not associated with precipitated particles. It is also unlikely to result from heating by transverse electric fields to the geomagnetic field. Walker & Rees (1968b) in a discussion of the SARARC which is equally applicable here, show that electric fields of more than 180 mV/m would be required. While fields of this order are observed in aurorae (Föppl et al. 1968) and are necessary to account for the electrojet current (Boström 1964), they cannot exist at lower latitudes where such large magnetic effects are not observed. The remaining possibility considered by Walker & Rees, that of conduction from a high-temperature zone in the magnetosphere, thus seems an attractive possibility. Few electron temperature measurements in the magnetosphere have been made, the published results being those of Serbu & Maier (1966). The lack of evidence indicating that enhancements occur near the plasmapause in the midnight sector during geomagnetic disturbance is thus not conclusive. On the other hand, enhanced thermal conduction from a local hot spot in the magnetosphere would not alone be expected to result in the large density decrease actually observed. This suggests that some strong electrodynamic process actually removes ionisation from the F-region, either upwards into the plasmapause or downwards where it recombines. Such a process may actually heat the electron gas. Even if it does not, a large temperature enhancement will result, provided that thermal conduction is not actually inhibited. This is because the thermal conductivity of the electron gas rises as T_e (Spitzer 1956) and is effectively independent of N_e, while at altitudes above the F-peak the collisional loss rate is proportional to N_e^2. Any process which reduces N_e will thus lead to a rapid increase in T_e, provided that the magnetospheric temperature does not fall too far because of the increased downward thermal conduction. The temperature near the plasmapause is at least five to ten thousand degrees K (Norman, private communication), which is sufficient to sustain the observed temperatures. Then the marked variations in electron temperature must reflect the variations in electron transport, which in turn must arise from an electrodynamical effect of the plasmapause.

4. CONCLUSIONS

At magnetically quiet times, the F-region electron temperature generally falls to values only about 300°K above the neutral atmosphere temperature. During a magnetic disturbance a broad zone develops coincident with the region of particle precipitation but extending to higher latitudes, in which the electron temperature may be enhanced to 3000°K. In this zone electron density is also enhanced. This zone may result from ionisation and heating produced by precipitated energetic particles. For a limited portion of the main phase a second zone of yet higher temperatures develops in the midnight sector only. This high-temperature zone is coincident with the mid-latitude trough of the ionosphere, the electron density falling to a low value. The high temperatures here may result from the reduction in collisional cooling at low electron densities, which will both raise the temperature directly and then also increase the heat conducted down from the magnetosphere by raising the thermal conductivity of the electron gas.

Very similar phenomena, with maximum temperatures exceeding 8000°K, may also occur in a magnetically quiet period in association with fluxes of 'field-aligned' low energy protons. The high-latitude zone, which is also observed in this case, cannot be due to electron precipitation but there is insufficient evidence to enable a suggestion of its origin to be made.

Acknowledgements: We wish to express our appreciation to our colleagues and to other ESRO–I experimenters for permission to use data in advance of publication, to those of our colleagues who designed and built the experiment, especially to Mr. T. S. Bowling, who was responsible for the qualification and for its integration in the spacecraft, and to the many ESRO staff members who worked on ESRO–I.

REFERENCES

Binsack, J. H. 1967. *J. Geophys. Res.* 72, 5231.
Bosham, R. 1964. *J. Geophys. Res.* 69, 4983.
Boström, R. 1964. *J. Geophys. Res.* 69, 4983.
Bowen, P. J., Boyd, R. L. F., Henderson, C. L. & Willmore, A. P. 1964. *Proc. Roy. Soc, A281*, 514.
Chappell, C. R., Harris, K. K. & Sharp, G. W. 1970. *J. Geophys. Res. 75*, 50.
Föppl, H., Haerendel, G., Haser, L., Lüst, R., Melzner, F., Meyers, E., Neuss, H., Rabben, H. H., Reiger, E., Stockner, J. & Stoffregen, W. 1968. *J. Geophys. Res. 73*, 21.
Page, D. E. 1970. In Manno, V. & Page, D. E. (eds.). *Intercorrelated Satellite Observations Related to Solar Events*, p. 367, D. Reidel Pub. Co., Holland.
Raitt, W. J. 1970. In *Space Research X*, North-Holland Pub. Co., Amsterdam. In preparation.
Rees, M. H. & Walker, J. C. G. 1968. *Ann. Géophys. 24*, 193.
Riedler, W. 1970. In Manno, V. & Page, D. E. (eds.). *Intercorrelated Satellite Observations Related to Solar Events*, p. 577, D. Reidel, Pub. Co., Holland.
Rycroft, M. J. & Burnell, S. J. 1970. *J. Geophys. Res. 75*, 5600.
Rycroft, M. J. & Thomas, J. O. 1970. *Planet. Space Sci. 18*, 65.
Serbu, G. P. & Maier, E. J. R. 1966. *J. Geophys. Res. 71*, 3755.
Spitzer, L. 1956. In *Physics of Fully Ionised Gases*, Interscience, p. 86.
Walker, J. C. G. & Rees, M. H. 1968a. *Planet. Space Sci. 16*, 459.
Walker, J. C. G. & Rees, M. H. 1968b. *Planet. Space Sci. 16*, 915.
Willmore, A. P. 1970. *Space Sci. Rev. 11*, 607.
Wrenn, G. L. 1969. *Proc. IEEE 57*, 1072.

The Anomaly of the Neutral Wind at a Height of $\simeq 200$ km at High Latitudes

W. STOFFREGEN

Uppsala Ionospheric Observatory, Research Institute of National Defence, Stockholm, Sweden

Abstract: At F2-layer heights the neutral global wind is generally directed from the subsolar point near the equator in all directions towards an opposite area on the nightside. Theoretical wind models have been verified by experiments up to the geomagnetic latitude of $\simeq 60°$. Near the auroral zone, however, there are great deviations from the models because of the influence of the polar ionosphere. Releases of neutral clouds in this area indicate that, depending on the latitude and local time, the neutral wind at a height of > 200 km changes its direction sometimes by as much as 180°. Such great deviations are associated with high electric fields and high neutral-wind velocities. During the evening and early morning, a change of 180° brings the neutral wind into the direction of the drift of the ionospheric plasma. It is well known that there is a connection between ionization movements and neutral winds due to ion drag. This connection, however, is regarded as too weak to explain the observed great deviations. Additional heating on the nightside of the auroral zone is proposed as the main reason for the change of the wind system, consistent with the observed anomalies.

1. INTRODUCTION

Release experiments at the latitude of ESRANGE near Kiruna ($\varphi = 68°$, $\Phi = 65°$) have been carried out during the past four years. When barium is released, the cloud separates into an ion cloud, indicating the strength and direction of the electric field, and a neutral cloud, which drifts with the surrounding neutral atmosphere. Strontium clouds and other non-ionized clouds will not separate and only move with the neutral atmosphere. The effect of electric fields on ion clouds and the effect of winds on neutral clouds will, under quiet conditions, be in good agreement with the theories developed for both types of clouds. However, if the geomagnetic activity is high and is accompanied by strong electric fields and high auroral activity, the behaviour of artificial clouds becomes much more complicated. In this paper the neutral cloud only will be discussed.

Generally, a neutral cloud tends, shortly after release, to drift with the motion of the neutral upper atmosphere. According to King & Kohl (1967), who have calculated models of the global wind system, the atmospheric motion at the level of the F2-layer shows a change of 360° during one day. This rotation is clockwise in the northern hemisphere. At the latitude of ESRANGE ($\varphi = 68°$) a neutral cloud is therefore supposed to move towards the south at $\simeq 02^h$, towards the west at $\simeq 08^h$, towards the north at $\simeq 14^h$, and towards the east at $\simeq 20^h$ local time. The calculated models available do not take into account the highly variable conditions in the auroral zone. In Fig. 1, a global wind system according to King & Kohl (1967) is shown.

Data from 25 neutral clouds, obtained in 14 experiments between April 1967 and March 1971 at ESRANGE, differ systematically from the expected directions. In the present paper it is suggested that this discrepancy mainly depends on the increased temperature on the nightside of the auroral zone, which in turn introduces a remarkable change of the wind directions in the course of one day. The impact of energetic particles conveys a large amount of energy into the auroral zone, energy which is transformed into ionization and excitation. A considerable part of the energy is converted into heat. Depending on the duration of the auroral events, the temperature of the neutral particles will gradually rise. At the height of the clouds discussed here, the ion and electron temperatures will be of the same order. According to Rees & Walker (1968),

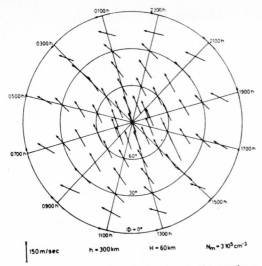

Fig. 1. The atmospheric wind system in the northern hemisphere, calculated for an altitude of 300 km and a peak electron density of 3×10^5 cm^{-3} (according to King & Kohl 1967).

who have calculated the ion and electron temperatures, the neutral particles will be heated at about the same rate as the ions, as a result of the friction between the ions and the neutrals. The primary source of heating of these particles is the electric field associated with the current flow in the auroral ionosphere. During auroral activity the horizontal current flow is mainly concentrated on the nightside of the auroral zone. At the edges of an auroral display the current may diffuse or, as Boström (1964) has shown, follow the geomagnetic field lines. Hence, a heating effect will be more pronounced on the nightside than on the dayside of

the auroral zone. From this point of view, an attempt is made to explain the observations in terms of temperature gradients in the auroral zone.

2. OBSERVATIONS

In Fig. 2, the calculated neutral wind directions at 68°N are shown, together with four theoretical wind models. The curves have been computed for levels of 250–400 km and are regarded as being still representative of heights of 180–230 km, the actual heights of the clouds discussed here. One of these curves refers to the wind model in Fig. 1. The 360° diurnal rotation of the wind vector is displaced about 2–3 hours with respect to local noon. This is the time difference eastward of the subsolar point near the equator, where the temperature is highest and from which the neutral wind is directed in different directions towards the opposite point on the night-side of the earth. Clouds above 200 km are indicated as open circles or squares and those somewhat below 200 km by black squares. The numbers indicate the velocity of each individual cloud.

It is striking that all the notations, except one, are in a clockwise sense with respect to the curves. All these clouds are released in *evening twilight*, while the exceptional one at about 02^h is released during *morning twilight*. It appears from the diagram that there is a clear tendency for clouds of higher velocity to show a greater deviation. It is furthermore important to note that the deviation does not exceed 180°. The fact that these release experiments have to be made during twilight only is the reason why the diagram is rather incomplete. The only cloud released during morning twilight

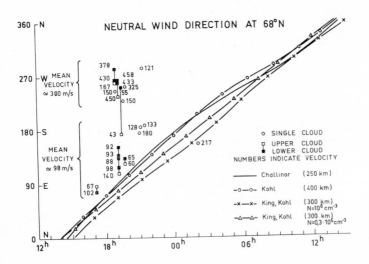

Fig. 2. Deviation of the drift directions of neutral clouds released at 68° latitude (ESRANGE) from the calculated wind directions.

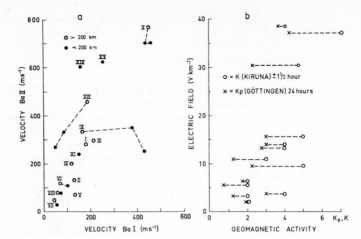

Fig. 3. a. The relation between the velocities of ionized clouds (Ba II) and neutral clouds (Ba I). The ratio was found to be approximately 2.5:1. b. Diagram showing that electric fields deduced from ion-cloud velocities are closely correlated with geomagnetic activity.

is plotted for a few degrees only in the opposite sense with respect to the model curves. This is in spite of the high cloud velocity of 217 mγs.

Some other observations should be discussed, in order to understand the general behaviour of a neutral cloud. The velocity of ion clouds, V_i, has been compared with that of the neutral clouds, V_n, from the same releases. As will be seen in Fig. 3a, there seems to be a correlation, in so far as higher velocities of ion clouds correspond to higher velocities of neutral clouds. The ratio between these velocities is, on the average:

$$\frac{V_i}{V_n} \simeq \frac{2.5}{1}.$$

There is further evidence that the velocity of ion clouds depends on the degree of geomagnetic and auroral activity. This is demonstrated in Fig. 3b, in which two different indices of geomagnetic activity (local and global) are used for comparison.

The global wind model in Fig. 1 has been computed assuming a global temperature model according to Jacchia (1965). The northern hemisphere of this model is shown in Fig. 4a. Approximate wind directions are indicated by arrows referring to the wind vectors in Fig. 1. The temperature difference between the dayside and the nightside is assumed to be 1000°–1300°.

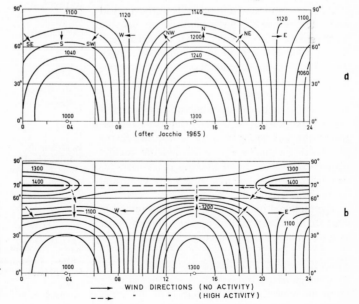

Fig. 4. a. Temperature distribution in the F-region for medium solar-cycle conditions (after Jacchia 1965). b. Temperature distribution, when an additional heating at the nightside of the auroral zone is introduced. The resulting change of wind directions is indicated by arrows.

85

The highly variable conditions in the auroral zone do not allow us to construct a modified wind model which is representative. In fact each auroral situation would need its own model, based on the actual degree of disturbance, its locality, and its time. Fig. 4b must be regarded only as an attempt to show how a modification of the quiet model in Fig. 4a can result in large changes of the neutral wind. When at $\simeq 70°$ latitude on the nightside an increase in temperature to $1400°$ is introduced, this will result in an *opposite* temperature and wind gradient during the *afternoon* and *evening hours*, as indicated by the dashed arrows. This is in agreement with the observed deviations during evening-twilight releases in Fig. 2. In the early *morning hours*, however, the direction of the wind will only be slightly changed and its velocity will increase. The single notation of a released cloud during *morning twilight* agrees very well with this statement.

3. DISCUSSION

In release experiments in Sardinia and the Sahara (Föppl et al. 1965) it was found that the observed wind directions were in good agreement with those expected from models (King & Kohl 1967). These models are based on the fairly stable ratio of 1.3:1 between the temperature in the subsolar area and that in the opposite area on the nightside.

The average wind models take into account the rather complicated processes of interaction of ionized and neutral particles in the presence of the geomagnetic field. These interactions become still more complicated and variable in the auroral zone. It has been pointed out clearly by the authors mentioned in Fig. 2 that at higher latitudes the models are more or less unreliable. Since wind directions are dependent on temperature and pressure gradients, it is obvious that additional heating sources will give rise to a change of wind speeds and directions. It is well known from spectral observations of N_2^+ bands that the temperature in the auroral zone increases with the degree of activity. Jacchia (1965) has found from satellite observations that the temperature increase towards the auroral zone may sometimes be several times the original value.

The modified temperature model, presented in Fig. 4b, must be regarded as a possible explanation. I would not argue that the additional heating alone is responsible for the drastic change of wind directions which is observed mainly during evening hours. Though this heating is believed to be of major importance, there is at least one more

influence which has to be considered seriously. This is the interaction between the movements of the ionized and neutral atmosphere due to drag forces. This interaction has been studied by Kohl (1969). He concludes that, although the ratio of ionization density to neutral density is very small, frictional forces can exert an important influence on the neutral air winds. The influence will increase when drag forces act for a long time on the neutral air motion. A shift of the wind direction of the order of 180°, however, would require an ion density which is considerably greater than the 10^4–10^5 el cm^{-3} usually measured during the experiments (Kohl, private communication).

In this connection it is of interest to consider the drift of the ionospheric plasma and its shift during the night. According to Harang & Tröim (1961), at latitudes slightly below the auroral zone, drift motions of ionized areas show a pronounced westward direction at 20^h L.T. and a maximum drift eastwards at 03^h L.T. The same tendency has been observed in the drift motion of auroral forms based on IGY data by the present author (Stoffregen 1961). This means that neutral clouds released during high activity in *evening twilight* drift in roughly the same direction as the ion clouds. This in turn is also the direction of both ionized areas and drift motions of auroral forms.

Acknowledgements: The work reported in this paper has been based on release experiments performed by the Max-Planck-Institut für Extraterrestrische Physik, Garching b. München. I wish to thank Professor R. Lüst and Dr. G. Haerendel for giving me the opportunity to take part in these experiments. My thanks are also due to my collaborators H. Derblom and H. Gunnarsson for their participation in the observations and analysis of data. Financial support from the Swedish Space Research Committee is gratefully acknowledged.

REFERENCES

Boström, R. 1964. *J. Geophys. Res. 69*, 4983.
Föppl, H., Haerendel, G., Loidl, J., Lüst, R., Melzner, F., Meyer, B., Neuss, H. & Rieger, E. 1965. *Planet. Space Sci. 13*, 95.
Harang, L. & Tröim, J. 1961. *Planet. Space Sci. 5*, 33.
Jacchia, L. G. 1965. *Space Research* V, p. 1152, North-Holland Publ. Co., Amsterdam.
King, J. W. & Kohl, H. 1967. *J. Atmos. Terr. Phys. 29*, 1045.
Kohl, H. 1969. *Annals of the IQSY*, 5, Solar-Terr. Phys: Terrestrial Aspects, M.I.T. Press.
Rees, M. H. & Walker, J. C. G. 1968. *Ann. Géophys. 24*, 193.
Stoffregen, W. 1961. *J. Atmos. Terr. Phys. 21*, 257.

Dynamical Behavior of the Polar Topside Ionosphere

P. M. BANKS

Department of Applied Physics and Information Science University of California, San Diego La Jolla, California 92037

Abstract: A review is given of magnetospheric interactions with the polar iono-sphere using recent experimental and theoretical results. The effect of the polar wind is discussed with reference to the observational data of J. Hoffman. These and the results of other experiments support the concept of polar wind ion flows as a general feature of the topside ionosphere for all regions outside the plasma-sphere. It is shown that most of the semi-permanent topside density features result from changes in plasma temperature and F_2-region effects rather than being associated with changes in ion composition. Finally, the polar peak density enhancement is discussed in terms of recent observations of the polar cusp.

1. INTRODUCTION

The global distribution of ionization in the top-side ionosphere is strongly controlled by the geo-magnetic field and the structure of the magnetos-phere. Reviews of this behavior have been given previously (Banks & Holzer 1969, Chan & Colin 1969, Banks 1970, Mange in press) and will not be repeated at length here. This paper is intended to provide a survey of measurements made in the past five years and their interpretation in terms of the dynamic model of magnetospheric plasma behavior.

As shown by Fig. 1, there are three essentially different regions of the topside ionosphere. The plasmasphere represents a region of high plasma density isolated to a large extent from the pro-cesses associated with magnetospheric convection. The plasmapause during magnetically quiet pe-riods forms at the boundary between those field tubes which co-rotate with the earth and those undergoing extensive motions under the influence of the magnetospheric electric field (Brice 1967, Nishida 1967). During magnetically disturbed times the plasmapause and convection is observed to move equatorward, while reduction of magnetic activity results in a gradual poleward develop-ment (Chappell et al. 1970).

During periods of low magnetic activity, mag-netic field tubes poleward of the plasmapause participate in the general magnetospheric convec-tion patterns first described by Axford & Hines (1961). Over a small area of the polar cap ($\Lambda_I >$ 80°), the field tubes open into the distant tail of the magnetosphere, while those at lower magnetic latitudes form closed loops. The circulation of field tubes through the magnetosphere can be plotted in the magnetic equatorial plane as shown in Fig. 2. In this diagram only the sunward mo-tions of the field tubes following reconnection can

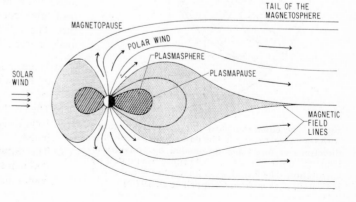

Fig. 1. The different regions of the magnetosphere. In the plasma-sphere field lines are closed and, to a large extent, co-rotate with the earth. At very high latitudes the field lines are open to the tail of the magnetosphere. Between the plas-mapause and open regions field lines are closed, but convect around the earth.

87

be seen. The original disconnection at the magnetopause and subsequent sweeping of field lines back into the tail occurs out of the equatorial plane and cannot be shown in this diagram.

The projection of the flow pattern given in Fig. 2 onto the north polar cap is shown in Fig. 3. The direction of field tube motion is asymmetric with respect to the magnetic pole. The dotted region corresponds to open field lines (those not intersecting the magnetic equatorial plane except in the far tail), while the dayside disconnection region is shown as a heavy line. This line also corresponds to the projection of the dayside neutral line of the magnetopause. Phenomena associated with this particular feature are discussed in a later section.

Numerous satellite measurements have shown that the plasmapause is equivalent to a light ion boundary, in the sense that both H^+ and He^+ densities poleward of the plasmapause are very low. In this region O^+ is observed to be the dominant ion up to altitudes of 3000 km, and a number of semi-permanent density features have been found which would appear to arise from both F_2-region density enhancements and differing topside plasma temperature profiles (Nishida 1967).

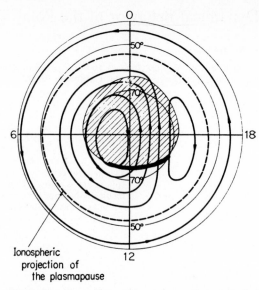

Ionospheric projection of the plasmapause

Fig. 3. The streamlines of flux tube motion projected into the north polar ionosphere. The plasmapause is shown by dotted lines, while the region of open field tubes is cross-hatched. The single dark line represents roughly the location of the polar cusp. (Adapted from Nishida 1967.)

2. THE POLAR WIND

The polar wind theory is based on theoretical studies of plasma transport for conditions appropriate to the high latitude ionosphere. Early work by Bauer (1966), Dessler & Michael (1966), and Nishida (1966) emphasized the possibility that H^+ could be lost from the polar regions through outward flow along open field lines into the tail of the magnetosphere. The ionospheric dynamics of this process were investigated in detail by Banks & Holzer (1968, 1969), Axford (1968), Holzer (1970), and Banks (1970). Adopting steady state conditions, calculations were made of the behavior of O^+, He^+, and H^+ along field tubes convecting over a summertime polar cap. The following points emerged from their analysis (see Figs. 4 and 5):

a) There should exist a substantial upward flux of H^+ with $\Phi(H^+) \simeq 2$ to 6×10^8 cm^{-2} sec^{-1}.

b) The H^+ flow speed becomes supersonic above 1000 to 3000 km for the conditions investigated.

c) The outward flow of H^+ leaves O^+ as the dominant ion up to altitudes greater than 3000 km.

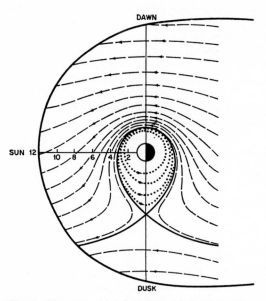

Fig. 2. The equatorial flow lines of the flux tubes with the magnetosphere. The dashed lines show flow directions of flux tubes dominated by convection, while the dotted lines trace field tubes dominated by co-rotation. The flow of field lines into the tail is not indicated. (Taken from Chappell et al. 1970.)

88

Fig. 4. Electron and ion density profile for a sunlit polar cap.

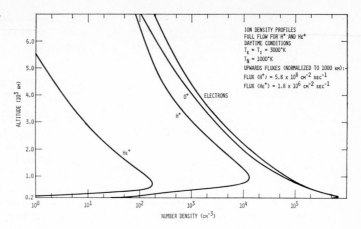

Fig. 5. H+ velocity profiles corresponding to summer conditions along open field lines.

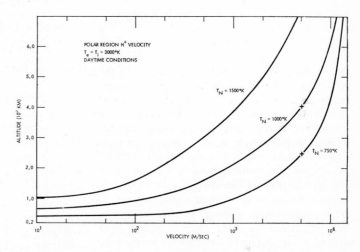

Although the polar wind calculations were made only for open field lines where steady state conditions have been reached, there are strong reasons to believe that the polar wind flow extends throughout the entire trans-plasmasphere region and is responsible for the formation of the plasmapause itself. As first pointed out by Nishida (1966) and later by Banks & Holzer (1969), reconnection of field tubes in the tail does not automatically terminate the upward H+ flow. Instead, an ion shock front must propagate along the convecting field tube to the ionosphere before the flow can be converted to subsonic speeds. As shown in Fig. 6, taken from the work of Banks et al. (1971), the time needed for this to happen is relatively long compared with typical convection times of four to ten hours. As a result, it is expected that essentially polar wind conditions will be found along all field tubes convecting outside the plasmasphere. Measurements of ion com-

position in the electron trough region have been interpreted to show the presence of the polar wind in the closed field tube region.

This last result has important consequences for

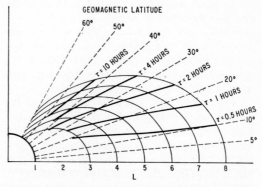

Fig. 6. Locations of shock fronts started from the geomagnetic equator. (Taken from Banks et al. 1971)

89

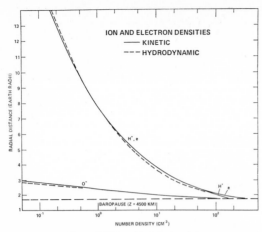

Fig. 7. Profiles of H$^+$ and O$^+$ densities computed using kinetic and hydrodynamic models. (Adopted from Holzer et al. 1971.)

the analysis of topside density variations in the polar regions, i.e. regions poleward of the plasmapause. Since O$^+$ in near diffusive equilibrium will remain the dominant ionic constituent up to altitudes of 2000 to 3000 km for most conditions, changes in the topside electron density can arise from increases in the F$_2$-peak density with an unchanged temperature profile, from increases in the topside plasma temperature with no change in peak density, or as a combination of effects. As we shall show later, many of the prominent density features of the polar regions appear to be related to the plasma temperature rather than the F$_2$-peak density.

There have been several criticisms of the polar wind theory (for a review see Donahue 1971). Dessler & Cloutier (1969) argued that hydrodynamic equations were inappropriate for describing the polar ionosphere. Lemaire & Scherer (1970) made ballistic exospheric computations along the direction suggested by Dessler & Cloutier and it appeared at first that the polar wind might become nothing more than a polar gasp. Revision and comparison of the exospheric work with the hydrodynamic results has shown, however, that there is little, if any, discrepancy between the results for the H$^+$ flow speed and density from the two mathematical approaches; in both models high speed H$^+$ flows are predicted with density and speed parameters similar to within a few percent. A comparison of this type is shown in Fig. 7, taken from the recent work of Holzer et al. (1971). It should also be pointed out that a series of detailed hydrodynamic calculations have also

been done by Marubashi (1971) with results virtually the same as those obtained by Banks & Holzer.

3. MEASUREMENTS OF POLAR ION DENSITIES AND FLOW SPEEDS

The first positive identification of a polar wind was obtained by Hoffman (1968) from the Explorer 31 satellite. Since that time more extensive analysis has been done, as reported by Hoffman (1971) and soon to appear in the literature.

A typical result for late afternoon summer conditions is shown in Fig. 8. The upper diagram gives the observed ion composition, while the phase shift, or angle of attack, between O$^+$ and H$^+$ ions is shown below. The phase shift is related to the H$^+$ velocity by the relation:

$$V(H^+) = V_s \tan \Phi,$$

where V_s, the satellite speed, is in the range 6–7 km sec^{-1}.

The plasmapause transition is clearly seen at

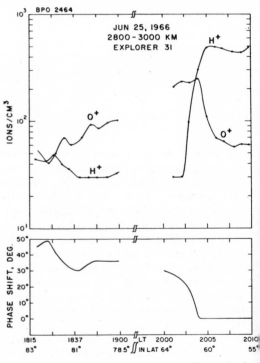

Fig. 8. Ion composition and H$^+$ phase shift obtained by Hoffman (1968, 1971) from Explorer-31. The plasmapause appears at 61° invarient latitude with increases of the H$^+$ flow speed to 4 km sec^{-1}. The escape flow continues within the polar cap, reaching 7 km sec^{-1} at 83°.

61° invarient latitude (Λ_I). Inside the plasmasphere H^+ is the dominant ion and there is no apparent ion flow. At the plasmapause, an H^+ upward speed of 4 km sec^{-1} is seen (64° Λ_I) while a rise occurs in the O^+ density. This latter behavior can be readily explained in terms of the plasma polarization electric field. When H^+ is a dominant ion, O^+ varies with altitude as exp $\left[-\dfrac{m(O^+)g}{k\,T_i} z \right]$ using conventional symbols. When O^+ becomes the dominant ion, the net electric field supporting the O^+ plasma is stronger and an altitude variation of exp $\left[-\dfrac{m(O^+)g}{k(T_e + T_i)} z \right]$ is found. Hence, although there is probably very little change in the F_2-peak density in going from 58° to 64° Λ_I, the O^+ density at 2800–3000 km changes by a factor of 4.

Within the polar regions the H^+ flow speed, shown in Fig. 8, remains high with 8 km sec^{-1} being seen at 83° Λ_I. The gradual change in ion composition with increasing ion speed is consistent with the polar wind results since the O^+–H^+ transition altitude depends upon the H^+ speed and the importance of the inertia term in the H^+ equation of motion.

To show the extent of the observed ion flows Hoffman (1971) has plotted all his available data for polar passes. The results, shown in Fig. 9 and

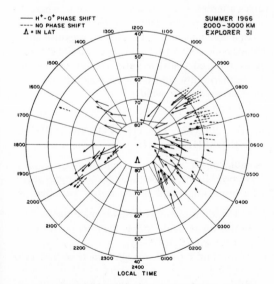

Fig. 9. Observations of polar wind flow in the summer polar cap. All available data is shown, with direction of satellite pass indicated by an arrow. The solid line indicates presence of ion flow, while the dotted line indicates its absence (Hoffman 1971).

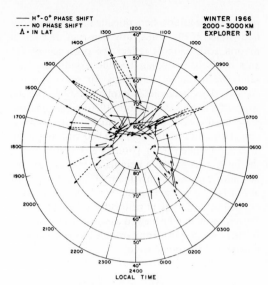

Fig. 10. Observations of polar wind flow in the winter polar cap (Hoffman 1971).

10, present data for all Explorer 31 polar passes for summer and winter conditions. The direction of each pass is shown by the arrow. The portion of the data when no ion flow was seen is indicated by dotted lines, while the presence of ion flow is given by solid lines.

The results indicate H^+ flow for both winter and summer over regions of the earth which generally lie outside the plasmapause. Hoffman (1971) indicates that the strongest flow occurs in the winter morning hours ($\Phi(H^+) \simeq 3$ to 5×10^8 cm^{-2} sec^{-1}) but is very structured, with many areas being depleted of all detectable ionization. The summer polar wind is, in contrast, rather steady, with H^+ fluxes in the order of 5×10^7 ions cm^{-2}.

Other measurements have been made which can be used to infer the existence of H^+ flows in the transplasmasphere region. Mayr et al. (1970) analyzed OGO–4 ion composition measurements taken in the light ion trough. They found it possible to explain their results only with an upward H^+ flow of 10^8 protons cm^{-2} sec^{-1} which had supersonic speeds above several thousand kilometers altitude.

Studies of the morphology of the polar ionosphere at 1000 km altitude reveal the general absence of H^+ through the presence of exceptionally low electron densities. Although it might be argued that such a condition reflects the absence of neutral hydrogen, in fact there is no evidence for an extremely low hydrogen concen-

91

tration in the atmosphere outside the plasmapause (see Meier 1970). Thus, low densities and small plasma scale heights reflect the presence of O^+ and analysis of polar topside conditions can safely be made on this basis for most circumstances. This behavior is explicitly shown in the work of Thomas & Rycroft (1970) where plasma scale heights have been evaluated at various magnetic latitudes for 500, 700, and 900 km. As shown in Fig. 11 (taken from Thomas & Rycroft 1970), the large plasma scale heights at 900 km at low latitudes can result only from H^+. Northward of about 60° magnetic latitude H^+ vanishes, leaving O^+ behind in a state of near diffusive equilibrium. Such a result can be viewed as subsidiary evidence for the presence of strong trough and polar region escape, i.e. the polar wind.

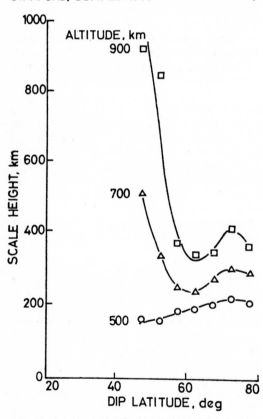

STANFORD, SUMMER 1963   LMT 02.00±00.30

Fig. 11. Average latitudinal variation of the electron density scale height as measured at Stanford, 0200 ± 0030 LMT during the summer of 1963. The rapid change in the 900 km scale height is expected for H^+ flow outside the plasmasphere. (Taken from Thomas & Rycroft 1970.)

It appears that most of the gross features of the polar topside ionosphere can be explained through ion escape into the tail of the magnetosphere. During periods when field lines in the deep polar cap are open to the tail, a steady escape flow is present. Upon reconnection, a shock front propagates down the convecting field tube toward the earth but, for sufficiently rapid convection, probably does not reach the flow critical point to convert the flow to subsonic speeds.

An interesting feature of the convection process is the associated plasma compression and rarefaction. In the tail of the magnetosphere field tubes filled with escaping polar wind plasma may extend far from the earth before reconnection occurs. Following reconnection, the closed loops must rapidly shorten (due to magnetic field line tension) and compress the trapped thermal plasma in an adiabatic fashion so that $TV^{\gamma-1}$ is approximately constant.

Likewise, in the daytime sector, field lines traversing the trough at $L \simeq 4$ must eventually move in such a way that connection can be made with the magnetopause. At ionospheric levels this implies a poleward motion, but in the equatorial plane a radially outward flow must result with a consequent increase in flux tube volume. To plasma trapped in the field tube such an expansion represents a cooling effect. For example, if $V \propto L^4$, then moving a flux tube from $L = 5$ to $L = 10$ gives a temperature ratio $T/T_0 = 1/6.4$, where T_0 is the initial plasma temperature.

In a similar manner, the plasma pressure along the dayside convecting field tubes can be substantially reduced. This, in turn, encourages further ionospheric flow and tends to maintain the daytime upward polar wind.

4. STRUCTURE OF THE POLAR TOPSIDE IONOSPHERE

A number of semi-permanent density features have been found in the polar topside ionosphere. The more important of these may be listed as:

a) the nighttime auroral zone maxima;
b) the polar peak found near magnetic noon between 75° to 79° Λ_I;
c) the mid-latitude trough which occurs near 65° Λ_I;
d) the polar cavity occurring above 80° Λ_I; (Nishida 1967, Maehlum 1969, Sato & Colin 1969, Thomas & Andrews 1969).

Particular interest centers about the polar peak

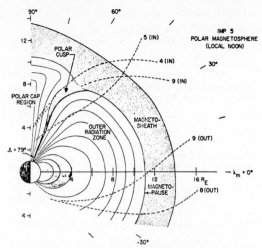

Fig. 12. View of the polar mangetosphere showing the extension of the polar cusp from the magnetosheath to the ionosphere. The plasmasphere is shown at 4 R^E as well as the meridian projections of the IMP-5 satellite. (Adopted from Frank 1971.)

density maximum (recently referred to as the polar cusp) since direct observations by Heikkila & Winningham (1971) and Frank (1971) have shown that this is a region where magnetosheath plasma has direct access to the polar ionosphere. (It also corresponds to the neutral points of the magnetopause where field line disconnection occurs. See Fig. 1 and 12.) As a consequence, it is expected that the magnetosheath electrons and protons (average energy $\sim$ 100 to 300 ev) will interact with the ionosphere in such a way that secondary ionization and thermal plasma heating will result. Although the measurements of Frank (1971) indicate that the polar cusp should be no more than 30 to 150 km wide and located near 79° Λ_L, the data of Heikkila & Winningham (1971) show regions of enhanced particle fluxes over the range 75° Λ_I to 79° Λ_I. Airborne observations of the mid-day aurora (Buchau et al. 1969), which is a manifestation of the polar cusp, tend to agree with those of Heikkila & Winningham.

Observations of ionization enhancement associated with the polar cusp have been made by Oguti & Marubashi (1966), Thomas et al. (1966), Nishida (1967), Bratteng & Frihagen (1969), Miller & Brace (1969), Sato & Colin (1969), Brace et al. (1970), Dyson & Zmuda (1970), and others. Although the source of the heating and ionization was not known at the time of these studies, suggestions were made that solar wind plasma could explain the phenomenon.

Typical meridional profiles of the polar peak density enhancement have been given by Nishida (1967). These show that changes in ionization density become more pronounced with increasing altitude. Furthermore, there is no dramatic change in the density at the peak of the F2-layer. Consequently, it may be thought that the polar peak or polar cusp density enhancement is primarily caused by local heating of the topside plasma with a consequent increase in the scale height of the O⁺.

A direct observation of the polar cusp ionization maximum has been made by Hoffman (1971) for a winter polar cap at a relatively low altitude (2000–2300 km). The results, shown in Fig. 13, indicate a dramatic enhancement of O⁺ and overall electron density in the region 74° < Λ_I < 83° with H⁺ flow speeds as large as 19 km sec⁻¹. The latitude behavior of the ions equatorward of the cusp region is peculiar and has yet to be explained.

A previous measurement of ion concentrations by Hoffman also appears to show the polar cusp enhancement (see Banks 1970, Fig. 2).

The presence of a permanent heat and particle source between 75° to 80° Λ_I at magnetic noon appears to explain the earlier polar peak observa-

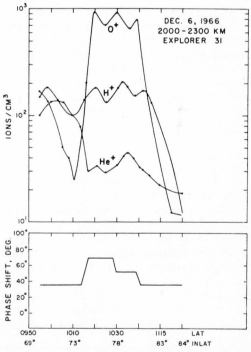

Fig. 13. Ion composition and H⁺ flow velocity measured in the polar cusp. A peak H⁺ speed of 19 km sec⁻¹ was noted. (Taken from Hoffman 1971.)

93

tions. A difficulty now arises, however, in considering the action of convection. If we adopt convection flow lines such as those shown in Fig. 3, plasma initially in the cusp region should be convected directly over the polar cap, producing a much broader region of enhanced electron density than is actually observed. The accumulated data of Thomas & Andrews (1969), for example, showed the presence of a polar ring of enhanced density surrounding the polar cavity, a region of exceptionally low density (see Hagg 1967, Timleck & Nelms 1969). If convection were to carry ionization directly over the polar cap, one would not expect to see a sharply defined polar cavity.

One explanation which would link the polar cusp with Thomas & Andrews' rings can be made on the basis that convection flows in such a way as to avoid the deep polar cap. In this way, polar cusp ionization could move around the polar cap at reasonable speeds before passing through the auroral zones into the trough regions. In the winter time only sporadic ionization sources would be present in the polar cavity, while in the summer photoionization would dominate.

It should be noted that the Injun-5 electric field measurements of Cauffman & Gurnett (1971) are consistent with such an interpretation and give quiet time convection speeds in the order of 0.2 to 0.5 km sec^{-1} while in disturbed periods speeds greater than 1.5 km/sec frequently occur. Northward of the auroral zones the convection speed is low and directed in an anti-solar sense. Between the auroral zone and the plasmapause small (10 to 20 mV/m) electric fields are sometimes observed, corresponding to westward convection.

5. SUMMARY

The idea that plasma outflow is a general phenomenon of the regions outside the plasmapause appears to agree with a number of different experiments. To understand the polar topside ionosphere in detail, however, will require an improved knowledge of both the spatial and temporal variations of plasma convection and the nature of localized heating and ionization regions. The existence of a polar cavity leads to the strong suspicion that convection of polar plasma does not pass directly over the pole, but keeps to the outskirts just northward of the dawn-dusk auroral oval.

Acknowledgement: This research was supported in part through NASA Grant NGR-05-009-075.

REFERENCES

Axford, W. I. 1968. *J. Geophys. Res. 73*, 6855.
Axford, W. I. & Hines, C. O. 1961. *Can. J. Phys. 39*, 1433.
Banks, P. M. 1970. In Skovli, G. (ed.). *The Polar Ionosphere and Magnetospheric Processes.* Gordon & Breach, New York.
Banks, P. M. & Holzer, T. E. 1968. *J. Geophys. Res. 73*, 6846.
Banks, P. M. & Holzer, T. E. 1969. *J. Geophys. Res. 74*, 6317.
Banks, P. M., Nagy, A. F. & Axford, W. I. 1971. *Planet. and Space Sci.* In press.
Bauer, S. J. 1966. In Frihagen, Joh. (ed.). *Electron Density Profiles in Ionosphere and Exosphere*, p. 387. North-Holland Publishing Company, Amsterdam.
Brace, L. H., Mayr, H. G. & Mahajan, K. K. 1970. *J. Atmos. Terr. Phys. 32*, 1945.
Bratteng, O. M. & Frihagen, J. 1969. *J. Atmos. Terr. Phys. 31*, 1017.
Brice, N. M. 1967. *J. Geophys. Res. 72*, 5193.
Brinton, H. C., Grebowsky, J. M. & Mayr, H. G. 1970. Goddard Space Flight Center Technical Report X–621–70–311.
Buchau, J., Whalen, J. A. & Akasofu, S. I. 1969. *J. Atm. Terr. Phys. 31*, 1021.
Cauffman, D. P. & Gurnett, D. A. 1971. *J. Geophys. Res.* In press.
Chan, K. L. & Colin, L. 1969. *Proc. IEEE 57*, 990.
Chappell, C. R., Harris, K. K. & Sharp, G. W. 1970. *J. Geophys. Res. 75*, 50.
Dessler, A. J. & Cloutier, P. A. 1969. *J. Geophys. Res. 74*, 3730.
Dessler, A. J. & Michael, F. C. 1966. *J. Geophys. Res. 71*, 1421.
Donahue, T. M. 1971. *Rev. Geophys. 9*, 1.
Dyson, P. L. & Zmuda, A. J. 1970. *J. Geophys. Res. 75*, 1893.
Frank, L. 1971. *J. Geophys. Res.* In press.
Hagg, E. L. 1967. *Can. J. Phys. 45*, 27.
Heikkila, W. J. & Winningham. J. D. 1971. *J. Geophys. Res. 76*, 883.
Hoffman, J. H. 1968. *Trans. Am. Geophys. Union 49*, 253.
Hoffman, J. H. 1971. *Trans. Am. Geophys. Union 4*, 301.
Holzer, T. E. 1970. In Skovli, G. (Ed.). *The Polar Ionosphere and Magnetospheric Processes.* Gordon and Breach, New York.
Holzer, T. E., Fedder, J. A. & Banks, P. M. 1971. *J. Geophys. Res. 76*, 2453.
Lemaire, J. & Scherer, M. 1970. *Planet. Space Sci. 18*, 103.
Maehlum, B. 1969. *J. Atmos. Terr. Phys. 31*, 531.
Mange, P. *Space Research 10*. In press.
Marubashi, A. 1971. *Rept. Ionos. Space. Res. Japan.* In press.
Mayr, H. G., Grebowsky, J. M. & Taylor, H. A. 1970. *Planet. Space Sci. 18*, 1123.
Meier, R. R. 1970. *J. Geophys. Res. 75*, 6218.
Miller, N. J. & Brace, L. H. 1969. *J. Geophys. Res. 74*, 5752.
Nishida, A. 1966. *J. Geophys. Res. 71*, 5669.
Nishida, A. 1967. *J. Geophys. Res. 72*, 6051.
Oguti, T. & Marubashi, K. 1966. *Rept. Ionos. Space. Res. Japan 20*, 96.
Sato, T. & Colin. L. 1969. *J. Geophys. Res. 74*, 2193.

Thomas, J. O. & Andrews, M. K. 1969. *Planet. Space Sci. 17*, 433.

Thomas, J. O. & Rycroft, M. J. 1970. *Planet. Space Sci. 18*, 41.

Thomas, J. O., Rycroft, M. J., Colin, L. & Chan, K. L. 1966. *The Topside in Electron Density Profiles in Ionosphere and Exosphere*, p. 322. North-Holland Publishing Company, Amsterdam.

Timleck, P. & Nelms, G. L. 1969. *Proc. IEEE 57*, 1164.

Distribution of ELF/VLF Noise in the Polar Ionosphere

R. E. BARRINGTON AND F. H. PALMER

Communications Research Centre, Ottawa

Abstract: The distribution of ELF and VLF noise, as observed by electric dipoles on Alouette II, is shown as a function of invariant latitude and local time for latitudes above 40°N. ELF noise usually has a bandwidth of less than 500 Hz but is sufficiently intense to control the AGC of a wide-band VLF receiver most of the time. This feature is important when percentage occurrence studies are made of other types of noise within the receiver passband. ELF noise is most intense near local noon and is distributed over a wide range of latitudes. Comparison with studies made using magnetic loop antennas, and with satellites at both high and low altitudes, leads to the conclusion that the noise is electromagnetic in nature. It seems likely that the noise is generated in the plasmasphere and is loosely guided down the plasmapause boundary to lower altitudes. Of the many known types of VLF noise the one discussed here usually has a lower frequency cutoff near the LHR frequency and is termed LHR noise. This noise is also most intense in the vicinity of the plasmapause near local noon. At the plasmapause itself individual records show a secondary minimum which is not always evident in studies of average noise intensity.

1. DISTRIBUTION OF NOISE IN THE POLAR IONOSPHERE

Naturally occurring VLF and ELF radio noise is an important source of information about processes that occur in the ionosphere and the magnetosphere. Noise observations from satellites require relatively simple instrumentation, yet they provide information concerning both the immediate surroundings of the spacecraft and regions at great distances from the vehicle. This information comes from the intensity, frequency, spectral distribution, polarization, and the type of waves that give rise to the noise observed by the satellite receivers. Broad-band, narrow-band, and swept receivers in conjunction with both electric dipoles and magnetic loops have been employed on a variety of spacecraft for investigations of ionospheric and magnetospheric noise.

In this paper, noise at ELF and VLF will be considered and, in keeping with the theme of the meeting, only observations made at invariant latitudes above 55° will be discussed. Noise occurs frequently at latitudes below this, but generally its characteristics and sources are different from those of noise found at higher latitudes. Only noise occurring below both the local electron gyrofrequency and the plasma frequency will be discussed. Noise at higher frequencies is common, but, apart from cosmic noise, it is not well understood and is only beginning to provide useful information on ionospheric and magnetospheric processes.

Much of the data presented here has been obtained from the broad-band VLF receivers of the Alouette and ISIS satellites (Barrington & Belrose 1963). These receivers are connected to long electric dipole antennas. Since all of the satellites of this series have an orbital inclination of 80° or more, they have provided a large number of noise observations in polar regions. The characteristics of various types of high-latitude noise are described and an attempt is made to interrelate some of these types. The relationship between particle observations and noise observations is not discussed, although some work has been done in this area and there is increasing evidence of the close connections between these two types of observations. Some aspects of this relationship are shown in other papers presented at this meeting.

2. ELF NOISE

The most intense and most frequently occurring noise seen by the broad-band receivers of the Alouette and ISIS satellites is found in the ELF part of the spectrum. Although this noise seldom has frequency components above 1 kHz it appears to control the AGC level of the receiver more than 50% of the time. This is remarkable since the

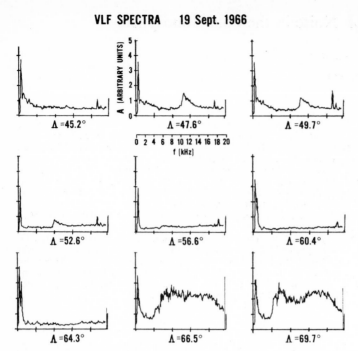

VLF SPECTRA   19 Sept. 1966

Λ =45.2°   Λ =47.6°   Λ =49.7°

Λ =52.6°   Λ =56.6°   Λ =60.4°

Λ =64.3°   Λ =66.5°   Λ =69.7°

Fig. 1. Typical VLF noise spectra obtained from Alouette II, 19 September 1966. Spectra are 10-second averages. Ordinate is in decibels.

receiver has a bandwidth of 30 kHz and the bandwidth of the ELF noise is usually less than 500 Hz. Fig. 1 shows some typical spectra selected from a pass of the satellite, in which ELF noise was present at all times. Throughout this pass, noise is found in various spectral regions, but the ELF noise remains quite distinct from any noise found at higher frequencies. Occasionally, as can be seen in Fig. 1, some of the spectra from the middle of the pass show an ELF noise band with a double peak. Often, when this occurs, it is found that the higher frequency peak is associated with chorus, whereas the lower frequency peak seems to have very little temporal fluctuation.

A study of the distribution of the ELF noise in local time and latitude was made using data from the Alouette II satellite. In this study the peak intensity of the ELF noise was scaled from spectra such as those of Fig. 1, and averaged for latitude intervals of five degrees and local time intervals of two hours. These average intensities are shown as a function of latitude and local time in Fig. 2. The large number in each box refer to the average intensity, and the small number gives the rms deviation of the observations about the mean value. This plot shows the ELF noise to be most intense around local noon, and to have a broad maximum intensity in the latitude range 55° to 65°.

A more refined picture of the distribution of

ELF noise in latitude and local time can be obtained only if it is possible to reduce significantly the standard rms deviations of the average intensities shown in Fig. 2. In an attempt to understand the reason for the large rms deviations of the data shown in this Figure a number of plots of ELF noise intensity as a function of invariant latitude were made from individual satellite passes. Four such plots are shown in Fig. 3. Here the triangles represent the intensities scaled from each spectrogram, and the solid line joins the average value of noise intensity calculated for every two degrees of latitude. There is a general tendency toward a maximum in intensity at high latitudes, but the shape and location of the maxima on individual records are highly variable. It is not possible, from the available satellite data, to determine whether the observed variations of Fig. 3 are primarily spatial or temporal in nature. The plots do, however, indicate the difficulty in trying to obtain a more precise picture of the distribution of ELF noise than that given by Fig. 2.

Generally, the distribution of ELF noise as seen by the Alouette satellite using an electric dipole antenna is similar to that observed by the Injun III satellite employing a magnetic loop antenna (Gurnett 1966). This would suggest that the waves giving rise to the noise seen by these satellites are electromagnetic. Both in the Alouette

98

LMT(hrs) / INV.LAT.	0-2	2-4	4-6	6-8	8-10	10-12	12-14	14-16	16-18	18-20	20-22	22-24
85-90					5 / 2	3 / 0.4	7 / 12	6 / 5	5 / 3	14 / 8	6 / 4	
80-85	3 / 0.3	14 / 9	16 / 6	9 / 10	8 / 4	5 / 2	5 / 3	9 / 5	7 / 6	6 / 3	7 / 3	5 / 2
75-80	10 / 5	19 / 13	25 / 10	16 / 17	38 / 32	87 / 58	14 / 5	17 / 15	15 / 9	16 / 37	11 / 9	6 / 3
70-75	17 / 19	17 / 13	16 / 14	18 / 62	40 / 41	55 / 63	16 / 4	22 / 17	14 / 12	18 / 25	15 / 13	13 / 35
65-70	15 / 18	10 / 8	10 / 16	25 / 40	39 / 43	43 / 46	35 / 39	27 / 22	24 / 16	15 / 16	13 / 15	8 / 4
60-65	9 / 14	7 / 5	7 / 7	21 / 24	51 / 208	42 / 46	62 / 48	27 / 18	24 / 19	24 / 62	9 / 11	12 / 44
55-60	7 / 8	7 / 24	7 / 4	15 / 14	21 / 33	41 / 35	98 / 84	30 / 20	40 / 54	19 / 18	9 / 10	6 / 2
50-55	8 / 10	5 / 4	6 / 3	11 / 7	8 / 4	25 / 26	44 / 33	14 / 11	34 / 47	11 / 8	6 / 2	8 / 3
45-50	6 / 5	8 / 8	9 / 6	10 / 9	9 / 5	12 / 10	18 / 11	9 / 6	15 / 10	10 / 4	9 / 4	8 / 6
40-45	7 / 4	7 / 8	10 / 7	4 / 3	9 / 4	9 / 8			49 / 26	12 / 4	6 / 2	8 / 6

Fig. 2. Mean ELF noise intensity as a function of invariant latitude and local mean time. The large numbers represent the mean intensity while the small numbers represent the standard deviation of the data from the mean. Total data points: 11,000.

and Injun observations the noise frequently has a sharp lower frequency cutoff, in the vicinity of the ambient proton gyrofrequency. Harvey (1969) and Guthart et al. (1968) have presented arguments based on this fact to support the idea that the ELF noise is, at least in some cases, due to electrostatic waves. Gurnett & Burns (1968), on the other hand, have explained this sharp cutoff feature as due to the reflection of electromagnetic waves at or near the multi-ion cutoff frequency that lies closest to the proton gyro-resonance.

Further support for the view that the ELF noise is primarily electromagnetic in nature comes from observations made using the search coil magnetometer of the OGO III satellite (Russel et al. 1969). Fig. 4 shows plots of the distribution of ELF noise as seen by the OGO 3 magnetometer and the Injun and Alouette satellites. When allowance is made for the fact that in this Figure the Alouette data are plotted in local time, whereas the Injun and OGO 3 data are plotted in magnetic local time, the three spacecrafts observe approximately the same temporal distribution for the ELF noise. The distribution of this noise in latitude is not, however, the same for these three sets of observations. The Alouette and Injun data agree fairly well, as would be expected if the noise is electromagnetic, since these spacecrafts made their observations at similar heights of a few hundred kilometres. The OGO 3 observations are from heights of many thousands of kilometres and show that steady ELF noise is

prevalent throughout a large volume of the magnetosphere.

The distribution of ELF noise with L value as seen by OGO-3 suggests a high latitude cutoff at about 60°, i.e. the mean position of the plasmapause. In contrast, the Alouette data indicate a broad peak in intensity at about 60° with a very gradual fall-off in intensity at higher latitudes. In fact, there is some evidence of a second peak in intensity between 75° and 80° which is close to the position of the cusp. At low latitudes the intensities observed by Alouette II show a more rapid fall-off with decreasing latitude than is indicated by the OGO-3 data.

3. VLF NOISE

Many types of noise are found in the VLF part of the spectrum, and often it is difficult to distinguish among them (Helliwell 1965). Here, the various types of discrete emissions such as whistlers, risers, hooks, etc. will not be considered. In such emissions the bandwidth at any given instant is small and the duration of an event is typically one second or so. The noise considered here is primarily hiss in which the intensity and spectrum change slowly with time. Chorus represents a superposition of many discrete events and is sometimes difficult to distinguish from hiss. Where possible, chorus has been eliminated from the data presented here.

One of the discoveries of early satellite observa-

7*

ELF NOISE INTENSITY

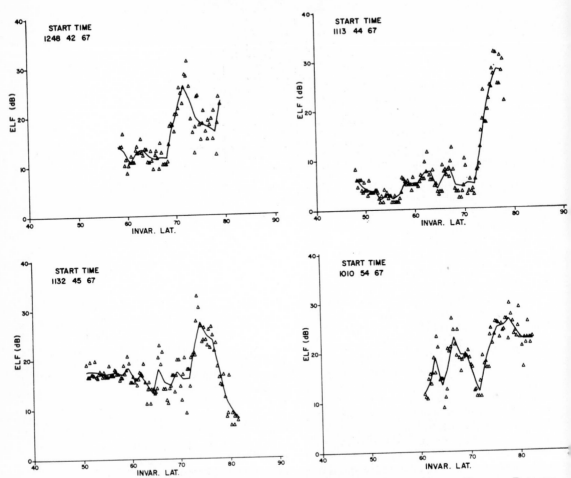

Fig. 3. ELF noise intensity as a function of invariant latitude for four different Alouette II passes. Data are from days 42, 44, 45, and 54 in 1967. Times given are local mean time.

tions of VLF noise was the fact that very frequently the low frequency edge of such noise bands coincided with the lower hybrid resonance (LHR) frequency of the plasma surrounding the spacecraft (Brice & Smith 1964). In Fig. 1, the spectra at 47.6°, 49.7°, and 52.6° invariant latitude have VLF noise bands with a sharp lower frequency cutoff at the LHR frequency. At latitudes below the plasmapause boundary such noise, having a very well-defined cutoff at its lower frequency edge and typically having a bandwidth of 2–4 kHz, is relatively common and has been termed LHR noise. In fact, such noise has been used to determine the LHR frequency. By combining

this frequency with measurements of the plasma frequency, information concerning the mean mass of the ions surrounding the spacecraft has been derived (Barrington et al. 1965).

At latitudes well above the plasmapause boundary VLF noise tends to be very broad band, and although its lower frequency boundary is frequently well defined, the cutoff frequency tends to vary rapidly with time. Often, erratic fluctuations in the cutoff frequency of several kHz in one second or less are found. In Fig. 1, the VLF noise observed at invariant latitudes of 66.5° and 69.7° is of this type. Since these spectra represent 10-second averages, and since the lower cutoff fre-

ELF/VLF NOISE DISTRIBUTIONS

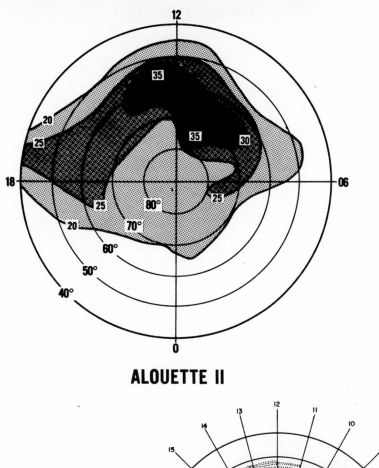

ALOUETTE II

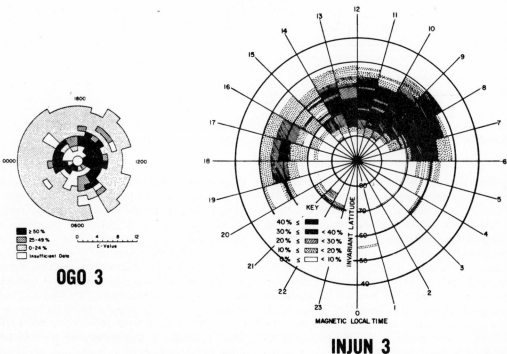

OGO 3

INJUN 3

Fig. 4. ELF/VLF noise distributions as determined using data from Alouette II, OGO 3, and INJUN 3.

LHR NOISE INTENSITY

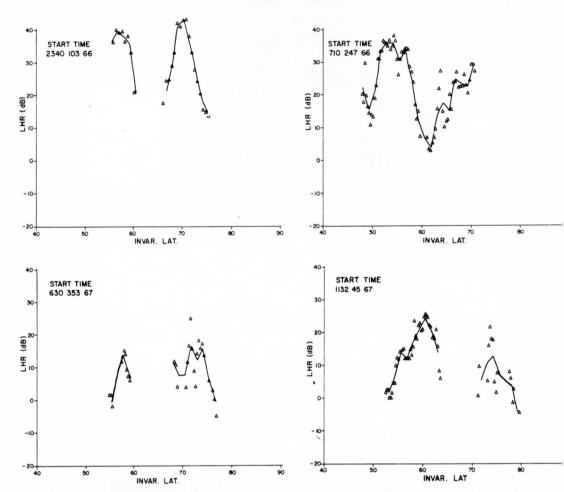

Fig. 5. LHR noise intensity as a function of invariant latitude for four different Alouette II passes. Data are from days 103 and 247, 1966, and days 45 and 353, 1967. Times given are local mean time.

quency varies rapidly throughout this period, the lower frequency edges of these bands are not as sharp as those found at lower latitudes.

Another significant feature of the noise spectra observed throughout the pass shown in Fig. 1 is the absence of VLF noise in the latitude region between 56° and 64°. Fig. 5 shows a plot of the maximum intensity of VLF noise as a function of latitude at four different local times. Again the triangles represent the intensities scaled from each spectrogram and the solid lines join the mean intensities found in each two-degree latitude interval. In all of these plots there is a region in which the VLF noise is either very low or not seen

at all. At both higher and lower latitudes intense VLF noise bands are found. This intensity minimum occurs at just the invariant latitude range in which the ionospheric trough and plasmapause are located.

In Fig. 6 the mean intensity of the LHR noise and the rms deviations about this mean are shown for intervals of two hours in local time and five degrees in invariant latitude. This Figure covers all local times and invariant latitudes from 40° to 65°. Data are absent above 65° since LHR noise is difficult to identify at high latitudes because of the absence of a sharp lower frequency cutoff. From this plot it is clear that the LHR

LMT(hrs) / INV.LAT	0-2	2-4	4-6	6-8	8-10	10-12	12-14	14-16	16-18	18-20	20-22	22-24
60-65	8 7	5 6	7 13	11 15	37 109	57 35	27 2		10 9	19 53	10 19	9 26
55-60	12 12	11 81	5 5	11 16	5 7	73 41	54 33	9 6	23 34	10 9	15 17	5 4
50-55	11 19	3 2	2 2	3 4	2 0.7	28 19	21 14	3 2	4 1	6 7	5 4	2 1
45-50	5 5	3 2	3 2	1 0.5	1 0.8	2 0.8		2 0.0		2 0.7	1 0.8	3 1
40-45		1 0.6			1 0.2					1 0.3		

Fig. 6. Mean LHR noise intensity as a function of invariant latitude and local mean time. The large numbers represent the mean intensity while the small numbers represent the standard deviation of the data from the mean. Total data points: 4300.

noise observed at latitudes below the plasmapause is most intense around local noon. Previous studies (Barrington & McEwen 1966) found that LHR noise was observed most frequently in the night sector. However, those studies did not deduce intensities but simply plotted percentage occurrence of the noise. If the intensity data presented here is considered along with the intensity data already presented for the ELF noise, the relationship between the old and new results can be understood. The receiver used to observe these two noise types has an AGC system which is controlled by the mean intensity of the noise over the entire pass band of the receiver: 50 Hz to 30 kHz. Thus, the intense ELF noise band found around local noon tends to reduce the sensitivity of the receiver at that time. The apparent intensity of the VLF noise bands is often reduced to the point where they are neglected in percentage occurrence studies. During the night hours the intensity of the ELF noise is much smaller. The receiver sensitivity is therefore higher and more VLF noise bands are apparent, even though their intensity is somewhat smaller than those observed around local noon.

The very broad band noise observed at latitudes above the plasmapause region and having a lower frequency cutoff near the LHR frequency has been termed auroral hiss. This name arises because the noise is found to be most intense at auroral latitudes and to have a distribution similar to that of the aurora (Feldstein et al. 1968). As yet, there have been no detailed studies made to determine the relationship between the two phenomena. Intercomparison of the VLF observations and those made by the sounding receiver of Alouette II indicate that the auroral hiss extends from the LHR frequency up to the vicinity of the plasma or electron gyro-frequency, whichever is lower (Barrington et al. 1971). There is also increasing evidence that the occurrence of auroral hiss is associated with the precipitation of electrons with energies of the order of a few hundred electron volts (Hartz 1971). These features of the auroral hiss are consistent with the view that it arises from Cerenkov radiation generated as low energy particles are precipitated into the upper ionosphere.

4. SUMMARY

The data that have been presented show clearly that noise in the ELF and VLF range of the spectrum is an important feature of the polar ionosphere and magnetosphere. The main features of only the strongest and most frequently occurring types of noise have been outlined. After almost a decade of noise observations in space from many satellites using several techniques, the morphology of the noise has become fairly well established. Less is known about the processes that give rise to the noise, and about the wave-particle interactions that may lead to its amplification or attenuation. Once these processes are understood, noise observation will be an important tool for monitoring the occurrence of phenomena throughout the ionosphere and magnetosphere.

REFERENCES

Barrington, R. E. & Belrose, J. S. 1963. *Nature 198*, 651.
Barrington, R. E. & McEwen, D. J. 1966. *Can. J. Phys. 45*, 13.
Barrington, R. E., Belrose, J. S. & Nelms, G. L. 1965. *J. Geophys. Res. 70*, 1647.
Barrington, R. E., Hartz, T. R. & Harvey, R. W. 1971. *J. Geophys. Res.* In press.
Brice, N. M. & Smith, R. L. 1964. *Nature 203*, 926.
Feldstein, Y. I. et al. 1968. *Ann. Géophys. 24*, 517.
Gurnett, D. A. 1966. *J. Geophys. Res. 71*, 5599.
Gurnett, D. A. & Burns, T. B. 1968. *J. Geophys. Res. 73*, 7437.
Guthart, H., Crystal, T. L., Ficklin, B. P., Blair, W. E. & Yung, T. J. 1968. *J. Geophys. Res. 73*, 3592.

103

Hartz, T. R. 1971. In McCormac, B. M. (ed.). *The Radiating Atmosphere*, p. 215. D. Reidel Publishing Co., Dordrecht, Holland.

Harvey, R. W. 1969. *J. Geophys. Res. 74*, 3969.

Helliwell, R. A. 1965. *Whistlers and Related Ionospheric Phenomena*. Palo Alto, Stanford University Press.

Russell, C. T., Holzer, R. E. & Smith, E. J. 1969. *J. Geophys. Res. 74*, 755.

Recent High-Latitude Optical Observations

J. F. NOXON

Blue Hill Observatory, Harvard University
Cambridge, Mass. U.S.A.

Abstract: Recent developments in five areas: conjugate effects, pulsating aurora, red (6300Å) arcs, infrared aurora, and oval morphology are discussed.

1. INTRODUCTION

My intention is to provide a selective review of certain optical topics of current interest; I am not attempting an exhaustive survey. In each case the optical measurements involve emission processes which either derive their energy from the magnetosphere or are influenced by it. Somewhat arbitrarily I am excluding such topics as the use of artificial luminous clouds to study electric fields, atmospheric motions and temperature, and the various atmospheric uses of optical radar. Most of the work I shall discuss has been reported in the last year or two and nearly all of it has been carried out by effective use of high-altitude platforms of one sort or another, principally jet aircraft and satellites.

2. CONJUGATE EFFECTS

Until recently photometric work in this area has focused upon the OI (6300 Å) enhancement associated with an influx of conjugate photoelectrons (see Noxon & Johanson 1970 for a summary). At least part of the interest has arisen from the hope that the enhancement could be utilized to investigate the poleward boundary of closed field lines or the attenuation of the flux at high L values where the tube opacity might become large. The red line turns out to have rather severe limitations however; one problem is the appreciable and varying airglow background for which reliable correction must be made. In addition the 6300 Å enhancement is not uniquely related to the magnitude of the incident electron flux but depends also upon the relative abundance of ambient electrons and atomic oxygen in the dark F-region.

An important new development has been the detection, by satellite, of a conjugate enhancement in the 1304 Å resonance line of atomic oxygen (Meier 1971); the considerably higher excitation energy largely eliminates both of the problems associated with the red line. Meier reports measurements of the conjugate enhancement up to nearly $L = 6$; if anything the magnitude is increased at higher L value (Fig. 1). A related observation (Meier 1970) indicates a polar depression in 1304 Å dayglow which is taken to be the result of an imbalance between escaping and incident electron flux in the region of open field lines. The same paper describes a similar small depression in Ly α dayglow; in this case it is suggested that the reduced hydrogen abundance is the consequence of efficient conversion of H atoms to protons via charge exchange with O^+ followed by escape of the protons in the polar wind. It seems reasonable to suppose that the present gap in the 1304 Å measurements will be filled in so that a more detailed study of conjugate propagation and attenuation of the electron flux can be performed.

Aircraft study of conjugate auroral forms has continued (Peterson et al. 1971) and suggests a tendency towards brighter forms in the northern hemisphere. Full details have not been published but the hemispherical asymmetries do not appear to be a seasonal effect.

3. PULSATING AURORA

Rosenberg et al. (1971) have studied the relationship between pulsations in auroral X-rays and the 5577 Å oxygen line. The higher energy electrons responsible for the X-rays contribute appreciably to the optical pulsations; the conclusion is that the entire energy spectrum of the electrons is modulated by a single process. The importance of higher energy electrons (> 15 keV) is borne out in a combined rocket/ground-based study reported by Whalen et al. (1971a). During pulsations the electron spectrum in the 15–60 keV

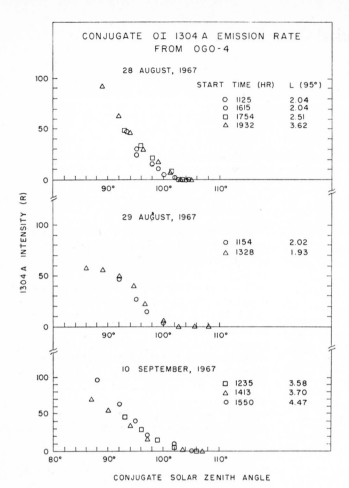

Fig. 1. The conjugate photoelectron enhancement of OI (1304Å) taken from Meier (1971). The observations are ordered with respect to L value and conjugate solar zenith angle.

range softens, whereas higher energy electrons and protons exhibit negligible pulsations. The rocket measurements confirm Eather's (1968) report of negligible pulsation in proton flux as deduced from observations of Hß. The softening of the electron flux during its increase does not seem to be a universal process, however, since Hilliard & Shepherd (1966) found a decrease in 5577 Å Doppler temperature during pulsations which suggests a hardening in the spectrum.

A related paper by Moore (1971) shows that the time delay between N_2^+ emission and the green line decreases with higher pulsation frequency; presumably the faster pulsations are associated with a harder electron spectrum which moves the pulsation altitude deeper into the $O(^1S)$ quenching region.

Parkinson et al. (1970) describe an in situ observation of a single pulsation in which both the

incident particle flux and the optical intensity were measured, the latter using an up-down photometer. They were able to show that the pulsation propagated downward at the modest rate of about 5 km/sec; the more energetic particles in the pulse must have arrived rather later than the softer ones. No change in the shape of the electron energy spectrum was observed between 1 and 12 keV, so that the effect must have involved higher energies. There appears to be a qualitative similarity between these findings and those of Whalen et al. (1971a), who state that in the 15–60 keV range the softer particles arrive first. The limited nature of these observations is such that the complete description of particle flux changes during pulsations has presumably not yet been achieved.

A recent study of pulsations observed optically at conjugate ground stations has been described by Gokhberg et al. (1970). Pulsations were coincident to better than one second; this again supports the interpretation that they are due to a pitch-angle redistribution of trapped electrons in the equatorial region (see Coroniti & Kennel 1970).

4. RED (6300 Å) ARCS

A recent summary of the properties of red arcs has been presented by Nagy et al. (1970). The very high ratio of 6300 Å to 5577 Å in these arcs makes it clear that the excitation must involve very low energy electrons. The association of high electron temperature and red arcs (Norton & Findlay 1969) supports this notion (Fig. 2). Until recently it remained unclear as to whether the production of $O(^1D)$ was due to a soft electron flux (< 20 eV) or to excitation by hot ambient electrons. There also remained the question as to whether, in the second case, the hot electrons in the F-region were produced by thermal conduction of heat from the high magnetosphere or by a heat input between 500 and 1000 km due to a soft electron flux. These questions appear to have been resolved by Chandra et al. (1971) who not only found an electron temperature gradient between 1000 km and 2000 km over red arcs, but also noted that no enhancement in the flux of soft ($E > 5$ eV) electrons existed over the arc. Since the electron temperature structure reported leads to the conclusion that a downward heat flow of $1.5 \cdot 10^{10}$ eV/cm^2 sec existed over the arc, it is probable that the 100–200 R arc intensity can be accounted for as a consequence of ambient electron heating in the F-region (see Walker & Rees

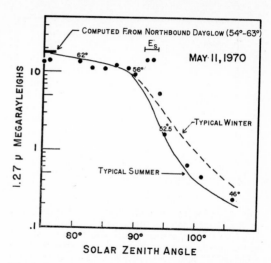

Fig. 3. Twilight decay of $O_2(^1\Delta_g)$ emission measured from a southbound aircraft; the geographic latitude is indicated. The solid and dashed lines are theoretical calculations; the former assumes a constant 5.2 km ozone scale height above 40 km while the latter assumes that the ozone density at 85 and 90 km is, respectively, twice and equal to the 80 km value. These two choices fit summer and winter measurements respectively; the theoretical curves are adjusted at $\chi = 75°$ to fit the observations at a smaller solar zenith angle made on the northbound leg. There is an obvious enhancement near $\chi = 93°$ which is exactly coincident with auroral sporadic E_s measured by an airborne ionsonde, (Noxon 1971).

1968, Roble et al. 1970a). The positive electron temperature gradient at high altitude also suggests that processes depositing heat at lower altitude, such as soft electrons or electric fields, are unimportant. It now seems fairly clear that the existence of a red arc implies selective plasma heating in a relatively narrow L shell at very high altitude.

An extraordinary stability in arc emission intensity must also be kept in mind. For example, in the 31 October 1968 arc, as observed over Boston, the intensity in a fixed direction varied less than 0.5 % for nearly an hour, apart from a small linear decrease in time. Such behavior is rather difficult to reconcile with any mechanism which deposits heat locally in the F-region; it also implies a marked stability in the plasma temperature structure at very high altitude, even if one accepts the conduction mechanism.

It has also become apparent that red arcs tend to lie at the feet of field lines which map out to the plasmapause (Glass et al. 1970, Chappell et al. 1971). There is often an obvious tilt between the

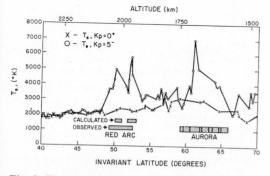

Fig. 2. Electron temperatures measured over a red arc and aurora compared with quiet day values (from Norton & Findlay 1969, as presented by Nagy et al. 1970).

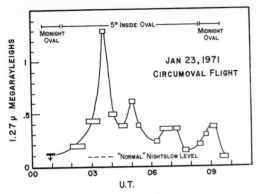

Fig. 4. Aurorally associated enhancement of 1.27μ in the polar cap; the flight path crossed the oval twice, as shown, and only then was there significant visual aurora overhead. The major infrared enhancement of 1.3 mR was coincident with a major substorm in the oval, several degrees to the south (Noxon 1971).

5. INFRARED AURORAS

There is recent evidence which suggests that enhanced emission from $O_2(^1\Delta_g)$ at 1.27 μ is sometimes associated with auroral (or magnetospheric) activity (Evans et al. 1970, Megill et al. 1970, Noxon 1970, Schiff et al. 1970). In some cases there is a high degree of spatial correlation between a major 1.27 μ enhancement and such quantities as visual aurora, aurorally induced E-region ionization, explosive substorms, and the statistical auroral oval (Figs. 3 and 4). Yet, on the whole, extended aircraft observation over the past few years shows that in a majority of cases intense active aurora is not accompanied by any significant enhancement in $O_2(^1\Delta_g)$ emission. There is certainly no evidence that a particle in-

direction of an arc and the contours of constant L; the tilt appears to be correlated with the equatorward movement of the arc, particularly in the evening hours when the plasmapause decreases more rapidly in radius. The observations on the October 31, 1968 arc reported by Roble et al. (1970b) bear this out; simultaneous observations at Boston, when compared with the Ann Arbor data, make it clear that in the early evening the tilt angle approached 25° at a time when the southern movement was rapid.

The association of red arcs with a film of hot plasma in the magnetosphere appears to be fairly well established; the coincidence of the film with the plasmapause seems plausible. Certainly there exists a fairly close coincidence between the two in the limited number of cases studied so far. Generally the red arcs exist somewhat equatorward of aurora (Hoch & Clark 1970) with a gap in luminosity between; a similar gap exists in the electron temperature measured at high altitude (Norton & Findlay 1969).

The arcs may then at least give a qualitative picture of the shape of the plasmapause under disturbed conditions when the latter has shrunk under magnetospheric attack. The picture must necessarily remain somewhat qualitative, however, since the actual arc intensity is strongly influenced by local ionospheric plasma and neutral density; the latter determines the actual electron temperature attained near 400 km, where arcs occur, for a given downward heat flow from high altitude.

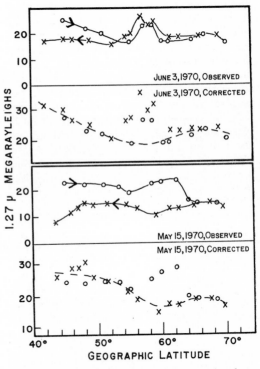

Fig. 5. Two examples of aurorally associated enhancement in the 1.27μ dayglow. The measurements on both north- and southbound legs of the flight are shown. The corrected intensities are referred to a solar zenith angle of 0° and were obtained from the simple ozone photolysis theory which predicts zenith intensity as a function of solar zenith angle. It is clear that the legs are mutually consistent with the theory except near 60° where, in each flight, an enhancement existed which is located at the expected latitude of the auroral oval at the local time of observation (Noxon 1971).

flux directly stimulates an enhancement; indeed there are many cases in which the energy radiated in an enhancement exceeds the total energy input from particle precipitation as deduced from N_2^+ band measurements. In such cases the 1.27 μ enhancement often appears as a very large-scale phenomenon in which the intensity over a large portion of the polar cap is ten or twenty times larger than the minimum values observed (20 kR). It is not yet clear what other geophysical quantity (if any) has also increased under such circumstances, although in the most pronounced cases we have examined, the K_p index was high. It is well to point out that when 1.27 μ reaches a level of, say, 700 kR over the cap then the total energy *radiated* is about $3 \cdot 10^{17}$ ergs/sec; this exceeds the total rate of energy deposition in the auroral oval, according to Feldstein & Starkov (1971), when $K_p < 6$. Some dayglow and twilight observations imply an aurorally associated enhancement of 10 Megarayleighs (Fig. 5); the column abundance of $O_2(^1\Delta_g)$ corresponding to the enhancement equals the abundance of O_2 above 120 km.

It is quite conceivable that the day and twilight effects could be the result of an enhanced ozone concentration in the D-region. In the dayglow one finds that about 4 mR of 1.27 μ comes from altitudes above 70 km and about 1 mR from above 80 km (see Evans & Llewellyn 1970). Since the dayglow is thought to arise from production of $O_2(^1\Delta_g)$ through photolysis of ozone it follows that a 10 mR enhancement would require a doubling of the ozone abundance above 70 km or a factor of 10 increase in abundance above 80 km. A similar enhancement in twilight, at a solar depression of 2.5°, would require a factor of 10 increase in ozone abundance above either altitude, owing to the reduction in solar input at lower altitude in twilight. It appears out of the question that such changes should be produced directly by a particle flux (Maeda & Aiken 1968); it seems more likely that the auroral environment in some way perturbs the ozone chemistry, either through temperature, dynamical transport, or an effect on the hydrogen–oxygen compounds which appear to determine the ozone abundance at such altitudes.

The alternative to ozone changes in the day, and chemiluminescent reaction changes at night, is to suppose that the $O_2(^1\Delta_g)$ enhancement is produced by hot electron excitation in the lower E-region. This possibility has been discussed in some of the papers mentioned, and also by Walker (1970). There is, at present, little direct evidence favoring such a mechanism; the fraction of electrons with energies above the 1 eV threshhold for $O_2(^1\Delta_g)$ production must be equivalent to that in a Maxwellian distribution at a temperature of nearly 2500°K. This is not an easy temperature to sustain in the E-region.

Some enhancement of infrared emission from OH in aurora has been reported (Brown 1970, Stair 1971) although there are many reports which note an absence of such enhancement (see Harrison 1970). Since the total energy radiated by OH in the nightglow is very large, any aurorally associated enhancement implies, as in the case of $O_2(^1\Delta_g)$, that a major increase in radiated energy has occurred.

The position on infrared aurora may be summarized by saying that some major enhancements exist which appear to be closely associated in space and time with auroral activity; these must surely be classified as 'infrared aurora'. In many other cases the association is much less obvious; but even here it may ultimately turn out that the energy source is the magnetosphere, even if only very indirectly.

6. OVAL MORPHOLOGY

From this vast subject we select a few recent observations from satellites and jet aircraft. An outstanding advance is the study of far UV aurora reported by Chubb & Hicks (1970) (see Figs. 6 and 7). The photometric measurements were capable of distinguishing proton and electron aurora under sunlit conditions as well as at night. Their observations bring out the diurnal changes in the latitude distribution; they also confirm nicely the tendency of proton aurora to occur equatorward of electron aurora in the night sector. An almost instantaneous picture can be realized of the overall precipitation pattern. The current question of the relative position of proton and electron auroras on the dayside is not resolved by their few measurements; these show a separation with the proton aurora occurring poleward. Recent aircraft (Eather & Mende 1971) and ground-based (Rees & Benedict 1970) observations suggest that an intermingling is more common. There is little doubt, however, that the satellite method applied to UV aurora will provide the extensive data needed to improve the picture of gross auroral morphology as revealed by optical means.

On a finer scale there has been a considerable amount of new information brought forth on oval

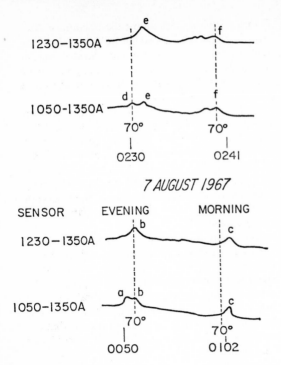

1230-1350A

1050-1350A

70°   70°

0230   0241

7 AUGUST 1967

SENSOR   EVENING   MORNING

1230-1350A

1050-1350A

70°   70°

0050   0102

Fig. 6. Ultraviolet auroral observations (Chubb & Hicks 1970). The 1230–1350Å detector responds mainly to electron produced 1304Å while the other channel includes Lyman α. The separation of proton and electron flux in latitude in the evening sector is apparent.

structure from recent aircraft investigations. Eather (1969), Eather & Mende, (1971), and Whalen et al. (1971b) have all used jet aircraft to study the spectral changes associated with crossings of the oval. The latter authors also include additional information from an airborne ionosonde. On both the day- and nightside the optical measurements give clear evidence of a softening in the particle energy spectrum when the pole is approached (see Fig. 8 and accompanying paper by Eather & Mende). The question of the continuity of the oval in the longitudinal sense has been investigated by Buchau et al. (1970); they performed 'circumoval' flights which followed the predicted (Feldstein) location of the oval through a full magnetic day. Analysis of the ASCA plots so obtained revealed no latitudinal discontinuity

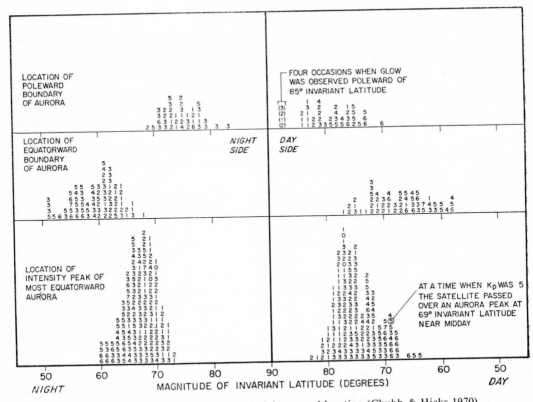

Fig. 7. Comparison of satellite-measured day and night auroral location (Chubb & Hicks 1970).

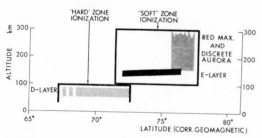

AIRCRAFT OBSERVATIONS
compared with
SATELLITE MEASUREMENTS
of "HARD" (>21keV) AND "SOFT" (0.08–21keV) ELECTRON PRECIPITATION ZONES

Fig. 8. A representation of noontime particle precipitation inferred by Whalen et al. (1971b) using combined optical and ionosonde airborne measurements. 'Red max' refers to the 6300Å oxygen line, a sensitive indicator of soft electron precipitation.

in the optical oval. A great deal of data has been obtained from such aircraft flights which awaits analysis or publication, and it would be premature to guess the outcome. At present one can conclude that the gross picture agrees rather well with that inferred from satellite particle measurements on the time energy, and spatial structure of precipitation.

Acknowledgement: The author's work was supported by a grant to Harvard University from the National Science Foundation, GP 4293.

REFERENCES

Brown, N. B. 1970. Abstract. *Trans. Am. Geophys. Union 51*, 370.

Buchau, J., Whalen, J. A. & Akasofu, S.-I. 1970. *J. Geophys. Res. 75*, 7147.

Chandra, S., Maier, E. J., Troy, B. E. & Narasinga Rao, B. C. 1971. *J. Geophys. Res. 76*, 920.

Chappel, C. R., Harris, K. K. & Sharp, G. W. 1971. *J. Geophys. Res. 76*, 2357.

Chubb, T. A. & Hicks, G. T. 1970. *J. Geophys. Res. 75*, 1290.

Coroniti, F. V. & Kennel, C. F. 1970. *J. Geophys. Res. 75*, 1279.

Eather, R. H. 1968. *Ann. Géophys. 24*, 525.

Eather, R. H. 1969. *J. Geophys. Res. 74*, 153.

Eather, R. H. & Mende, S. B. 1971. *J. Geophys. Res. 76*, 1746.

Eather, R. H. & Mende, S. B. 1971. In Folkestad, Kr. (ed.). *Magnetosphere–Ionosphere Interactions,* Universitetsforlaget, Oslo.

Evans, W. F. J. & Llewellyn, E. J. 1970. *Ann. Géophys. 26*, 167.

Evans, W. F. J., Wood, H. C. & Llewellyn, E. J. 1970. *Planet. Space Sci. 18*, 1065.

Feldstein, Ya. I. & Starkov, G. V. 1971. *J. Atmos. Terr. Phys. 33*, 197.

Glass, N. W., Wolcott, J. H., Miller, L. W. & Robertson, M. M. 1970. *J. Geophys. Res. 75*, 2579.

Gokhberg, M. B., Kazak, B. N., Raspopov, O. M., Roldugin, V. K., Troitskaya, V. A. & Fedoseyev, V. I. 1970. *Geomagnetism and Aeronomy 10, 289*.

Harrison, A. W. 1970. *J. Geophys. Res. 75*, 1330.

Hilliard, R. L. & Shepherd, G. G. 1966. *Planet. Space Sci. 14*, 383.

Hoch, R. J. & Clark, K. C. 1970. *J. Geophys. Res. 75*, 2511.

Maeda, K. & Aiken, A. C. 1968. *Planet. Space Sci. 16*, 371.

Megill, L. R., Despain, A. M., Baker, D. J. & Baker, K. D. 1970. *J. Geophys. Res. 75*, 4775.

Meier, R. R. 1970. *J. Geophys. Res. 75*, 6218.

Meier, R. R. 1971. *J. Geophys. Res. 76*, 242.

Moore, J. G. 1971. *Planet. Space Sci. 19*, 119.

Nagy, A. F., Roble, R. G. & Hays, P. B. 1970. *Space Sci. Rev. 11*, 709.

Norton, R. B. & Findlay, J. A. 1969. *Planet. Space Sci. 17*, 1867.

Noxon, J. F. 1970. *J. Geophys. Res. 75*, 1879.

Noxon, J. F. & Johanson, A. E. 1970. *Planet. Space Sci. 18*, 1367.

Noxon, J. F. 1971. Unpublished observations.

Parkinson, T. D., Zipf, E. C. & Dick, K. A. 1970. *J. Geophys. Res. 75*, 1334.

Peterson, R. W., Wescott, E. M., Nielson, H. C. S. & Glass. N. W. 1971. Abstract. *Trans. Am. Geophys. Union 52*, 334.

Roble, R. G., Hays, P. B. & Nagy. A. F. 1970a. *J. Geophys. Res. 75*, 4261.

Roble, R. G., Hays, P. B. & Nagy. A. F. 1970b. *Planet. Space Sci. 18*, 431.

Rosenberg, T. J., Bjordal, J., Trefall, H., Kvifte, G. J., Omholt, A., & Egeland, A. 1971. *J. Geophys. Res. 76*, 122.

Rees, M. H. & Benedict, P. C. 1970. *J. Geophys. Res. 75*, 4763.

Schiff, H. I., Haslett, J. C. & Megill, L. R. 1970. *J. Geophys. Res. 75*, 4363.

Stair, A. T. 1971. In McCormac, B. M. (ed.). *The Radiating Atmosphere*. Reinhold Publ. Co., Dordrecht, Holland.

Walker, J. C. G. 1970. *Planet. Space Sci. 18*, 1043.

Walker, J. C. G. & Rees, M. H. 1968. *Planet. Space Sci. 16*, 915.

Whalen, B. A., Miller, J. R. & McDiarmid, I. B. 1971. *J. Geophys. Res. 76*, 978.

Whalen, J. A., Buchau, J. & Wagner, R. A. 1971b. *J. Atmospheric Terr. Phys. 33*, 661.

Morphology of the Pulsating Aurora

G. J. KVIFTE AND H. PETTERSEN

The Auroral Observatory, PO Box 387 – 9001 Tromsø, Norway

Abstract: Observations of pulsating aurora have been made on a routine basis from Tromsø during the winters of 1967–1969 with several photometers pointing in different directions in the magnetic meridian plane. Special emphasis has been placed on obtaining observations in the late afternoon and early evening. The results are presented in morphologic maps, which show that the pulsating aurora mainly occurs in an oval-shaped region, which at medium geomagnetic activity is near Tromsø most of the night. An interesting feature is the finding of rather high pulsation occurrences in the early evening. An investigation of the latitudinal extension of the pulsating region near Tromsø shows a typical width of about 100 km in the evening, increasing to 300 km or more late in the night, the increase being greatest at high magnetic activity.

1. INTRODUCTION

In this paper we shall present results additional to those shown in a recent morphologic investigation by Kvifte & Pettersen (1969). The main purpose of the present work has been to study the late afternoon and evening geomagnetic sector, which has been more or less neglected in previous works. For the midnight region and morning sector much more data are presented than in the above-mentioned paper, thus making the statistical results more reliable. The latitudinal extension of the pulsating region is also investigated.

2. OBSERVATIONS

The observations were performed with four identical photometers at Tromsø (67°N, 117°E geom. coord.) during the winters 1967/68 and 1968/69. The photometers were equipped with 4278 Å interference filters to observe the auroral N_2^+ emission and had a 10° field of view. The instruments responded to pulsations in the frequency range 0–20 Hz and to intensities down to about 20 R. In 1967/68 the photometers were directed along the magnetic meridian at elevations of 30° and 45° to the south, towards the zenith and at 45° in the north. The next winter the photometer at 30°S was directed towards 30°N. In this way a latitude interval of about 3° around 67°N geomagnetic latitude was covered. During the first winter the observations were started at about 20^h local time (19 GMT or 22^h geomagnetic time) and ended at dawn. The next winter a great effort

was made to start as early as possible after sunset, and good coverage was obtained from 19 to 09^h geomagnetic time. Altogether, 1100 minutes of observations were obtained during the first hour of this interval, increasing to 3500 min/h in the midnight region, and again decreasing to 1500 min/h in the morning. The instruments were working during almost all clear periods and also when no pulsating aurora was present.

3. RESULTS

The data were sorted into three groups according to geomagnetic activity. To separate the groups the sum of local K indices from 12 GMT to 12 GMT was computed for every night that observations were obtained. The sum values limiting the three groups were set to 14 and 22, resulting in approximately equal amounts of data in each group. For all groups the fraction of all time that pulsating aurora in some form occurs has been calculated for each hour in the interval $19–09^h$ geomagnetic time. Only pulsations with amplitudes exceeding 25 R have been used for the computations. The results are shown in Figs. 1–3, where the data are presented with geomagnetic latitude and time as variables for the three groups. Also included are some observations from Ny-Ålesund, Spitsbergen, at 75°N geomagnetic latitude made by Brekke & Pettersen (1971). Since no significant dependence on magnetic activity was found there, all data are included in all three Figures.

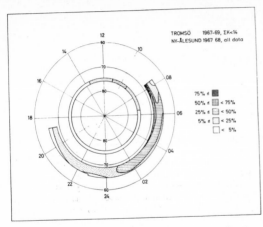

Fig. 1. The occurrence of pulsating aurora in geomagnetic coordinates for low magnetic activity.

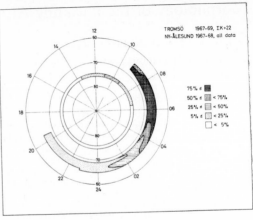

Fig. 3. The occurrence of pulsating aurora in geomagnetic coordinates for high magnetic activity.

The diagrams for the high and low activity groups show the same features as those presented in the previous paper by Kvifte & Pettersen (1969) for the midnight and morning hours. The new observation is that pulsations also occur in the afternoon sector, at least from 19ʰ geomagnetic time, and with the same percentage of occurrence at high and low activity. In this paper a third diagram is presented, showing the relations during medium activity, when we see a region of increased occurrence compared to both high and low activity on the evening side. However, the frequency of occurrence is always low compared to the morning sector. Also the pulsation amplitude is low on the evening side and usually well below 100 R for all activities. As shown in the paper by Kvifte

& Pettersen, a mean amplitude of 400–500 R is found in the morning sector at high activity. However, on rare occasions pulsating aurora may also be seen by the naked eye in the evening.

From the previous Figures it is apparent that the latitudinal extension of the pulsating region depends on geomagnetic time as well as geomagnetic activity. These problems are investigated and some results given in Fig. 4. This shows the percentage distribution of large versus relatively small pulsating areas as a function of time for the three groups of magnetic activity. The curves showing the occurrence of the 'less than 100 km extension' are constructed as the fraction of all the time we observe pulsations in one, and only one, of the two centre directions, compared to the time pulsations that are found in at least one of these photometer channels. The latitudinal width limit of 100 km refers to the rough distance between any two neighbouring photometers in the usual auroral height of 100–110 km. The 'large extension' curves correspondingly show the fraction of all the time we find pulsations simultaneously in all four directions to the time we have pulsations in at least one of the two centre directions. The reference curves are also given in the Figure. At all activities we see that the latitudinal extension of the pulsating areas is relatively small in the evening. Later in the night the pulsating region increases in latitude, reaching a maximum near 2ʰ GMT at low geomagnetic activity, when more than half of the observations show a width greater than 300 km, and at high activity reaching a maximum near 4ʰ GMT, when the pulsating region is nearly always broader than 300 km in

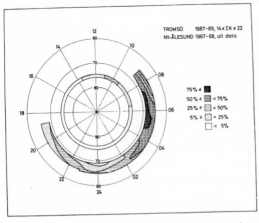

Fig. 2. The occurrence of pulsating aurora in geomagnetic coordinates for medium magnetic activity.

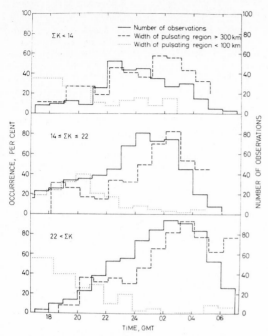

Fig. 4. Percentage distribution of the latitudinal width of the pulsating region above Tromsø.

the south-north direction. It should be stressed that the widths of coherent pulsating areas are usually much smaller than the dimensions found here.

In spite of rather limited coverage in latitude, these data show auroral optical pulsations to occur in a more or less oval- or spiral-shaped region around the geomagnetic pole, the distance to the pole being shortest on the dayside. However, the percentage of occurrence and the amplitude of the pulsations are far from constant along the oval.

At low magnetic activity the pulsating region is seen to be situated north of Tromsø all through the night. At medium activity the oval-shaped pattern has expanded towards the south, being still north of Tromsø in the early evening and crossing Tromsø near 22^h geomagnetic time. Around midnight the maximum is seen to be in the south and in the morning hours Tromsø is again underneath the oval. At greatest activity the pulsating region is far south of Tromsø, except in the morning, when the oval crosses it. On the morning side the expansion with increasing activity seems to be a broadening of the pulsating area towards the south, and the evening and midnight sectors show a real movement of the pulsating oval to the south.

Campbell & Rees (1961) state that the pulsa-

tions observed before midnight are probably due to movements or variations of structure in the aurora. In the evening we have observed visual pulsations only rarely. However, these few occasions seem to indicate that the evening pulsations at the latitude of Tromsø are of the ordinary stationary type. An indication of this may also be found in Fig. 2, where the oval is seen to form a continuous pattern from the evening to the morning side. However, at times we also observe intensity variations due to apparent movement of structures, but not preferentially during the evening hours.

The finding of an area with increased frequency of occurrence on the evening side (Fig. 2) is supported by Victor (1965), who found a secondary maximum in occurrence at 22^h geomagnetic time from Byrd station (70°S geom. lat.) in 1961. However, his data are not classified with respect to magnetic activity and should not be used in a detailed comparison with the data reported here. In a recent paper Roldugin & Starkov (1970) report pulsations in the latitude interval 60–64°N geomagnetic latitude during several nights in the winter of 1967–68. At low magnetic activity (Q = 3) they found pulsations during a few hours only. These occasions were shortly after midnight. At high activity (Q = 6) they observed pulsations during the period 22–06 hrs geomagnetic time, in good agreement with the results presented here. From Oslo Omholt (private communication) has observed pulsating patches on some occasions, and after exceptionally strong storms Störmer (1942) has observed the same type of pulsations as far south as 57–58°N geomagnetic latitude. In view of this it seems important to extend the region of systematic observations towards the south.

In addition it seems important to investigate the pulsating aurora in relation to the substorm model. As is well known from the works of Akasofu (e.g. Akasofu 1968), pulsating patches are characteristic features of the post breakup phase of the auroral substorm on the morning side of the break-up centre. Consequently the pulsating oval should be looked upon, not as a quasi-stationary pattern, but rather as a pattern which is present at times following shortly after the onset of auroral substorms. The results shown here, in particular those in Fig. 2 for medium activity, seem to establish the existence of pulsations on the evening side of the break-up centre as well. The percentage of occurrence is, however, low compared to that of the morning hours, and may be further lowered when using a more appropriate

8*

coordinate system. Since the substorm centre is not always placed at the midnight meridian (Akasofu, 1968), some of the pulsation events observed in the evening may still be morning events compared to the break-up centre. Choosing origo in the break-up centre at the time of break-up may then result in decreased occurrence values in the evening and a corresponding increase later in the night. In the substorm picture one will possibly find a less pronounced difference in occurrence from high to low magnetic activity as the high values at high activity may be caused by an increased frequency of the auroral substorm under these conditions.

REFERENCES

Akasofu, S.-I. 1968. *Polar and Magnetospheric Substorms.* Reidel Publishing Company, Holland.
Brekke, A. & Pettersen, H. 1971. *Planet. Space Sci. 19,* 536.
Campbell, W. W. & Rees, M. H. 1961. *J. Geophys. Res. 66,* 41.
Kvifte, G. J. & Pettersen, H. 1969. *Planet. Space Sci. 17,* 1599.
Roldugin, V. K. & Starkov, G. V. 1970. *Geomagn. Aeronomy. 10,* 72 (English ed.).
Störmer, C. 1942. *Geofys. Publ. 13,* No. 7, 1.
Victor, L. J. 1965. *J. Geophys. Res. 70,* 3123.

Properties of Low Energy Particle Impacts
in the Polar Domain in the Dawn and Dayside Hours

R. A. HOFFMAN

Goddard Space Flight Center, Greenbelt, Maryland

Abstract: In the dawn and dayside hours of the polar domain, two regions of electron precipitation have been identified: a very high latitude 'soft zone', and a lower latitude 'hard zone'.

The electrons in the soft zone produce a large number of interesting phenomena both above and in the ionosphere, such as the generation of VLF hiss, magnetic effects from the currents they constitute, electron concentration enhancement peaks at 1000 km altitudes, and the dayside auroral oval, with emissions predominantly at 6300Å. Electron precipitation is continuously present in this zone.

On the other hand, fewer phenomena appear associated with the lower latitude hard zone, which exists through the morning hours to noon, and is related to substorm activity. The higher energy precipitating electrons (> 50 keV) produce D-layer events. The lower energy electrons (a few keV) produce the mantle aurora, but because of a likely energy dispersion from local time drift of the electrons originating in the midnight region, the morphology of E-layer absorption events is more difficult to observe.

1. INTRODUCTION

Two regions of electron precipitation have been identified in the dawn and dayside hours of the polar domain, a very high latitude 'soft zone' and a lower latitude 'hard zone'. The characteristics of the radiation in the two regions, that is, the energy spectrums, structure, and morphology, are entirely different, and so is the relationship of the radiation to magnetic activity. The electron precipitation in the 'soft zone' produces a large number of interesting phenomena both above and in the ionosphere. On the other hand fewer phenomena appear associated with the lower latitude 'hard zone'.

In this review the particle precipitation regions will first be defined. Their spectral and spatial characteristics will be displayed and their relationship with magnetic activity exhibited. The second part of the review will discuss the effects of the 'soft zone' precipitation both above and in the ionosphere, including the generation of VLF hiss, magnetic effects from the currents the precipitation constitutes, electric effects, ionization effects, and production of the dayside auroral oval. The third part of the review will emphasize the relationship of the lower latitude 'hard zone' with the morphology of ionospheric absorption events, as well as the production of the mantle aurora.

The data base for this review is data from the OGO–4 Auroral Particles Experiment, although considerable use will be made of data from other satellites and ground stations.

1. DEFINITION OF PARTICLE PRECIPITATION REGIONS

The definition of the particle precipitation regions in the dayside and morning hours of the magnetosphere is based primarily on measurements made of low energy precipitating electrons in the energy range of 100 ev to tens of kilovolts. In the morning hours up until local noon two regions have been identified, the lower latitude hard zone (68° to 75°) and a higher latitude soft zone (75° to 80°). After local noon only the soft zone appears to be present. A polar cavity exists at latitudes above about 80°, where only small fluxes of electrons precipitate.

Examples of measurements in the regions

The first really clear evidence of the existence of two regions of precipitation at high latitudes was obtained by the Lockheed group from two short-lived satellite flights in 1963 and 1965 (Sharp & Johnson 1968). In the 1965 flight the detection of the soft zone was made by a differential energy detector measuring electrons at an energy of about

117

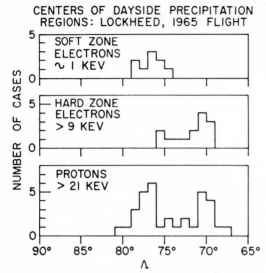

Fig. 1. The dayside zones of precipitation identified by charged particle detectors flown on low altitude polar satellites (Sharp & Johnson 1968).

one kilovolt, whereas the detection of the hard zone was made by an integral energy detector measuring electrons having energies greater than about nine kilovolts (Fig. 1). While only a few passes of data were available, the data clearly showed the existence of the two zones. On the same satellite a detector measuring protons having energies greater than about 21 kilovolts gave indication of the possibility of two zones of proton precipitation as well. Note in the Figure that the centers of the dayside precipitation regions have been plotted, not the extent of the regions of precipitation.

Additional information regarding the existence of two precipitation regions came from the Aurora 1 satellite (Burch 1968). In Fig. 2 a very weak hard zone extending from about 62° to 75° can be seen in the detector measuring electrons in the energy

range 6.2 to 25 keV. The soft zone appears in the 46- to 280-ev channel, commencing abruptly at a latitude of 75° and ending at 80°. A small portion of the polar cavity appears at latitudes above 80°.

More extensive measurements of the morning and daytime precipitation regions have been made with the Auroral Particles Experiment on the OGO–4 satellite (Hoffman 1969). Fig. 3 contains data comparing the regions of precipitation in the afternoon and morning hours. This pass of data begins in the afternoon hours at a latitude of 70° where there is no evidence of a low latitude hard zone because of the lack of electrons at 7.3 keV below 78°. The soft zone commences at a latitude of 75°, where the 0.7 keV detector counting rate begins to show structure, exists through the noontime hours even at a latitude of 84.6°, and ends abruptly in the morning hours at 79°. The morning hour lower latitude hard zone is evident in the counting rate from the 7.3 keV detector and commences at a latitude of about 75° and extends down to about 69° at a local time of about 7.5 hours. Another example from the OGO–4 satellite (Fig. 4) reveals especially clearly the two regions of precipitation as well as the polar cavity.

More recent measurements of these precipitation regions have been made by a detector having excellent energy resolution aboard the ISIS–1 satellite (Heikkila & Winningham 1971). Data from a pass in the late morning hours are shown in Fig. 5. The top portion of the Figure contains a spectrogram from precipitating electrons, where the density of the trace qualitatively indicates the spectral energy density as a function of particle energy. The hard zone can be identified by the presence of electrons in the energy interval 10^3 to 10^4 ev from an invariant latitude of 66° to about 74°. For this pass the precipitation produced a total energy flux of about 0.1 ergs/cm^2-sec-ster. The soft zone is characterized by precipitating electrons having an energy slightly above

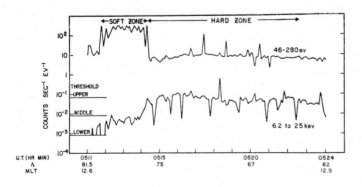

Fig. 2. The hard (auroral) zone and soft zone at magnetic local noon as measured by the Auroral satellite (Burch 1968).

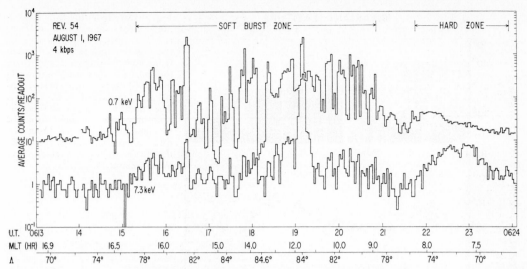

Fig. 3. Data from the Auroral Particles Experiment on OGO-4 during a pass in the northern hemisphere from dusk to dawn. K_p was O +. The two detectors at 0.7 keV and 7.3 keV measured electrons with pitch angles near 0° in an energy band + 18 % − 13 % about the center energy listed. The counting rate profiles are used to show the existence of the soft zone in the afternoon and morning hours and the hard zone only in the morning.

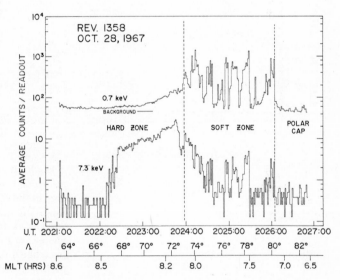

Fig. 4. A late morning hour pass from the OGO-4 satellite revealing the hard and soft regions of pre- cipitation as well as the polar cavity. K_p was 4- during this pass.

10^2 ev, and extends from 74° to almost 80° in- variant latitude. The almost total lack of precipi- tation with energies above 10^2 ev at latitudes higher than 80° indicates the polar cavity.

Spectrums in the regions

Typical energy spectrums obtained in the soft zone from three different experiments appear in Fig. 6. Only the ISIS–1 electron spectrometer measured sufficiently low energy electrons with

adequate energy resolution to identify a peak in the spectrum at about 100 ev. Data from the Aurora 1 and OGO–4 experiments indicate an extremely steep energy spectrum at energies above the peak in the spectrum. The particle flux falls off at least as steep as E^{-3} at energies above a couple 100 ev. This Figure indicates that data from the lowest energy channels of the latter two experiments, 46 to 280 ev on Aurora 1 and 0.7 keV on OGO–4, do indeed indicate the presence of the soft zone.

119

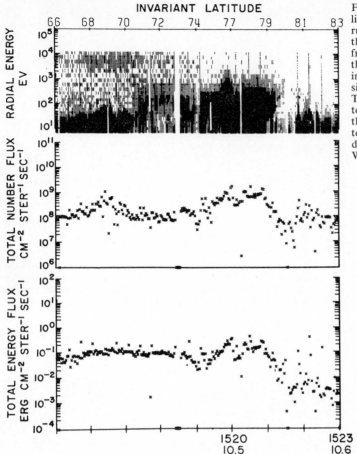

Fig. 5. Data from the ISIS–1 satellite at local magnetic noon on February 3, 1969. The top portion of the Figure contains a spectrogram from precipitating electrons where the density of the trace qualitatively indicates the spectral energy density as a function of particle energy. The middle frame contains the total integrated number flux and the bottom frame contains the total integrated energy flux. K_p during the pass was 4 (Heikkila & Winningham 1971).

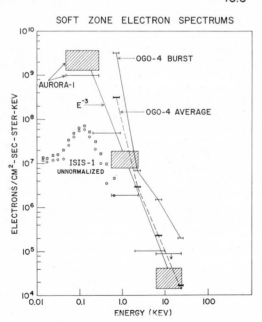

The hard zone appears predominantly at energies from 1–10 keV (Fig. 7), and often displays a knee in the energy spectrum between 5 to 10 keV. Note that the 0.7 keV detector on OGO–4 measured a flux only about 10 times the flux at 7.3 keV, whereas in Fig 6 the ratio of these two fluxes was more like a factor of 10^3. It is on the bases of the grossly different spectrums as well as structures in the two regions that in the remainder of this paper we use the output of the 0.7 keV detector as an indicator of the soft zone and the 7.3 keV detector as the indicator of the hard zone.

Fig. 6. Typical energy spectrums obtained in the soft zone from three different experiments. The published Aurora 1 data (Burch 1968) were based upon efficiencies by Frank and have been modified to agree with the Arnoldy efficiencies for energies above 0.5 keV (Paschmann et al., 1970, Archuleta & DeForest 1971). The ISIS–1 spectrum is relative only (Heikkila & Winningham 1971).

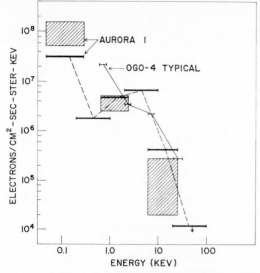

HARD ZONE ELECTRON SPECTRUMS

Fig. 7. Electron spectrums in the hard zone from Aurora 1 and OGO–4. The Aurora 1 data have again been modified for channel electron multiplier efficiencies.

Spatial extent of the regions

The spatial extent and frequency of occurrence

of the soft zone have been studied using data from the 0.7 keV detector aboard OGO–4 (Hoffman & Berko 1971b). For this study all data from the 0.7 keV detector collected from July 30, 1967, through February 26, 1968, were analyzed. The criteria used to define this region were rapid fluctuations in the counting rate from the detector with peak electron fluxes of at least 10^8 electrons/cm^2-sec-ster-keV. An attempt was made to eliminate the effects of magnetic activity, especially in the midnight region. Data were used during times when K_p was less than or equal to 2. Additional data were eliminated in the midnight region on the basis that precipitating electrons with fairly hard energy spectrums are usually associated with magnetic activity even though the counting rate profiles may be highly structured (see Fig. 14 from 70° to 73°) (Hoffman 1969). Therefore when the counting rate of the 7.3 keV detector rose rapidly and in coincidence with increases in the 0.7 keV detector counting rate, it was assumed that the precipitation was associated with magnetic activity and these data were simply not counted.

The resulting soft zone frequency of occurrence map appears in Fig. 8. The most striking feature of this map is the concentration of high probabilities (i.e. $\geq 40\%$) between 5 and 14 hours and from 75° to $82\frac{1}{2}$° invariant latitudes in these hours.

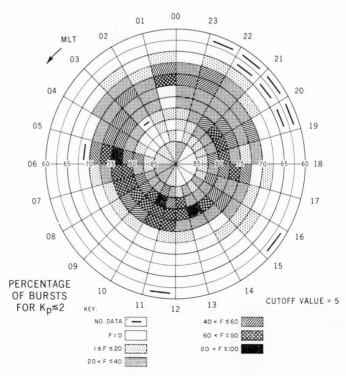

Fig. 8. Soft zone frequency of occurrence map for $K_p \leq 2$ based on OGO–4 data in an invariant latitude magnetic local time coordinate system (Hoffman & Berko 1971).

PERCENTAGE OF BURSTS FOR $K_p \leq 2$

KEY:

NO DATA	40 < F ≤ 60
F = 0	60 < F ≤ 80
1 ≤ F ≤ 20	80 < F ≤ 100
20 < F ≤ 40	

CUTOFF VALUE = 5

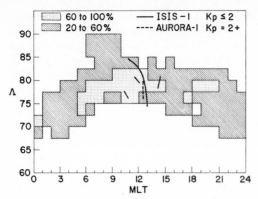

Fig. 9. The OGO–4 soft zone with the location of the soft zone on the dayside as defined by data from ISIS–I and Aurora 1 superimposed.

On the nightside the probabilities are generally smaller and tend to appear at lower latitudes than during the daytime hours. The probabilities in the daytime hours are so high that one finds that the soft zone is always present. (See Hoffman & Berko 1971b for the distribution of samples used to prepare Fig. 8).

To again exemplify that data from the 0.7 keV detector on OGO–4 could define the soft zone, at least during the daytime hours, we have superimposed the location of the soft zone as defined by data from ISIS–1 and Aurora 1 on a simplified version of the frequency of occurrence map (Fig. 9). The spectral and spatial considerations presented give us confidence that data from the OGO–4 experiment can indeed be used to determine certain properties of the soft zone radiation.

We next wish to investigate the dependence of the soft zone on magnetic activity and universal time. For these studies we have measured the low latitude and high latitude boundaries of the soft zone as defined by the response of the 0.7 keV detector on OGO–4 when the satellite was within two and three hours respectively of local magnetic noon. The latitudes of these boundaries as a function of K_p are plotted in the upper two panels of Fig. 10 and the average locations of the boundaries for each integral value of K_p in the lower panels for data acquired during the late winter and early summer of 1968. The magnetic parameter K_p appears to order the location of the lower boundary better than the location of the upper boundary. It is surprising that such a magnetic parameter, which depends upon the nightside auroral electrojet, should produce any ordering in the location of the daytime soft zone. This implies that the location of the soft zone is dependent upon the magnetospheric configuration rather than upon any local magnetic effects. The move-

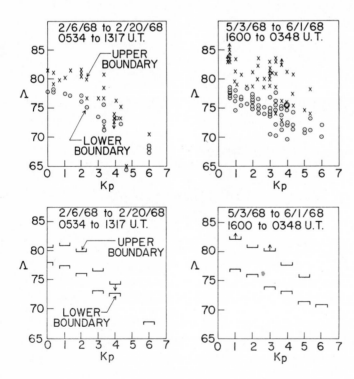

Fig. 10. The latitudes of the high and low latitude boundaries of the soft zone from OGO–4 near local noon for two different epochs plotted as a function of K_p. The top two panels contain all the data points and the bottom two panels contain averages over each integral value of K_p.

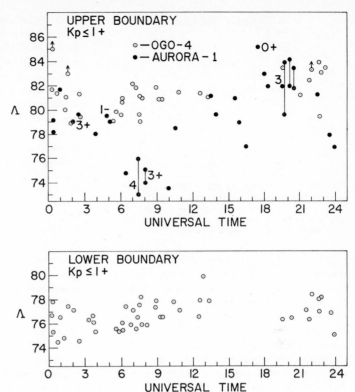

Fig. 11. The upper boundary and lower boundary of the soft zone for magnetic quiet periods as a function of UT. In the top figure the solid dots were obtained from the Aurora 1 satellite (Maehlum 1968). The numbers by some Aurora 1 data points are K_p during the time of the boundary acquisition.

ment of the soft zone is almost 2° equatorward for each value of K_p.

We next plot the upper boundary location and the lower boundary location as a function of universal time for those passes when $K_p \leq 1^+$. In neither case does there appear to be a U.T. effect greater than about 2°. In the top portion of Fig. 11 we have included data from the Aurora 1 satellite (Maehlum 1968), which indicated a rather strong U.T. effect. Unfortunately geomagnetic activity during the early portion of the lifetime of Aurora 1 as measured by K_p indicated moderate activity; in fact, at least two of the four data points between six and ten hours U.T. occurred when K_p was 3^+ and 4. Taking into account the shift in latitude of the upper boundary of the soft zone with increasing K_p as well as the fairly large scatter of data points at moderate K_ps (see Fig. 10), it appears possible that the Aurora 1 data might be explained as a magnetic effect rather than a U.T. variation.

A universal time control of phenomena occurring at high latitudes can be ascribed to the variation in angle which the geomagnetic axis makes with the earth-sun line (β) as a function of

U.T., and therefore the solar wind flow direction (Maehlum 1969). This variation in tilt could cause geomagnetic field distortions which vary the boundary locations. In the northern hemisphere the geomagnetic axis dips towards the sun near 1800 to 2000 U.T. and away from the sun near 0600 to 0800 U.T. Since the tilt of the geomagnetic

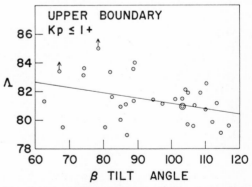

Fig. 12. The latitude of the upper boundary of the soft zone at noon when $K_p \leq 1 +$ as a function of β, the angle between dipole axis projected onto the noon-midnight meridian plane and the earth-sun line.

123

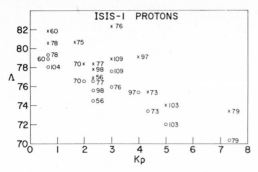

Fig. 13. The location of the dayside soft zone as defined by precipitating protons as a function of K_p. The data were obtained from Winningham (1970). The geomagnetic tilt angle β is indicated by each data point. See Fig. 10 for symbols.

axis is even more dependent upon the season of the year, we have plotted all upper boundary locations when $K_p \leq 1^+$ as a function of β in Fig. 12. The data points with β greater than 100° were acquired primarily during February, whereas the data points less than 90° were acquired primarily in late April and May. The wintertime data show less scatter of the data points than the summertime data. The least squares fit of a linear relationship to all the data points shows not more than a combined $2\frac{1}{2}°$ seasonal and U.T. variation in the high latitude boundary of the soft zone.

So far all boundary studies have been performed using low energy electron precipitation data. The ISIS–1 experiment also measured low energy protons, which seem to occur concurrently with the electron precipitation, although more narrowly confined in latitude (Winningham 1970). While only a small amount of proton precipitation data are available, the location of this region also seems to depend strongly upon K_p (Fig. 13). In the Figure we have indicated by each data point the geomagnetic tilt angle β. Note that for the lower boundary, when $K_p = 1^-$, the tilt angle varied between 60° and 104° for the three data points, yet the boundary changed by less than 3°. Thus the proton precipitation displays the same relations to magnetic activity and tilt angle as electron precipitation.

While it was previously suggested by Vernov et al. (1966) and Thomas et al. (1966), there is now evidence that the high latitude soft zone is due to direct penetration of the magnetosheath plasma to low altitudes through the dayside magnetospheric cusps (Frank, 1970, Heikkila & Winningham, 1971). The soft zone would then occur necessarily on open field lines and the low latitude boundary would be nearly synonymous with the last closed field line on the dayside. If this is the case, one can explain the lack of U.T. control and the strong dependence on magnetic activity

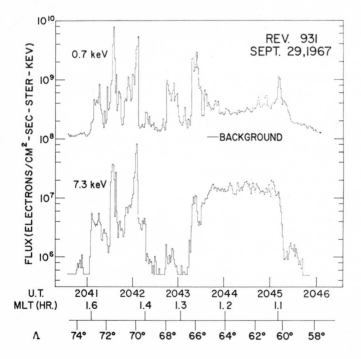

Fig. 14. Data from an OGO–4 satellite pass acquired near midnight during a substorm when K_p was 5. See Fig. 3 caption for a description of the detector.

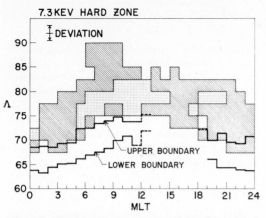

Fig. 15. The hourly average location of the hard zone as defined by the 7.3 keV detector on OGO–4 as a function of magnetic local time irrespective of magnetic activity. The mean deviations of the boundary locations are slightly less than 2° at each hour.

on the location of the dayside soft zone by the following. While the outer reaches of the magnetosphere may be distorted in various ways by a variation in the tilt of the geomagnetic axis, the number of closed field lines on the dayside would remain the same, thus negating any low altitude effect. On the other hand the number of closed field lines and, therefore the latitude of the last closed field line when measured at low altitudes, would be more strongly dependent upon the magnetospheric configuration, which changes during magnetic activity (Cummings et al. 1968).

We next turn to the location of the hard zone. Because the hard zone extends into the midnight regions, we show in Fig. 14 data obtained from a near midnight pass of the OGO–4 satellite in order to define the region at such hours. These data were acquired during a geomagnetic substorm. Large fluxes of 7.3 keV electrons were observed precipitating between latitudes of 60° and 66°, but the small fluctuations in the counting rate from the detector should be especially noted. At higher latitudes, from 70° to 73°, this detector measured even larger fluxes, but they coincided exactly with very large fluxes at 0.7 keV. At these hours we will again define the hard zone as the region of 7.3 keV precipitation with rather small fluctuations in the counting rate from the detector.

On the basis of these criteria the location of the hard zone is shown in Fig. 15. Note that it begins in the early evening hours, about 1900 M.L.T., continues through midnight at its lowest latitude (64 to 68½°) and ends at local noon in the latitude range of about 70 to 74°. On only very few occa-

sions out of about 200 passes through the afternoon hours has anything even resembling a hard zone been observed. In the Figure the spatial definition of the hard zone is based upon all observations, independent of magnetic activity. Note that the upper boundary of the hard region and the lower boundary of the soft zone are nearly coincident. On an individual pass basis these two boundaries may be slightly separated, as in Fig. 3, or at times slightly overlapping, as in Fig. 4.

Previously we presented evidence (Hoffman 1970) that the electrons precipitating in the hard zone originate on closed field lines in the midnight region at the time of substorms, and subsequently drift around through the morning hours, where they encounter a strong pitch angle scattering mechanism to cause the precipitation. The character of the radiation throughout the entire region is essentially the same (Hoffman & Berko 1971a). The average energy spectrum everywhere is similar to that shown in Fig. 7. As evidence of this we plot in Fig. 16 the ratio of 0.7 keV flux at three different local times as a function of invariant latitude. There appears to be a slight tendency towards softening of the spectrum to higher latitudes, although this situation is not always observed on a pass-to-pass basis.

If indeed these electrons do drift in local time on closed field lines, we must explain the large five- to six-degree shift in latitude from midnight to noon in the boundaries of the region. In such a model we must assume that a particle measured as precipitating at a particular local time has spent most of its lifetime with a mirror point near the magnetic equator where the bulk of particles in

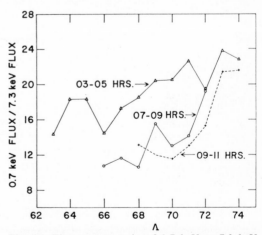

Fig. 16. The average ratio of 0.7 keV to 7.3 keV fluxes at three different local times as a function of invariant latitude.

125

normal distributions are always found. The magnetospheric distortions can account for only about one to two degrees' shift in latitude in the lower boundary of this region (Fairfield 1968). The apparent increased distortion could be accounted for by several things. First, in the late morning hours at latitudes just below the indicated lower boundary of the hard zone, the fluxes could be too low for measurement. Since the longitudinal drift time is inversely related to latitude, the population could have been depleted prior to arrival at the late morning hours. Second, the electrons could be driven out towards the boundary of the magnetosphere by electric fields. There is a slight bit of evidence for cross-L drift because the ratios in Fig. 16 indicate a slight softening with increase in latitude. On the other hand it could equally well indicate an inward drift with a slight energization of the electrons.

2. EFFECTS OF SOFT ZONE PRECIPITATION

In section 2 of this review we will discuss the effects of the soft zone precipitation as a function of decreasing height; that is, as the electrons proceed from the outer regions of the magnetosphere down into the atmosphere, they produce different phenomena. These effects are divided into five categories: auroral hiss, magnetic effects (both DC and AC) electric effects, ionization effects, and the dayside auroral oval.

Auroral hiss

Auroral hiss is a wide-band noise observed from a few hertz to several hundred kilohertz at high magnetic latitudes. It is generally ascribed to the incoherent Cerenkov radiation process, where emissions are generated from incoming electrons

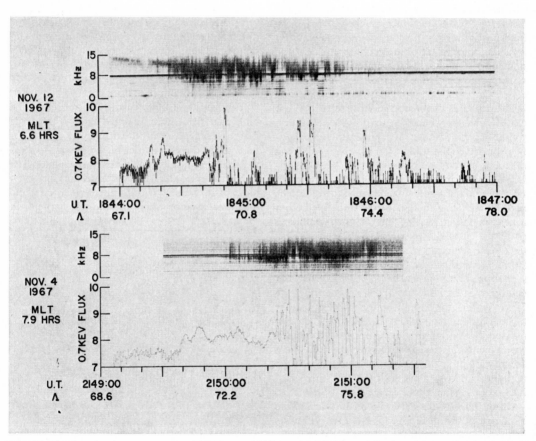

Fig. 17. Simultaneous measurements of VLF auroral hiss and 0.7 keV precipitating electrons by the OGO-4 satellite. The bandpass of the VLF experiment which used an electric dipole antenna was 100 Hz–18kHz. The logarithm of the flux at 0.7 keV is plotted. The soft zone begins at about 1844:45 U. T. for the November 12 event and at 2150:33 for the November 14 event.

with velocities that exceed or are comparable to the phase velocity of the radiation in the medium (Jørgensen 1968). If the hiss propagates in the whistler mode it will occur at frequencies below the plasma cutoff and the electron cyclotron frequency, but above the local lower hybrid resonance. In his paper Jørgensen discussed a model for a region in space in which the auroral hiss is believed to be generated. He showed that the total power generated in this region is comparable to the observed power, and concluded that auroral hiss may be generated by incoherent Cerenkov radiation from electrons with energies of the order of 1 keV. He acknowledged the fact that the inclusion of electrons with energies below 1 keV in his calculations of the noise spectrum would increase his spectral density, but could not perform the calculations because the knowledge of auroral electrons with energies below 1 keV was very poor at that time.

Hartz (1970) studied the broad-band noise emissions observed by Alouette II in the frequency range of the Cerenkov radiation. On the basis of the spatial distribution of this noise he concluded that the emissions arose from the Cerenkov radiation and were related to fluxes of electrons having energies in the range 0.1 to 1 keV. From the general characteristics of the noise band he concluded that the region of generation was localized to the height interval near and not too far above the satellite.

We have compared the electron precipitation measurements from the OGO–4 satellite with the VLF observations from an electric dipole antenna on the same satellite (Laaspere & Hoffman 1971) (Fig. 17). Data in this Figure show the general coincidence of the region of 0.7 keV electron precipitation with the region of auroral hiss. The hiss seems to spread slightly beyond the location of the particle precipitation, especially to lower latitudes. Fig. 18 contains one of the VLF records for comparison with electron precipitation at energies above one kilovolt. The broad, rather structureless, region of precipitation defines the location of the hard zone. While the hiss begins to appear in this region of harder radiation, it is predominantly at higher latitudes. By these two Figures we show that the auroral hiss is associated

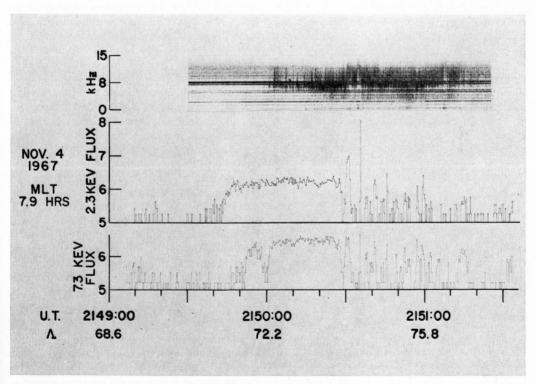

Fig. 18. Simultaneous measurement of auroral hiss and precipitating electrons with energies around 2.3 and 7.3 keV. The hard zone extends from about 2149:52 to 2150:28 U. T.

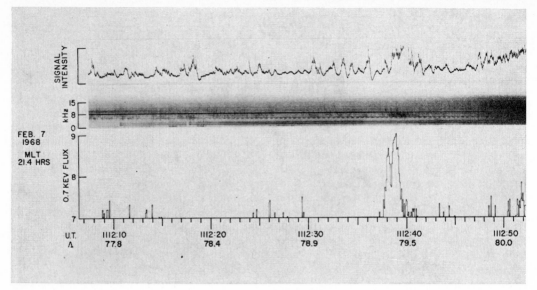

Fig. 19. An exact correlation between auroral hiss and 0.7 keV electron precipitation at 1112:39 U. T.

with electrons having energies less than one kilovolt and is not related to the precipitation in the hard zone.

In general it is difficult to find a one-to-one correlation between specific bursts of electrons and a dominant feature in the auroral hiss. This would be expected because of some propagation of hiss across field lines, as well as the fact that the particle measurements refer to the precipitation measured at an extremely small cross-section of magnetic lines of force. However, in Fig. 19 we do show an exact relationship between the 0.7

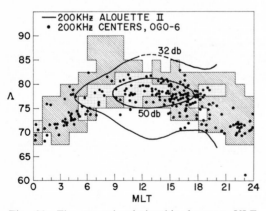

Fig. 20. The general relationship between VLF auroral hiss measured by electric dipole experiments aboard the OGO–6 (Laaspere & Hoffman 1971) and Alouette II (Hartz 1970) satellites and the precipitation of structured 0.7 keV electrons.

keV precipitation and a particular auroral hiss event. In this case a very isolated burst of the 0.7 keV electrons was observed with no appreciable precipitation for some tens of seconds on either side. By far the most prominent feature in the VLF record occurs simultaneously with the burst of electrons. The very dark feature at the end of the VLF record is due to loss of satellite telemetry signal.

These correlations between VLF and particle precipitation events are easiest to find in the morning hours in the soft zone. The general relationship between the auroral hiss and the soft zone is shown in Fig. 20. This Figure contains VLF data from electric dipole experiments aboard OGO–6 and Alouette II satellites. The dots are the locations of the centers of 200 khz radiation measured from the OGO–6 satellite (Laaspere & Hoffman 1971), whereas the contours of 200 khz radiation were obtained from the Alouette II satellite (Hartz 1970). Both sets of VLF data were taken irrespective of magnetic conditions. In spite of this there is remarkable coincidence between the hiss and the location of the soft zone.

Magnetic effects

The movement of the electrons along the magnetic field lines constitutes electric currents along the field lines. The magnetic effects of such currents should be and are measured by magnetometers flying through the region of the soft zone.

128

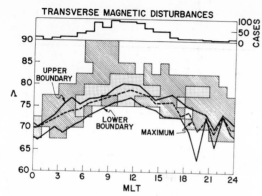

TRANSVERSE MAGNETIC DISTURBANCES

Fig. 21. The relationship between the average locations of transverse magnetic disturbances greater than 30γ at 1100 km altitude (Zmuda et al. 1970) and the precipitation of structured, 0.7 keV electrons. The magnetic data were compiled when $K_p \leq 2 +$ and the particle data when $K_p \leq 2$. Note that most of the measurements of the magnetic disturbances occurred in the daytime hours in the lower portion of the soft zone.

We first consider the transverse magnetic disturbances observed at 1100 km by magnetometers aboard the satellites 1963–38C and 1964–64A (Zmuda et al. 1970). Magnetic disturbances greater than 30 gammas could be measured by the detectors. Fig. 21 contains the boundaries of the quiet time diurnal variation of the magnetic disturbances. The two solid lines are the hourly averages of the upper and lower boundaries respectively, and the dashed line is the average location of the maximum of the disturbance. Quiet conditions were defined by K_p being less than or equal to 2^+, whereas the soft zone frequency of occurrence map on which the data are superimposed was compiled from magnetic conditions less than or equal to 2. The coincidence between the regions of magnetic disturbance and particle precipitation is remarkable. Zmuda et al. (1970) have also shown that the average locations of the transverse magnetic disturbances move equatorward slightly less than $2°$ per value of K_p, similar to the particle observations. To account for the magnetic disturbances they estimate that the particle fluxes must be between 10^8 and 3.5×10^9 particles/cm²-sec. As we shall see (Table I), the intensity of the electron precipitation in the soft zone is sufficient to produce these magnetic fluctuations.

The electron precipitation measurements indicate either spatial or temporal structures, often of the order of one second or less in extent. The motion of search coil magnetometers through

Table I.

	Total flux precipitated	Total energy precipitated	Average energy
OGO–4 Morning	$2–3 \times 10^8$	0.3	1.3
OGO–4 Afternoon	1×10^8	0.1	0.9
ISIS–1 Noon*	3×10^9	0.5	–

Total flux in electrons/cm²–sec
Total energy in ergs/cm²–sec
Average energy in keV

* Heikkila & Winningham (1971)

these regions of field aligned currents should produce signals in the few hertz or few tens of hertz frequency range. Such AC magnetic variations are indeed observed, as shown in Fig. 22. The search coil magnetometer data was also obtained from an experiment aboard OGO–4 (Burton et al. 1969). The X and Y magnetometers were oriented $45°$ and $135°$ respectively to the radius vector from the earth and the Z axis magnetometer made an orthogonal set. They responded primarily to the frequency range around one hertz. Field aligned currents at high latitudes where the magnetic field lines are nearly vertical would produce a magnetic field in the horizontal direction, and therefore the X and Y magnetometers should show fluctuations exactly in phase and in the same sense. The small variations at the beginning of the Figure are due to spacecraft boom vibrations. Coinciding exactly with the first observation of the electron precipitation, the search coil magnetometers showed an increase in the fluctuations. The phase relation between the X and Y signals should be noted throughout the record. At times the search coil signals were so strong that the signal saturated. This is especially seen from one to five seconds after 2324 UT. Note at the end of the Figure at 2324:05.4 the exact coincidence in the cessation of both the particle flux and the search coil magnetometer outputs. Since the magnetic field was apparently not changing outside of the particle beam, this measurement probably indicates the existence of a sheet current with an edge at 2324:05.

Electric effects

Similar to magnetic field effects, electric field probes flying through this region of extremely structured radiation should also measure field fluctuations in the one to several tens of hertz range. Such fields could be due to polarization

9

129

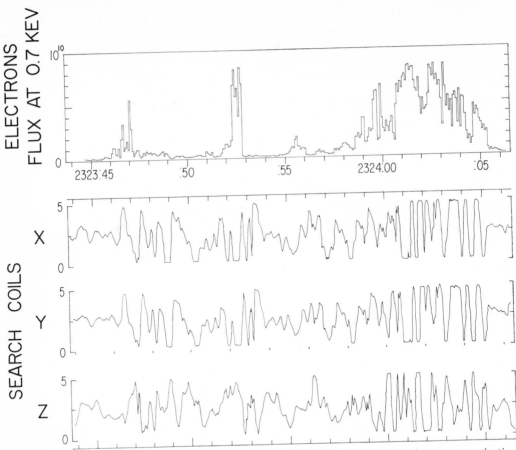

Fig. 22. Detailed association between AC magnetic variations (Holzer & Burton private communication) and 0.7 keV electron precipitation from experiments on OGO-4. The frequency response of the search coil magnetometers had a maximum of 1 Hz.

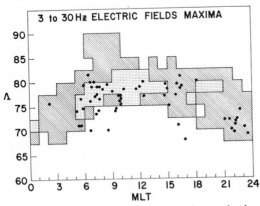

Fig. 23. The relationship between maximums in the 3 to 30 Hz irregularity signal from the OV 1–10 satellite electric field antennas in early 1967 (Maynard & Heppner 1970) and the precipitation of structured 0.7 keV electrons. Both sets of data were acquired when $K_p \leq 2$.

electric fields, the primary field which might possibly cause the field aligned currents, or to electron density irregularities. We show in Fig. 23 the locations of the maximums in the 3 to 30 Hz irregularity signal from the electric field probe aboard the OV1–10 satellite when $K_p \leq 2$ (Maynard & Heppner 1970). The data acquisition from this experiment was not evenly distributed in magnetic local time, causing a lack of observations after midnight and at dusk. Again the maximums of the irregularity signals seem to lie predominantly at latitudes of the soft zone.

Ionization effects

Sato & Colin (1969) have studied electron concentration enhancements from measurements made by the top-side sounder aboard Alouette I at a height of 1000 km at polar latitudes during

1962 to 1964. In an initial analysis of these data, Thomas et al. (1966) suggested that these peaks of electron concentrations were due to electrons diffusing upwards along the lines of force to 1000 km from lower down in the F-region, where they were produced by energetic particles from the magnetosphere which were accelerated along neutral lines and entered the Earth's atmosphere.

Sato & Colin plotted the distributions of the locations of electron concentration enhancement peaks for a variety of epochs and magnetic conditions. In order to compare these distributions with the location of the soft zone as defined by the OGO–4 data, we have chosen the November 1962 to January 1963 plot with $K_p \leq 2$. The superposition of these data sets appears in Fig. 24. Except for a few scattered points, the locations of electron concentration enhancement peaks fall within the soft zone. With an increase in magnetic activity the distribution seemed to spread to both lower and higher latitudes and essentially fill the morning and noon portions of the polar cavity. The spreading to lower latitudes is in agreement with the relationship of the soft zone to K_p, but the soft zone upper boundary usually also moves equatorward with increasing magnetic activity. However, during substorms electron precipitation has been observed within the polar region, although usually with a slight break in the precipitation pattern to allow for the identification of an upper boundary to the soft zone.

The high altitude ionization from the very soft electron precipitation spectrum is also evident as

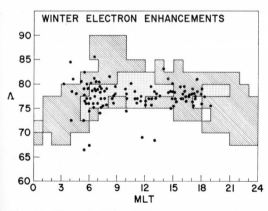

Fig. 24. The association between electron concentration enhancement peaks measured by the topside sounder aboard Alouette I at a height of 1000 km from November 1962 through January 1963 (Sato & Colin 1969) and the precipitation of structured 0.7 keV electrons. Both sets of data were acquired when $K_p \leq 2$.

an anomalously high E-layer. The ionospheric sounder aboard the AFCRL flying ionospheric laboratory measured an E-layer virtual height of about 140 km from 75 to 78° latitude at local noon (Whalen et al. 1971).

The energy input into the soft zone in the form of superthermal charged particles is, of course, highly variable. While the high altitude electron concentration enhancement peaks may be localized because of collimated influx beams, average energy input values may be more appropriate for use in calculating the effects on the ionosphere. The apparent fleeting nature of dayside auroras suggests rather short-term beams, so localized effects may become averaged out. We list in Table I some average values of particle influx, energy influx, and average energies for typical passes of OGO–4 and a single pass of ISIS–1 through the soft zone during low K_p, keeping in mind that the numbers quoted for OGO–4 are based on only a four-point spectrum and the 'total' values pertain to electrons between 0.7 and 25 keV only. One sees that typically the OGO–4 experiment measured about 10% of the total particle flux, whereas it observed closer to half of the total energy influx. Peak values were roughly ten times these average values for OGO–4 and two to four times for ISIS–1.

Dayside auroral oval

Auroras in the dayside auroral oval, when observed visually during the winter, appear considerably different in form from auroras observed during auroral breakup in the midnight region (Fig. 25). The dayside auroras are discrete rayed auroral forms as shown in this photograph taken from an airplane by the Air Force Cambridge Research Laboratories (Buchau, private communication, 1971). In movies of all-sky camera pictures of daytime auroras, the forms are very short-lived and fleeting. Because they are weak structured forms, they are usually seen primarily in the zenith; that is, they are extremely aspect-sensitive.

We have sought an association between the electron precipitation in the soft zone (daytime portion of the frequency of occurrence map) and optical measurements of the daytime auroras. Many investigators have used all-sky cameras and photometric data to determine the frequency of occurrence of auroral forms at different local times. In order to make a meaningful comparison of any optical data with the frequency of occur-

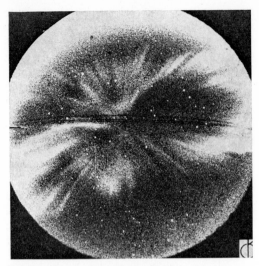

Fig. 25. All-sky-camera photograph of auroras at high latitude on the dayside of the dipole during winter (Buchau private communication).

rence map we want to choose the optical study which employed procedures most analogous to those we used to compile the map. We considered the published data of Feldstein (1966), Stringer & Belon (1967), Sandford (1968), and Lassen (1969) and determined that the Stringer & Belon work was the one most suitable for comparison with the particle precipitation observations (Hoffman & Berko, 1971b). Using data acquired by an all-sky camera network based in Alaska during the winter of 1964–65, Stringer & Belon produced contour maps showing the probabilities of observing dis-

crete and homogeneous auroral forms in 15-minute intervals during magnetically quiet periods. It is their isoauroral diagram for discrete auroral forms which we wish to compare with the frequency of occurrence map in the daytime hours, because discrete auroras are the dominant auroral form in these hours and have been used by the previously listed investigators to define the auroral oval during these hours.

In Fig. 26 we have shaded the region between 4 and 18 hours local time where the probability of occurrence of the soft zone is greater than at least 50%. The cross-hatched area in these same hours denotes the region of greater than 15% probability of discrete auroral optical emissions presented by Stringer & Belon. The superposition of these two regions during the daytime hours is very apparent. Furthermore, both regions are considerably broader in latitude during the pre-noon hours than the afternoon hours.

It has been shown previously that there is sufficient energy in the more intense structures in the dayside soft zone to produce auroras visible on all-sky-camera photographs (Hoffman & Berko 1971b).

Photometric measurements of dominant auroral emission lines, taken especially from aircraft in the daytime hours, clearly display the effects of the soft radiation on the optical emissions. On the basis of five flights through the daytime hour auroral regions, Eather & Mende (1971) have plotted the average ratio of the 6300 OI/4278 N_2^+

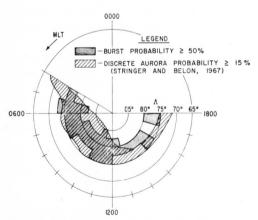

Fig. 26. A polar plot in invarint latitude-magnetic local time of the high probability of structured 0.7 keV electron precipitation during the dayside hours in comparison with the region of high probability of discrete auroras (Stringer & Belon 1967).

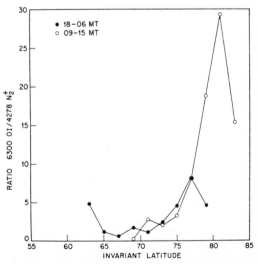

Fig. 27. The average ratio of 6300 O I/4278 N_2^+ auroral emissions as a function of invariant latitude for nighttime and daytime (Eather & Mende 1971).

132

as a function of invariant latitude (Fig. 27). The ratio goes from a low typical nighttime value between 70 and 75° to the very large ratio at the three points plotted at 79, 81, and 83° invariant latitude. This large ratio is caused, of course, by the fact that the soft zone spectrum produces excitations at high altitudes where the $\lambda6300$ oxygen emission predominates.

3. EFFECT OF MORNING HARD ZONE PRECIPITATION

Absorption events

The analysis of energetic electron data (≥ 50 keV energy) has clearly shown that these electrons are injected into the trapping region in the restricted local time sector near midnight during substorms. The electron groups are then observed to move eastward about the earth with a mean speed, velocity dispersion, and change in profile characteristic of gradient and curvature drift motion in the distorted dipole field (Arnoldy & Chan 1969, Pfitzer & Winckler 1969, Lezniak & Winckler 1970). Other observations have shown a very close correlation between the appearance of electron increases at synchronous orbit and the precipitation of electrons into the atmosphere which are detected as auroral x-rays by balloon instrumentation (Parks & Winckler 1968). One is led to the conclusion that the injection of these electrons in the midnight sector during substorms is accompanied by simultaneous scattering and precipitation into the atmosphere as these electrons drift eastward in longitude. One would therefore expect that the zone of precipitation and ionization in the ionosphere would also sweep eastward around the Earth. To study this question, Rosen & Winckler (1970) analyzed data from the Alaskan chain of riometers operated by ESSA. This series of seven instruments covered the range of L-values from 3.9 to 8.0.

When examining substorm absorption events recorded by the stations of the riometer chain, it was observed that the absorption did not always begin simultaneously at all stations. Instead the onset progressed either northward or southward along the chain. If the chain of stations was located in the morning hours and a substorm occurred in the midnight region, where a body of electrons would be injected into close field lines, one would expect the precipitation and therefore the riometer absorption, to be measured first at high L-values or high invariant latitudes, with a progression of absorption onsets toward low

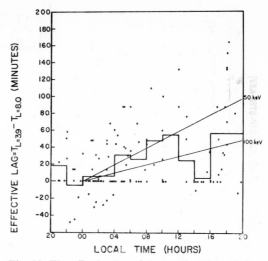

Fig. 28. The effective lag of the starting time of riometer events associated with substorms normalized to an L difference of 8.0 to 3.9 as a function of local time. The histogram represents the average effective lag during 2-hour intervals of local time. The lines labeled 50 keV and 100 keV are theoretical predictions of drift times from midnight in a dipole field for electrons of the listed energies.

values. This is because the drift rate at higher L-values is faster than at lower L-values, and in fact it is roughly linear with the L-value. Therefore the lag time to the onset of the event should be longer at the low L-value stations than at the high L-value stations. Rosen & Winckler normalized these lag times to L-values of 3.9 and 8 and plotted the difference in the lag times for the L-values as a function of the local time of the stations at the onset of the storm (Fig. 28). Both positive and negative lags were seen around midnight but the average lag shifted with local time towards a predominantly positive value. This means that the electrons at low L-values did indeed take longer to arrive at the local time of the chain of stations than the electrons at the higher L-values. Assuming that these precipitating electrons had energies of 50 kilovolts during their drift times, the lag difference is given by the solid line labeled 50 kilovolts in the Figure. This agrees with the average measured lag times from 0 to 12 hours local time. The 50-kilovolt electrons have the correct energy to produce the ionization in the D-region to cause riometer absorption, because their maximum ionization rate occurs at an altitude of 90 km.

It is well known that most of the energy precipitating into the atmosphere in the midnight hours during a substorm is carried by electrons

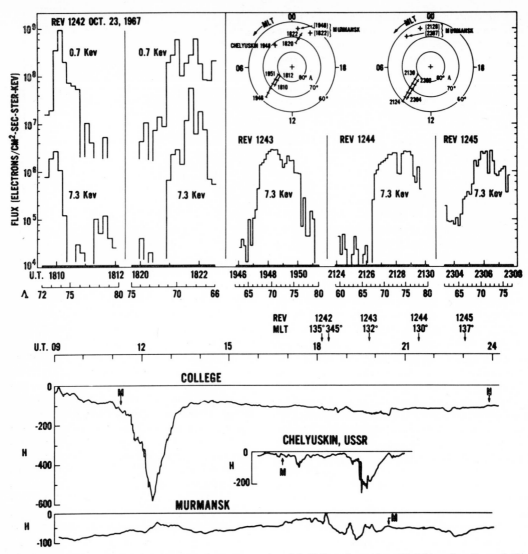

Fig. 29. Evidence of drift of low energy electrons on closed field lines from the midnight region through the morning hours. The M on the magnetograms denotes the time the observatory passed magnetic midnight. The precipitation during revolutions 1244 and 1245 at about 00 hours MLT occurred after the magnetic activity in the region of midnight had ceased.

having energies in the few kilovolt range rather than at 50 kilovolts. In light of the morphology of these 50-kilovolt electrons, one wonders what happens to the kilovolt electrons after a substorm. We have evidence that these electrons also drift in local time through the morning hours and precipitate to form the hard zone (Hoffman 1970). An example of such a precipitation event in the morning hours is shown in Fig. 29. A substorm occurred around 1200UT as seen in the College magnetogram, followed by a small disturbance

noted especially at Chelyuskin from 1700 to almost 2100 hours UT. A series of four late morning satellite passes occurred between 18 hours and 23 UT. At the top of the Figure, the first, third, fourth, and fifth panels show the 7.3 keV precipitation at about 10 hours magnetic local time. In the first panel of data which occurs during the small disturbance at Chelyuskin, only the high latitude portion of the hard zone is seen. On Revolutions 1243, 1244, and 1245, the latter two after all activity had ceased in the midnight region, the hard zone is clearly observed. Instead of requiring only from tens of minutes to an hour for these electrons to drift from midnight to noon, drift times are measured in several hours. Thus, if this interpretation is correct, following a substorm the hard (> 50 keV) electrons will precipitate first at a morning hour station and the average energy of the precipitation will slowly soften as a function of time. The morphology of ionization over a ground station situated in the morning hours is complicated by the fact that the initial ionization is produced some tens of minutes after the onset of a substorm in the D-region. Then there should be a very slow transition over a period of several hours, during which time the station would move to later morning hours, to a more typical E-layer absorption event from the hard zone electrons.

Auroral events

In section 2 of this review we associated the soft zone electron precipitation with the daytime portion of the auroral oval. We also saw in section 1 that the hard zone was situated immediately on the low latitude side of the soft zone. Since the energy spectrum of precipitating electrons in the hard zone is typically shaped like the spectrums in the midnight regions, it would be expected that auroral phenomena produced by these electrons in the morning hours would be dominated by the more typical auroral emission features that one finds in the midnight region.

In searching for an auroral optical phenomenon

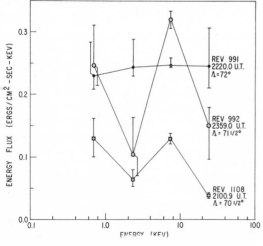

Fig. 30. Typical energy spectrums of the energy influx to the hard zone in the morning hours.

which could be associated with the hard zone, we found that the auroral type defined as the 'mantle aurora' by Sandford (1968) is consonant with our particle observations (Hoffman 1970). This aurora, measured photometrically at the $\lambda 3914$ and $\lambda 5577$ emissions, is a relatively steady, diffuse, subvisual aurora covering a large area of the sky, and occurring in the absence of discrete auroral forms as recorded on ground level all-sky camera photographs (Gowell & Akasofu 1969). Sandford (1968) found that on integrating the emissions over the entire high latitude region, the mantle auroral emissions were on the average the predominant optical phenomenon during solar maximum, giving rise to the majority of all auroral emissions, while at solar minimum such emissions dropped to form about half the total number of emissions. This suggests that the mantle aurora region of space is an important sink for energy from the magnetosphere.

On the assumption that the precipitating electrons were isotropic over the upper hemisphere at all energies, three typical energy spectrums of the energy influx are shown in Fig. 30. Note that energy is carried into the atmosphere at energies all the way up to at least 25 kilovolts. Rees (1970) calculated the column emission rates for $\lambda 3914$, $\lambda 5577$, and $\lambda 6300$ from the spectrum shown in Fig. 30, marked Revolution 1108. Assuming that the energy spectrums of precipitation events in the hard zone are consistently shaped like spectrum 1108 in Fig. 30, the flux of 10^6 electrons/cm²-sec-ster at 7.3 keV, which was used to define the boundaries of the hard zone in Fig. 15, would correspond to the energy influx which would produce 0.25 kR contours of $\lambda 3914$ emissions.

Sandford (1968 Fig. 3) published contours of this emission from data obtained by photometric methods in the southern hemisphere. We compare this 0.25 kR contour and the 0.5 kR contour with the region of 7.3 keV electron precipitation in Fig. 31. At higher latitudes we also show the location of the auroral oval as defined by Stringer & Belon (1967) with the same contour as that which appears in Fig. 26. All data in the Figure are compiled irrespective of K_p. The coincidence between the 7.3 keV electron precipitation region and the $\lambda 3914$ emission region is not exact. However, note from 05 through 11 hours MLT the strikingly identical shift in the boundary locations with respect to MLT, particularly between the particles and the 0.5 kR contour, and that the optical emissions decrease in intensity in the late morning hours, especially where the 7.3 keV pre-

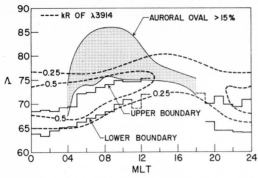

Fig. 31. A comparison of the region of 7.3 keV electron precipitation, which defines the hard zone and regions of optical emissions. The dashed contours are kR of λ3914 emissions in the absence of discrete auroras in 1963 in the southern hemisphere (Sandford 1968). The shaded area shows the location of the auroral oval during the morning and daytime hours as defined by Stringer & Belon (1967).

cipitation region seems to end. Certainly there is no relationship between the 7.3 keV precipitation and the auroral oval in the morning hours. Exact agreement between the electron precipitation and λ3914 emission regions would not be expected because the optical data were acquired during the southern winter of 1963, whereas the particle measurements were made during the last half of 1967 and the beginning of 1968. In addition criteria established to define the respective boundaries are not necessarily entirely compatible. No relationship between particle precipitation and Sandford's contours in the nighttime hours has been established. The general coincidence in the afternoon hours between Stringer & Belon's auroral occurrence contours for discrete aurora and Sandford's λ3914 emission contours during periods of no discrete aurora is also not understood.

On the basis of the following facts: (1) that the electron energy influx is sufficiently intense and has the proper spectrum to produce the optical emissions which Sandford has defined as the mantle aurora; (2) that the regions of precipitation and light emissions are reasonably associated spatially; and (3) that both the electron influx and the optical emissions are diffuse in nature, we concluded that the precipitation of these drifting electrons, apparently originating near midnight during substorms, is the cause of the mantle aurora (Hoffman 1970).

4. CONCLUDING REMARKS

In this review we have attempted to collect and integrate the various low energy charged particle measurements from satellites in the dawn and dayside hours of the polar domain, and to present some of the properties of the particles observed in this region. It is obvious that only the grossest characteristics of the radiation have been investigated, but hopefully the material presented here will be a base from which more definitive studies can originate. A thorough analysis of specific events and more careful statistical studies of the collective behavior of these particles are required, utilizing larger data bases and additional, more physically meaningful, supporting data, in order to understand the origin, history, and control of these particles.

If indeed the soft zone electrons are the result of the penetration of the magnetosheath plasma through the dayside magnetospheric cusps or 'neutral points', specific relations between the location of the soft zone, the magnetospheric configuration, and interplanetary conditions should exist. At first glance it appears that, in addition to field line interconnection between the magnetosphere and the magnetosheath, the particles must experience interactions within the magnetosphere in order to account for the spectral shapes, pitch angle distributions (Hoffman & Evans 1968), and the structure of the radiation, which rapidly vary with space or time, and the apparent overlap of the soft zone with closed field lines.

We have not specifically addressed the question of how far the soft zone extends into the nighttime hours, or what relationship might exist between the low energy, structured precipitation during magnetically quiet periods in the nighttime hours with the soft zone.

The temporal history of the hard zone in the morning hours requires considerably more analysis. We have not been able to find any analysis of ground-based observations relating to the effects of less than 50 keV precipitation in the hard zone which considered the possibility that the source of particles drifted in local time. Perhaps the most definitive studies of drifting electron clouds must be performed from equatorially stationed satellites, but unfortunately the synchronous orbit may be too low except for extraordinary events. Hopefully, data already acquired from such satellites will be able to illuminate the particle precipitation mechanism.

The observation of a large number of geophysical phenomena at high latitudes on the dayside of the dipole have been published, but we are only beginning to be aware that they probably have a common relationship with the electrons precipitating in the soft zone. For this reason we attempted to compile as many phenomena as possible which appear to have this common origin. We wish to point out that in those Figures which contain the superposition of soft zone phenomena on the rectilinear simplified probability map of the 0.7 keV structured electron precipitation, only the spatial relationship of the phenomena to the soft zone in the daytime hours is being considered.

The direct cause and effect relationships between the precipitating electrons and each of the individual phenomena have only begun to be investigated. For each type of event a host of questions remains to be answered.

● It is necessary to calculate from a well-measured electron spectrum the total power produced via the Cerenkov process to compare with the measured strength of the VLF auroral hiss. Further details of the electromagnetic radiation must be investigated, especially the effect of the ionosphere on the propagation of the hiss. This is possibly an area rich in wave-plasma phenomena.

● While the soft zone precipitation seems to constitute field aligned currents, the total current system and its relation to the magnetospheric configuration is still unknown. Since the types of ionospheric as well as magnetospheric currents which flow in the dayside ionosphere have not been determined, we have intentionally ignored the large body of ground-based magnetic measurements from these hours.

● The interaction of the soft zone electrons with the dayside ionosphere will be extremely difficult to study because of the great spatial gradients or rapid temporal variations which exist in the energy source and consequently the extremely localized and perhaps transient effects on the ionosphere. This is a region which has been almost totally ignored by investigators utilizing sounding rockets.

● While we believe that there is no direct relationship between the existence of the dayside portion of the auroral oval and the nighttime portion, and therefore that there are two major independent sources for auroral particles, the boundary conditions between these regions are not defined. The entire subject of polar cap auroras and the existence of the winter ionosphere has been neglected.

A large body of data from numerous experiments and satellites as well as associated ground observations now exist which certainly bear on these problems. These data, together with the increasing awareness of the interrelationships between the variety of phenomena which exist in the dawn and dayside hours, should enable a large number of these problems to be studied in depth in the succeeding years.

Acknowledgments: In the preparation of the material for this review, we wish to thank Mr. F. W. Berko for his participation in data analysis, Mr. R. W. Janetzke for data display support, Mr. R. D. Gribble for illustrations, and Mrs. Anne Thompson for her able assistance and patience in preparing and repeatedly revising the manuscript.

I spent an interesting and fruitful day learning about dayside optical and ionospheric measurements with Messrs. J. Buchau, J. A. Whalen, and C. P. Pike, and Mrs. R. A. Wagner at AFCRL, and appreciate their permission to reproduce the dayside aurora photograph. Professor R. E. Holzer and Mr. R. K. Burton have kindly allowed the publication of their search coil magnetometer data while we are engaged in a joint analysis project. Also I am grateful to Professor T. Laaspere for his permission to use his OGO–4 VLF data while we are preparing a joint publication. Mr. J. D. Winningham has kindly allowed me to use data from his very timely thesis. Quite a number of authors have granted me permission to use their published data.

I also wish to thank Drs. T. A. Fritz and S. J. Bauer for helpful discussions.

REFERENCES

Archuleta, R. J. & DeForest, S. E. 1971. *Rev. Sci. Instru. 42*, 89–91.
Arnoldy, R. L. & Chan, K. W. 1969. *J. Geophys. Res. 74*, 5019–5028.
Burch, J. T. 1968. *J. Geophys. Res. 73*, 3585–3591.
Burton, R. K., Holzer, R. E & Smith, E. J. April 1969. (Abstract) American Geophysical Union, Wash., D. C.
Cummings, W. D., Barfield, J. N. & Coleman, P. J. 1968. *J. Geophys. Res. 73*, 6687–6698.
Eather, R. H. & Mende, S. B. 1971. *J. Geophys. Res. 76*, 1746–1755.
Fairfield, D. H. 1968. *J. Geophys. Res. 73*, 73–7338.
Feldstein, Y. I. 1966. *Planet. Space Sci. 14*, 121–130.
Frank, L. A. 1970. Preprint 70–55, Dept. of Physics and Astronomy, The University of Iowa.
Gowell, R. W. & Akasofu, S.-I. 1969. *Planet. Space Sci. 17*, 289–290.
Hartz, T. R. 1970. In Skovli, G. (ed.). *The Polar*

137

Ionosphere and Magnetospheric Processes. Gordon & Breach, New York.

Heikkila, W. J. & Winningham, J. D. 1971. *J. Geophys. Res. 76*, 883.

Hoffman, R. A. 1969. *J. Geophys. Res. 74*, 2425.

Hoffman, R. A. 1970. Goddard preprint, X-646-70-205 (submitted to *J. Geophys. Res.*).

Hoffman, R. A. & Berko, F. W. 1971 a. (Abstract) American Geophysical Union, April 12–16, 1971, Washington, D. C.

Hoffman, R. A. & Berko, F. W. 1971 b. *J. Geophys. Res. 67*, 2967.

Hoffman, R. A. & Evans, D. S. 1968. *J. Geophys. Res. 73*, 6201.

Jørgensen, T. S. 1968. *J. Geophys. Res. 73*, 1055.

Lassen, K. 1969. In McCormac, B. M. & Omholt, A. (eds.). *Atmospheric Emissions*, p. 63. Van Nostrand Reinhold Co., New York.

Laaspere, T. & Hoffman, R. A. 1971. A comparison of VLF auroral hiss with precipitating low-energy electrons using simultaneous data from two OGO-4 experiments. (Abstract) COSPAR, Seattle.

Laaspere, T., Johnson, W. C. & Semprebon, L. C. 1970. Symposium on Upper Atmospheric Currents and Electric Fields, Boulder, Aug. 1970.

Lezniak, T. W. & Winckler, J. R. 1970. *J. Geophys. Res. 75*, 7075.

Maehlum, B. N. 1968. *J. Geophys. Res. 73*, 3459.

Maehlum, B. N. 1969. *J. Atm. Terr. Phys. 31*, 531.

Maynard, N. C. & Heppner, J. P. 1970. In McCormac, B. M. (ed.). *Particles and Fields in the Magnetosphere*, p. 247, Reinhold Pub. Co., New York.

Parks, G. K. & Winckler, J. R. 1968. *J. Geophys. Res. 73*, 5786.

Paschmann, G., Shelley, E. G, Chappell, C. R., Sharp, R. D. & Smith, L. F. 1970. Absolute efficiency measurements for channel electron multipliers utilizing a unique electron source. Preprint, Lockheed Palo Alto Research Laboratory, Palo Alto.

Pfitzer, K. A. & Winckler, J. R. 1969. *J. Geophys. Res. 74*, 5005.

Rees, M. H. 1970. In Skovli, G. (ed.). *The Polar Ionosphere and Magnetospheric Processes.* Gordon & Breach, New York.

Rosen, L. H. & Winckler, J. R. 1970. *J. Geophys. Res. 75*, 5576–5581.

Sandford, B. P. 1968. *J. Atmos. Terr. Phys. 30*, 1921–1942.

Sato, T. & Colin, L. 1969. *J. Geophys. Res. 74*, 2193–2207.

Sharp, R. D. & Johnson, R. G. 1968. *Earth's Particles and Fields*, (ed.). B. M. McCormac, Reinhold Pub. Corp., New York.

Stringer, W. J. & Belon, A. E. 1967. *J. Geophys. Res. 72*, 4415–4421.

Thomas, J. O., Rycroft, M. J. Colin, L. & Chan, K. L. 1966. *Electron Density Profiles in Ionosphere and Exosphere.* (ed.). J. Frihagen, p. 322–357. North-Holland Pub. Co., Amsterdam.

Vernov, S. N., Melnikov, V. V., Savenko, I. A. & Savin, B. I. 1966. *Space Res. VI*, 746–756.

Whalen, J. A., Buchau, J. & Wagner, R. A. 1971. *J. Atmos. Terr. Phys. 33*, 661–678.

Winningham, J. D. 1970. Ph. D. Thesis, Texas A&M University, Dec. 1970.

Zmuda, A. J., Armstrong, J. C. & Heuring, F. T. 1970. *J. Geophys. Res. 75*, 4757.

High Latitude Particle Precipitation and Source Regions in the Magnetosphere

R. H. EATHER AND S. B. MENDE

Physics Department, Boston College, Chestnut Hill, Massachusetts 02167
Lockheed Research Labs, 3251 Hanover, Palo Alto, California 94304

Abstract: In this review we present averaged properties of precipitating auroral protons and electrons (as deduced photometrically) and compare these with direct satellite measurements of similar parameters. The various distinct types of precipitating particles are defined and related to their source regions in the magnetosphere.

There are two distinct types of proton precipitation. On the nightside, the proton aurora locates equatorward of electron aurora before midnight, and overlaps electron aurora after midnight. The most probable source region in the magnetosphere is the ring current, and gradient drift may sometimes extend this region through the dusk meridian and as far around as midday. There is a second, higher-latitude zone of soft-proton precipitation on the dayside, which has its origin in magnetosheath plasma penetration through the cusp region.

There are three distinct types of electron precipitation. On the nightside, there is a broad zone of soft (~ 1 keV) precipitation that extends from the equatorward side of the nightside oval and up to invariant latitudes of $\sim 80°$; the probable source region is the plasma sheet via loss-cone drizzle. The auroral oval on the nightside is generated by higher-energy (~ 5 keV) electrons that superimpose on the low-latitude side of the soft zone. The most probable source region in the magnetosphere locates between the inner edge of the plasma sheet and the center of the plasma sheet (near neutral sheet) in the tail. Gradient drift of these electrons extends this region through the dawn meridian and past noon, resulting in a precipitation region locating just equatorward of the dayside oval. The third region of electron precipitation coincides with the high-latitude dayside protons and results from very soft magnetosheath electrons ($\lesssim 300$ eV) penetrating the cusp regions. It is these soft dayside electrons that generate the dayside oval.

These multiple zones of particicle precipitation, with their distinct and somewhat independent sources in the magnetosphere, comprise a much more complex picture than the simple concept of the auroral oval would suggest, but at the same time they provide a basis for clearer understanding of high-latitude precipitation phenomena.

1. INTRODUCTION

This review describes how ground-based optical techniques may be used to determine the type, flux, and energy of precipitating auroral particles. Recent experiments along these lines are described, and we arrive at a number of new conclusions on precipitation patterns and source regions in the magnetosphere. Comparisons with satellite data facilitate the identification of these source regions.

2. SPECTRAL–PHOTOMETRIC MEASUREMENTS

Within certain limitations, ground-based or airborne measurements of auroral emissions can be used to determine the type, energy, and flux of precipitating particles. The technique uses mainly 4861 Hβ, 4278 N_2^+, and 6300 OI measurements; the Hβ intensity is used to estimate the proton flux and the proton contribution to N_2^+ and OI excitation. The residual 4278 N_2^+ intensity then gives the total energy influx of precipitating electrons; at times when this residual is zero, airglow corrections can be made to the OI intensity. Finally the ratio 6300/4278 (proton corrected and airglow corrected) gives a measure of the average energy of the electrons.

There are certain precautions to observe in applying the procedure, such as van Rhijn and extinction corrections, perspective effects, lifetime effects, etc, but one can obtain confirming data

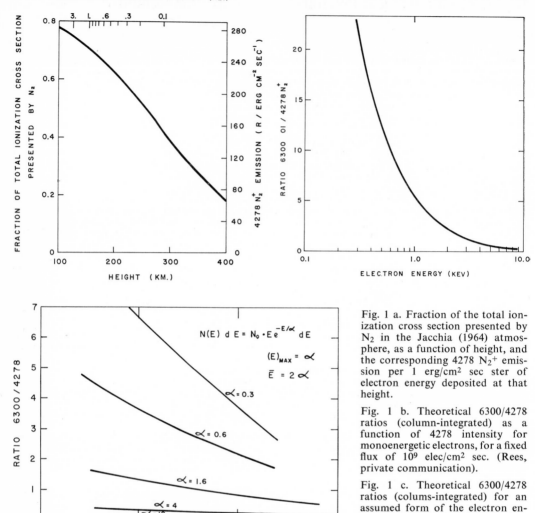

Fig. 1 a. Fraction of the total ionization cross section presented by N_2 in the Jacchia (1964) atmosphere, as a function of height, and the corresponding 4278 N_2^+ emission per 1 erg/cm² sec ster of electron energy deposited at that height.

Fig. 1 b. Theoretical 6300/4278 ratios (column-integrated) as a function of 4278 intensity for monoenergetic electrons, for a fixed flux of 10^9 elec/cm² sec. (Rees, private communication).

Fig. 1 c. Theoretical 6300/4278 ratios (colums-integrated) for an assumed form of the electron energy spectrum, with different peak energies α, as a function of 4278 intensity. (Rees, private communication).

by measuring additional emissions such as 3914 N_2^+, 5577 OI, and 5200 NI. Thus careful photometry can be a powerful technique for studying the details of energetic particle precipitation.

Relevant conversion data from emission intensities to energy are shown in Fig. 1. The conversion from 4278 N_2^+ intensity to total energy input would be independent of electron energy in a pure N_2 atmosphere (for electron energies $\gtrsim$ 100 eV), but because the fractional abundance of N_2 varies with height, we must use the correction factor as a function of height (or electron energy) as shown in Fig. 1a. Fig. 1b shows a theoretical curve (Rees, private communication) relating the 6300/4278 ratio to monoenergetic electron energy for an assumed model atmosphere. In practice, we have a distribution of precipitating electron energies, and the variation of 6300/4278 as a function of 4278 intensity (or total energy input) is shown in Fig. 1c (theoretical curves, Rees, private communication), for various energy spectra peaked between 0.3 and 10 keV. Thus if we assume a spectral form and measure the 6300/4278 ratio and 4278 intensity (for electron excitation), we

140

can uniquely define the parameter α giving the peak of the energy spectrum i.e. a measure of average electron energy.

3. DAYSIDE PRECIPITATION PATTERNS

Results of airborne experiments aboard the NASA Convair 990 have been published (Eather 1969, Eather & Akasofu 1969, Eather & Mende 1971). Only four north-south passes were made near the midday sector, so statistics are limited. Averaged latitude distributions of 4278 N_2^+ and $H\beta$ have been published (Eather & Mende 1971), and are replotted as a function of oval co-ordinates (invariant latitude minus latitude of theoretical position of equatorward boundary of the auroral oval, see Eather & Mende 1971) in Fig. 2. Note first that the peak average 4278 intensity is only 70 R (which corresponds to subvisual aurora). 4278 intensities of $\sim$ 300 R were observed in individual events, and such auroras were weak but visible. This average 4278 intensity is lower than nighttime averages by a factor of about 7. The peak $H\beta$ average intensity ($\sim$ 8 R) is also less than nighttime averages by a factor of $\sim$ 3; note too that the proton precipitation ($H\beta$) locates on the high-latitude half of a broader region of electron precipitation.

Fig. 3 shows the 6300/4278 ratios (electron excitation) plotted in oval co-ordinates, and indicates a number of important results. There are two distinct types of dayside precipitation: a re-

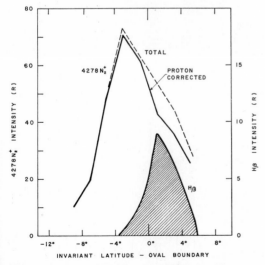

Fig. 2. Average 4278 N_2^+ and $H\beta$ intensities as a function of oval co-ordinates (see text) for dayside auroras.

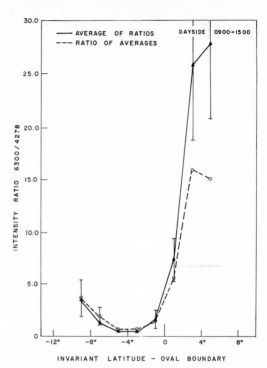

Fig. 3. 6300/4278 ratios as a function of oval co-ordinates for dayside auroras.

gion *equatorward* of the equatorial boundary of the auroral oval were high energy ($\gtrsim$ 5 keV) electrons precipitate, and a region *poleward* of the equatorial boundary (i.e. in the position of the oval) where soft electrons ($\lesssim$ 200 eV) precipitate. (These energies are derived from the ratios in Fig. 3, the intensities in Fig. 2, and the theoretical curves of Fig. 1c). This same effect may be seen by looking at the details of particular north-south flights (Fig. 4). It may be seen that for invariant latitudes less than about 77°, the 6300 intensity shows no relationship to the 4278 intensity, whereas above 77° the two curves show similar behavior. Both Figs. 3 and 4 show that the division between the regions of hard and soft electron precipitation is very sharp and that there is little overlap of these regions.

The red auroras excited in the soft precipitation region have been photographed in color, and there is a clear distinction between these auroras and the more typical green aurora further towards the equator (Akasofu, private communication).

Comparison of Figs. 2 and 3 shows that the protons precipitate in the same region as the *soft* electrons. An examination of the Doppler profile of the emitted $H\beta$ radiation shows that these pro-

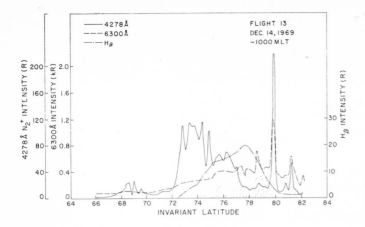

Fig. 4. 4278 N_2^+, 6300 OI, and 4861 Hβ intensities throughout a north-south meridian flight near noon.

tons are less energetic than on the nightside, so probably have energies $\lesssim$ 3 keV (Eather & Mende 1971).

These deductions from photometric measurements agree very well with detailed particle mea-

surements from the low-altitude satellite ISIS–1. Fig. 5 shows spectrograms for electrons and protons plotted against invariant latitude (Heikkila & Winningham 1971). The low-latitude, hard-electron precipitation, and high-latitude, soft-

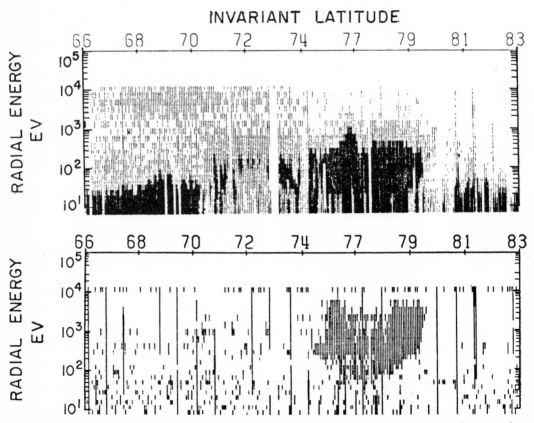

Fig. 5. Satellite measurements of electron (upper plot) and proton (lower plot) energy spectra for a crossing of the dayside auroral region. The density of the trace qualitatively indicates the spectral energy density as a function of particle energy and time (Heikkila & Winningham 1971).

electron and proton precipitation, with a sharp transition at 73° ($K_p = 5$), are all clearly shown. For quiet times ($K_p \sim 0 \to 1$), the sharp transition occurs at higher latitudes ($\sim 77.5°$) so that the soft precipitation of electrons and protons covers the Λ range $\sim 78–81°$ (Winningham 1970, Heikkila & Winningham, private communication).

The coincident precipitation of low-energy electrons and protons in a region adjacent to a lower-latitude region of hard electron precipitation led Heikkila & Winningham (1971) and Eather & Mende (1971) to suggest that these particles may penetrate directly from the magnetosheath. Such a penetration through the dayside neutral points would imply that the lower-latitude, hard-electron precipitation occurs on closed field lines.

There are a number of recent satellite results associating high-latitude precipitation of soft electrons and protons on the dayside with direct penetration of magnetosheath plasma through neutral points (or 'polar cusp' or 'cleft') (Heikkila & Winningham 1971, Frank 1971a). A summary of satellite observations of dayside precipitation, and a comparison with photometric results is presented in Fig. 6. Consideration of the experimental data (and remembering certain limitations on the energy coverage of some satellite detectors) leads to probable average energy influx of ~ 0.1 erg cm^{-2} sec^{-1} ster^{-1} for soft electrons, and ~ 0.05 erg cm^{-2} sec^{-1} ster^{-1} for soft protons. The spectral peak seems to be typically 100–200 eV for electrons and ~ 300 eV for protons. A summary of the average features of dayside precipitation as shown in Fig. 6 is presented in Table I.

The lower-latitude zone of hard electron precipitation has been discussed by Hoffman (1971a) and indirectly by Frank (1971a). This is a broad, diffuse and steady region of precipitation occur-

Table 1. Dayside aurora

	Hard zone electrons	Electrons	Soft zone protons	Total
Average energy input (erg/cm² sec ster)	0.1	0.1	0.05	0.15
4278 N₂ + (R)	85	70	~ 30	100
5577 OI	~ 200	~ 250	~ 80	330
6300 IO	20	1250	~ 80	1330
4861 Hβ			10	10

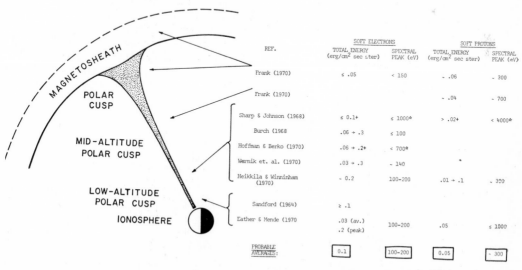

Fig. 6. Summary of measurements of proton and electron energy fluxes, and mean energies, in the polar cusp.

143

ring on closed field lines; the average energy flux being precipitated is similar to that in the soft zone (~ 0.1 erg cm^{-2} sec^{-1} ster^{-1}) and it seems clear that these electrons move by gradient drift from a nighttime source region (see full discussion by Hoffman 1971a). The width of the precipitation region is much broader before midday than after (Hoffman 1971a, Eather, Heikkila, and Akasofu, private communications) and often extends only a few hours into the afternoon sector (Hoffman 1971a). This extension into the afternoon would probably be a function of the nightside source strength and the loss rate along the drift path.

It is interesting to note that early satellite results from the Lockheed group (Sharp & Johnson 1969) showed a second zone of proton precipitation coincident with the hard electrons (Fig. 7). This zone was not detected photometrically by Eather & Mende (1971), nor has it been reported by other satellite experiments. However it occurs in the same region as the trapped ring current in the dayside (Frank 1971a) so it seems a likely explanation is that on some occasions these trapped ring current protons do enter the loss cone. Indeed the second proton zone is probably entirely analogous to the hard electron zone in that it has as its source a gradient drift from a nightside source region. Such protons drift through the evening sector towards noon, and their extent into the dayside would be a function of the nightside source strength and the loss rate along the drift path. Apparently the source strength and/or the loss rate near noon are only occasionally strong enough to give measureable precipitation.

It appears then that we have a quite satisfactory picture of dayside particle precipitation and the various source regions in the magnetosphere.

The only significant discrepancies between the satellite and photometric experiments listed in

Fig. 6 concerns the geometry of the polar cusp as a function of altitude. The low-altitude satellites and airborne photometric measurements show that the soft zone typically covers some 3° of latitude (i.e. ~ 300 km) and that the protons and electrons precipitate right across this region. Higher altitude measurements by Frank (1971a) indicate that the width of the soft precipitation region of protons, when projected to ionospheric heights, should be 10–200 km, with an average of ~ 100 km (Frank 1971b), and that these protons precipitate in a sheet located poleward of the soft electron precipitation. An explanation of the narrower widths observed by Frank might involve the limited energy range he considers (700–1100 eV), or uncertainties in field-line projections. A more serious question is whether the protons precipitate separately and poleward of the electrons; this certainly is not the case at low altitudes and it is difficult to see how the situation could be different further up the field lines. Again Frank has compared limited energy ranges of protons (700–1100 eV) and electrons (300–500 eV), so an energy variation with latitude could distort the picture, and if total number flux or total energy flux were considered, the situation may possibly be more in agreement with low-altitude measurements. We must await a more detailed presentation of Frank's data to see if a problem really exists.

4. THE DAYTIME AURORAL OVAL

The question arises as to what is meant by the auroral oval on the dayside. The oval has been determined from all-sky camera photographs and so represents aurora which exceed the sensitivity of the film used. Typically all-sky cameras will just detect about 500 R of 5577 OI and so respond to energy inputs ~ 0.1 erg/cm^2 sec ster. In Table I

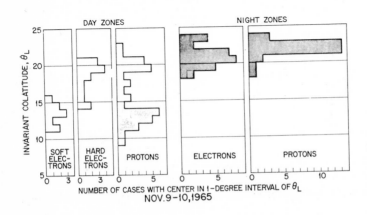

Fig. 7. Lockheed measurements of the location of peak particle precipitation; plotted are the number of auroral-zone crossings with peak response in the 1° interval centered on θ_L (Johnson et al. 1966).

we listed the energy inputs into the hard and soft zones and the expected optical emission intensities. Table I is based on *average* energy inputs. The normal, high-speed black and white films used in all-sky cameras (usually Tri-X, 2080, or equivalents) are panchromatic films and hence quite red-sensitive. Thus these films would respond preferentially to auroras in the soft zone (see Table I), *even though there may be as much or greater energy input into the hard zone*. Even so, the *average* soft zone energy input is only just at the sensitivity limit of the film, so we must ask what the statistical spread is about the average energy input in both the hard and soft zones. The soft zone auroral forms show a lot of spatial structure and are often short-lived (Eather 1969, Eather & Akasofu 1969, Lassen 1969) and this dynamic behavior is also confirmed by satellite measurements (Burch 1968, Hoffman & Evans 1968, Heikkila & Winningham 1971); in contrast, the hard zone seems much steadier. Indeed specific events would have to exceed the average by a factor of 4 to exceed all-sky camera sensitivity in the green. In the soft zone, the 6300 intensity on the *average* is near the all-sky camera sensitivity level.

We conclude that the presently accepted dayside auroral oval represents the soft-electron and proton precipitation, and Hoffman (1971b) has independently arrived at a similar conclusion. Fig. 3 confirms this as it shows the soft zone locates in a 3–5° band just above the equatorial boundary of the oval. However, hard electrons locating equatorward of the oval deposit as much or more energy in the atmosphere. As they probably result from a gradient drift of nighttime electrons, the concept of a continuous auroral oval might be more applicable to them. Thus we question the usefulness of the concept of a continuous auroral oval. It is a very artificial notion that only has meaning in terms of peak response of black and white all-sky camera film; this peak response evidently comes from 'normal green' auroral on the nightside, and from 'soft red' aurora on the dayside. These two types of aurora have entirely different source regions in the magnetosphere, and there is no obvious topological connection between these regions.

We strongly recommend that the use of the auroral oval as a means of ordering high-latitude geophysical data on a 24-hour basis be discontinued, and that instead the various different magnetosphere source regions of precipitating particles that are summarized at the end of this paper be kept in mind.

5. NIGHTSIDE PRECIPITATION PATTERNS

Statistical results from all NASA Convair expeditions in 1967–1968 and 1969 (some 40 flights, each of ∼ 6 hours duration) were used in this

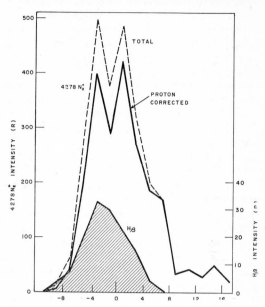

Fig. 8. Average 4278 N_2^+ and Hβ intensities as a function of 'oval co-ordinates' (see text) for nightside auroras.

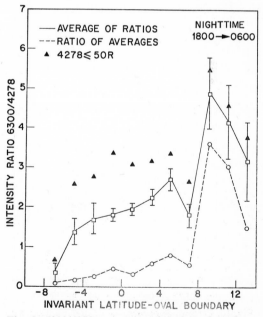

Fig. 9. 6300/4278 ratios as a function of oval co-ordinates for nightside auroras.

analysis. Fig. 8 shows average 4278 N_2^+ (electron excited) and Hβ intensities in oval co-ordinates, and for night hours. Fig. 9 shows the corresponding 6300/4278 ratio plot. (The difference between the two curves 'average of ratios' and 'ratio of averages' is discussed by Eather & Mende 1971, but is not important in our present discussion.)

The previously reported nighttime soft zone (Eather 1968, Eather & Mende 1971) is evident in the peaking of the average 6300/4278 ratio above the oval position. The peak ratio of ~ 5.0 corresponds to about a 500 eV peak in the energy spectrum (Fig. 1c). An alternate presentation (Fig. 10) shows the percentage occurrence of peak energies of < 1 keV and > 5keV. The > 5 keV precipitation maximizes in the position of the auroral oval, whereas the < 1 keV precipitation locates at much higher latitude; in fact $\sim 90\%$ of the occurrences of precipitation in the high-latitude soft zone are of < 1 keV electrons. A plot of percentage occurrence of 4278 N_2^+ exceeding 0.5 and 50 R (Fig. 11) shows, by comparison with Fig. 10, that the soft precipitation is typically

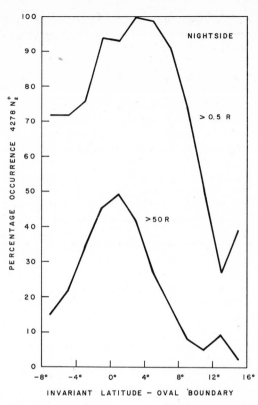

Fig. 11. Percentage occurrence of 4278 N_2^+ exceeding 0.5 R (limit of detection) and 50 R, as a function of oval co-ordinates.

low intensity (< 50 R). It is also interesting to note that there is a broad region centered on the oval where there is measurable precipitation virtually all of the time.

Various considerations led us to suspect that there may be a systematic relationship between the 6300/4278 ratio and the 4278 intensity, i.e. between average energy and total energy precipitated. The ratio 6300/4278 is plotted versus mean 4278 intensity in Fig. 12. The plotted numbers ($1 \rightarrow 11$) represent $4°$ latitude intervals centered from $8°$ equatorward of the equatorial boundary of the auroral oval to $12°$ poleward of that boundary (so, for example, the numeral 6 represents the interval $0°–2°$ in oval co-ordinates). There are no points plotted unless the number of data points in the appropriate latitude-intensity box exceeded 5.

We have drawn a division line at an intensity level of 50 R, and note that for $4278 > 50$ R, there is a reasonably systematic decrease of the 6300/4278 ratio with increasing 4278 intensity for all latitudes. For $4278 < 50$ R, it seems this rela-

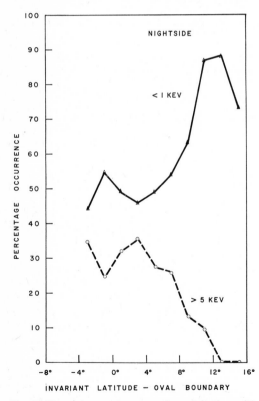

Fig. 10. Percentage occurrence of precipitation with mean electron energy < 1 keV and > 5 keV, as a function of oval co-ordinates.

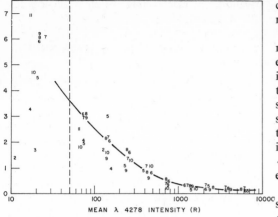

MEAN λ 4278 INTENSITY (R)

Fig. 12. The mean ratio 6300/4278 plotted as a function of mean 4278 intensity, for 11-latitude intervals. The plotted numbers (1→11) represent 4° intervals centered every 2° from 8° equatorward of the equatorial boundary of the oval to 12° poleward of that boundary (eg. the numeral 6 represents 0–2° in oval co-ordinates).

tion breaks down, but a reasonably systematic increase in the ratio with increasing latitude becomes evident. We interpret these results as follows:

a) There is a low level (< 50 R) of precipitation occurring in a very broad region from below the auroral oval position to well poleward of it, such that the average energy of precipitation softens with latitude (from ~ 1.5 keV to $\lesssim 500$ eV).

b) Higher intensity precipitation superimposes on this low level precipitation, and locates preferentially in the position of the oval. This pre-

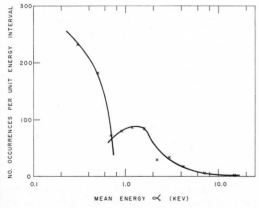

MEAN ENERGY ∝ (KEV)

Fig. 13. Number of cases of occurrence of a given α (defined in Fig. 1c, and is a measure of peak energy for the spectrum) per unit energy interval. Two separate particle distributions are indicated.

cipitation is characterized by an increasing average energy as total energy input increases.

We conclude that the so-called 'soft zone' does not only locate poleward of the auroral oval, but extends right across the auroral oval itself. There is a gradual softening with latitude throughout this broad region. Energetic electron precipitation superimposes on the lower-latitude half of the soft zone, and gives rise to the visual auroral forms that make up the auroral oval. As the 4278 N_2^+ intensity in the oval increases from 50 R to up to ~ 10 kR, there is a systematic hardening of the electron spectrum.

The division of Fig. 12 into two intensity divisions ($\gtrsim 50$ R), and our interpretation in terms of two distinct particle observations, is not as arbitrary as it may seem. In Fig. 13 we have plotted the occurrence frequency of α, where α is the parameter in the spectrum used in Fig. 1c, and is a measure of the average energy. It may be seen that there is a definite indication of two separate particle populations, one between $\lesssim 200$ eV and ~ 700 eV (our soft particle spectrum), and a wider distribution locating between ~ 1 and ~ 10 keV. Note that α exceeds 5 keV in only 11 % of all cases. However, if we exclude the low-α distribution, then for those more energetic electron spectra that excite visual aurora, α exceeds 5 keV some 25 % of the time.

6. VARIATION OF TOTAL ENERGY PRECIPITATED WITH MEAN ENERGY

For this analysis, the energy spectrum parameter α (Fig. 1c) and the total energy being precipitated were calculated. The resultant plot of total precipitated energy Φ (ergs/cm^2 sec) versus peak energy of the spectrum α (keV) is given in Fig. 14. (Note that average energy of spectrum $= 2\alpha$.) The data have been averaged over all latitudes and times, for nightside data only.

If these particles had been accelerated by an adiabatic compression process with negligible sources and losses, then Liouville's theorem predicts that if we plot Φ versus α on a log-log plot (as in Fig. 14), then we should get a straight line with a slope of 3. On the other hand, if acceleration was by static electric fields, we would expect a slope of 1.

The plot of total energy precipitated versus α gives a reasonable straight line, though there seems to be a flattening out at lower energies. In this respect it is interesting to note that if we subtract a constant 0.15 ergs cm^{-2} sec^{-1} from Φ, a

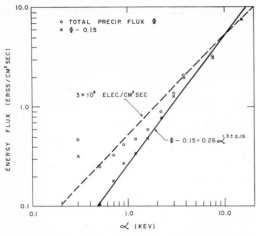

Fig. 14. Total energy precipitated Φ (ergs/cm^2 sec) as a function of energy spectrum parameter α, for nightside data. The relation for a constant number flux of 3×10^8 electrons/cm^2 sec is also shown.

much better straight-line fit results (Fig. 14). It is tempting to relate this 0.15 ergs cm^{-2} sec^{-1} (corresponding to ~ 40 R of 4278 N$_2^+$) to the average contribution of the soft precipitation, and then interpret the remainder as the harder, 'auroral' precipitation that superimposes on the soft zone. We do not claim to have proved this suggestion in Fig. 14, but it is consistent with the rest of our results, and is aesthetically pleasing.

Fig. 14 shows that for the particle population above about 0.5 keV there is a quite linear relationship with a slope of 1.3 ± 0.15. We could argue that this is more consistent with an electric field acceleration mechanism, but there are other ad hoc explanations for such a slope. For example, a combination of electric field acceleration and adiabatic compression, or adiabatic compression with strong losses of the higher energy particles, could give a slope in agreement with the experimental results.

In Fig. 14 we have also drawn in the Φ versus α relationship for an electron flux of 3×10^8 cm^{-2} sec^{-1}. It is interesting to note that our results suggest that the average number flux of precipitating electrons increases by less than 50% for two orders of magnitude increase in the total energy precipitated. The range plotted extends up to about 3 kR. We realize that there are times (especially at breakup) when very intense aurora are excited by much higher fluxes of 1–10 keV electrons. At those times fluxes in excess of 10^{10} cm^{-1} sec^{-1} have been reported. This must be a much more dynamic and transitory process than the lower-level, steady-state picture we envisage here for IBC 1–2 auroras.

7. COMPARISON WITH PLASMA SHEET ELECTRONS

In Fig. 15 we summarize plasma sheet data from 17 Re according to Hones (1968). We have plotted his data (originally published in tabular form) by performing averages as indicated and assuming equal weighting for his latitude-longitude boxes. In Fig. 14a we see that the average energy of plasma sheet electrons decreases from about 1.2 keV at the center of the plasma sheet to some 0.4 keV near the edge. This has led us to associate these electrons with our soft precipitation zone, as the zone shows a similar softening with latitude. As the energies match fairly well, we believe that the soft precipitation represents a loss-cone drizzle of plasma sheet electrons, with no important acceleration processes involved. If we assume isotropy, the $\sim 1°$ plasma sheet loss-cone maps down to the ionosphere and carries enough energy to excite some 10–50 R of $\lambda 4278$ N$_2^+$ emission, in

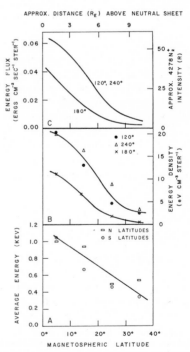

Fig. 15. Summary of Hones (1968) plasma sheet electron properties at 17 R$_E$. The 180° curve is for the midnight sector, and 120° and 240° for the dusk and dawn sectors. A. Average energy B. Energy density C. Energy flux and resultant 4278 N$_2^+$ emission if this flux was isotropic over the atmospheric loss-cone.

148

good agreement with energy inputs into the soft zone (Fig. 4 and 12).

The data presented in Fig. 15 were obtained for dipole tilts between $\pm 20°$, so an effective broadening of the latitude extent of the plasma sheet results. Typically the latitudinal width of the plasma sheet near midnight is only $\sim \pm 3\,R_E$, and the sheet thickens to perhaps double this value near the dawn and dusk meridians. According to Fairfield's (1968) model of the tail field, we would not expect the edges of the plasma sheet to map down to an invariant latitude that ever exceeds about 74°. But we observe soft precipitation up to about $\varLambda = 79–80°$, which we believe comes from the edge of the plasma sheet. Certainly there are not sufficient fluxes of low-energy electrons in the high-latitude magnetotail to explain the observed precipitation. We are forced to conclude that the edges of the plasma sheet must map down to higher invariant latitudes in the ionosphere that would be expected from Fairfield's (1968) model. Independent studies of the thickening of the plasma sheet and poleward movement of the electrojet (Hones et. al. 1970) also indicate that a given latitudinal interval in the plasma sheet near 17–18 R_E subtends a larger invariant latitude interval at the ionosphere than that indicated by Fairfield's model.

On the low-latitude side, our observation of aurora at invariant latitudes of 60° indicate, by comparison with Fairfield's model, that these aurora occur on closed field lines. Vasyliunas (1970a) has convincingly associated this equatorial boundary of aurora with the inner edge of the plasma sheet, which he also regards as being in a closed field line region.

We now consider the more energetic auroral precipitation (the $> 50\,R$ side of Fig. 12) that excites the visual auroral forms. Average energies are in the 1–10 keV range, and so exceed typical average energies in the plasma sheet. The average precipitated energy at the peak in Fig. 8 is ~ 0.6 erg/cm^2 sec ster, and this also exceeds typical plasma-sheet energy fluxes, though there are some discrepancies in reported fluxes. Hones (1968) and Vasyliunas (1968) agree on the electron mean energy ($\sim 0.2–2$ keV, average ~ 1 keV) but the 'most probable' energy density given by Vasyliunas is a factor of ~ 3 higher than Hones's 'average' values. In fact Hones's *maximum* energy flux (~ 0.3 erg/cm^2 sec ster) is about the same as Vasyliunas's average. In either case, both the average energy and energy flux of plasma sheet electrons are significantly less than for the pre-

cipitated electrons in the auroral oval, and it is only the cases of *very high* plasma sheet energy fluxes (~ 1 erg/cm^2 sec ster) that compare with *average* precipitated fluxes. Certainly the energy fluxes associated with commonly occurring IBC 2 aurora (~ 2 erg/cm^2 sec ster) are almost never seen in the plasma sheet.

The variability of plasma-sheet energy spectra is illustrated in Fig. 16a where we show a selection of published spectra; Figure 16b shows three schematic spectra derived from Figure 16a that represent typical 'soft', 'average', and 'hard' spectra. The energy carried by each of these spectra is 0.06, 0.30, and 1.00 erg/cm^2 sec ster respectively. The *'typical'* spectrum published by Vasyliunas (1970b) seems to be nearer to the *hardest* of published spectra.

The photometric data presented in this paper, together with arguments presented earlier by Vasyliunas (1970b) and Frank (1971a, b), seem quite convincing in associating the harder, auroral-oval precipitation with a magnetospheric source region locating from the inner edge of the plasma sheet and extending down the centre of the plasma sheet. We maintain that some accelera-

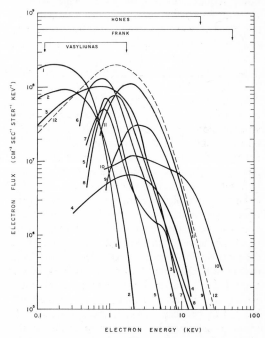

Fig. 16 a. A selection of published plasma sheet electron energy spectra. 1–4 at 18 R_E (Hones et al. 1971); 5–15.9 R_E, 6–10.5 R_E, 7–15.3 R_E, 8–19.7 R_E, 9–13.5 R_E, 10–10.1 R_E, (Frank 1967); 11–9.8 R_E (Schield & Frank 1970); 12– Vasyliunas (1970a,b) 'typical' spectrum.

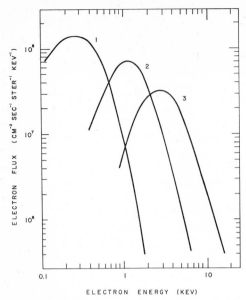

Fig. 16 b. Schematic representation of typical 'soft' (1) 'average' (2), and 'hard' (3) plasma sheet electron energy spectra.

tion is required between the plasma sheet at ~ 18 R_E and the auroral zone, and note that a simple adiabatic compression would be entirely adequate to provide the required energization (of about a factor of 5). We note that harder plasma sheet spectra in Fig. 16a were all measured closer to the earth (9–11 R_E) than the Vela orbit (17–18 R_E).

We are somewhat in disagreement with Vasyliunas (1970b), who also views the auroral oval as an extension of the plasma sheet to ionospheric heights, but requires no energization in the process. (We believe that loss-cone drizzle does occur, but gives rise only to the soft zone.) Vasyliunas (1970a, b) cites the contention of Chase (1969) that the electron energy spectrum in post-breakup auroral closely resembles, in both shape and intensity, the spectrum within the plasma sheet. We have examined Chase's (1969) published comparison (his Fig. 2), and note that the total energy in the plasma sheet spectrum is ~ 0.3 erg cm^{-2} sec, whereas that in the auroral spectrum is ~ 2.0 erg cm^{-2} sec and that the auroral spectrum has a peak between 5 and 10 keV that carries 2/3 of the total energy, and has no counterpart in the plasma sheet spectrum. Thus we conclude there is little reason to contend that these spectra are similar (even though they may appear so in a Figure that plots 7 1/2 orders of magnitude of flux in a space of just one inch (Chase 1969)). A

far more detailed comparisons of plasma sheet and auroral spectrum (Hones et al. 1971) reveal that the plasma sheet spectra are typically softer than auroral spectra, especially in that they do not show peaks in the 5–10 keV range as are often observed by rockets, and plasma sheet fluxes are typically an order of magnitude less than auroral fluxes as measured by rockets.

Vasyliunas also compares the averaged precipitated electron flux in the auroral oval (Sharp et al. 1969) with three OGO–1 passes in the plasma sheet. We again feel the 'agreement' is not convincing. First there is the problem of matching the plasma sheet data (at various estimated distances from the neutral sheet) with satellite data at various invariant latitudes; we have discussed above evidence that a given distance above the neutral sheet should correspond to higher latitude than indicated by Fairfield's model. Second, Vasyliunas's energy fluxes (~ 0.3 erg/cm² sec ster) are about three times Hones's average, and Sharp et al.'s peak average flux (~ 0.3 erg/cm² sec ster) is about half of our own average. So if we compare data from Hones with our data, we conclude that there is a discrepancy of a factor of 6. This argument reduces to the question of which data to believe, so it is not particularly profitable. But we feel the argument concerning the differences in average energy of plasma sheet and auroral particles is quite convincing.

A few final comments should be made on the character of the auroral precipitation. Fig. 11 shows that there is always measurable precipitation in the position of the oval, but that the energy flux only exceeds 0.6 erg/cm² sec ster about 50% of the time. At higher latitudes where mainly soft precipitation locates, emissions are detectable only $\sim 50\%$ of the time and exceed 50 R only 5–10% of the time. Thus in neither case is there a *continuous* precipitation of electrons with energy fluxes corresponding to their postulated plasma-sheet source levels. We are forced to conclude that there must be perturbing mechanisms in the plasma sheet that can turn precipitation on and off at certain times. It would be of interest to study this problem in more detail by considering statistics of occurrence of precipitation from given points in the oval and soft zones, rather than from a moving platform such as an aircraft or satellite.

8. PROTONS AND THE PLASMA SHEET

Hones (1968) and Frank (1970) have published plasma-sheet proton spectra. Proton peak fluxes during quiet times are ~ 10^6 protons/cm^2 sec ster with average energies near 1 keV. This would correspond to a precipitating energy flux of ≤ 0.005 erg/cm^2 sec ster if isotropic over the loss-cone, and so loss-cone drizzle would not give rise to any detectable optical emissions (Eather 1967). Vasyliunas (1970a) has suggested that the proton ring current could be filled by adiabatic compression of these plasma-sheet protons. We agree that this seems a likely source for the ring-current protons as the resulting increase in energy flux in the compression (Φ increases to about 0.6 erg/cm^2 sec as the energy increases from 1 to 5 keV) could excite ~ 50 R of Hβ if isotropic over the loss-cone. (Frank (1971a) believes that these plasma-sheet protons have their source in the front-side magnetosheath plasma.) Possible mechanisms involved in the consequent precipitation of the ring-current protons to generate the nighttime proton aurora have been discussed by Cornwall et al. (1970) and Eather & Carovillano (1971). Although there is no agreement yet on the details of the precipitation mechanism, we are quite confident that the ring current is the source region.

9. POLAR CAP AURORA

There is no continuous, low-level precipitation over the polar cap, and spectral-photometric measurements (Eather 1969) place an upper limit of ~ .001 erg/cm^2 sec ster for both protons and electrons. These measurements were made near the last solar maximum, and there are earlier reports indicating widespread emissions over the pole during IGY (Sandford 1964). However, we believe Sanford's diagrams may have been misleading as he extrapolated data from his highest latitude station (80°) across the polar cap. An examination of his data (Sandford 1968, Fig. 6) in 3914 N$_2^+$ emission (airglow corrections must be applied to data in 6300 or 5577 OI) indicates there is no polar cap precipitation for K$_p \lesssim 3$ for IGY. For K$_p \gtrsim 4$, an extrapolation of day and night data to connect over the pole would indicate polar cap precipitation, but there is not much justification for such an extrapolation as the day and night source regions are quite different. Similar comments apply to the IQSY data if we replace the K$_p$ conditions above about K$_p \sim 6$. We conclude that it is unlikely that there is very widespread precipitation across the polar cap, though note that this has yet to be proven for high K$_p$ conditions.

There are, however, short-lived (a few minutes) structured (spatially) bursts of precipitation across the polar cap. Eather & Akasofu (1969) showed from photometric data that the emissions were excited by soft ($\lesssim 1$ keV) electrons. Heikkila & Winningham (1971) and Hoffman & Evans (1968) see similar features from satellites. From the geometry of the magnetosphere, it seems these electrons must come from the high-latitude magnetotail, though we know of no reports of isolated plasma 'clouds' in that region.

10. PRECIPITATION PATTERNS AND SOURCE REGIONS

We have tried to summarize the basic precipitation patterns in Fig. 17 for both electrons and protons. Figure 17a shows the electron patterns, displayed on an invariant latitude-magnetic time grid, with the auroral oval for quiet times (Q = 1) added for reference. As discussed in section 4, the oval on the dayside locates in the soft zone and results from direct penetration of low-energy electrons from the magnetosheath. Immediately adjacent to it and on the equatorward side are the higher-energy electrons that have gradient-drifted from the nightside. Hoffman (1971a) associates these with Sandford's mantle aurora. The dayside precipitation of these electrons does not seem to extend much past noon, where it is thinner

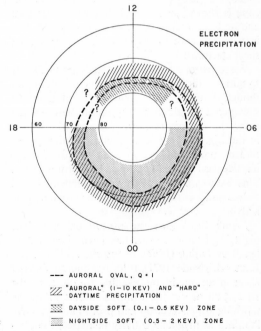

Fig. 17 a. Electron precipitation patterns.

151

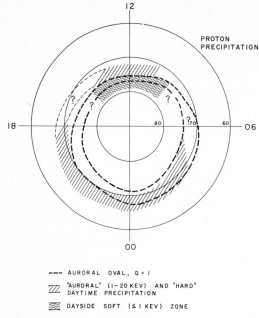

--- AURORAL OVAL, Q = I

▨ "AURORAL" (1–20 KEV) AND "HARD"
DAYTIME PRECIPITATION

▨ DAYSIDE SOFT (≤ I KEV) ZONE

Fig. 17 b. Proton precipitation patterns.

(in latitude) and less intense. On the nightside the auroral oval precipitation is shown, and has its origin in the region bounded by the inner edge of that plasma sheet and the region of the plasma sheet close to the neutral sheet. The wide, soft zone is shown extending right through the oval and up to latitudes of 79–80°, and we believe this is a consequence of loss-cone drizzle of plasma sheet electrons.

We know of no published data that allows us to connect the dayside and nightside soft zones, though Frank (1971b) has published a model showing a topological connection between the associated source regions. The question marks in the Fig. 17a indicate the uncertainties in this respect, and the uncertainty as to how far the dayside hard zone extends into the morning hours. This extension is probably very dependent on source and loss functions, and hence on magnetic activity.

Figure 17b shows the proton patterns. The nightside proton aurora has been discussed in detail by Eather (1967), Montbriand (1969), and Eather & Mende (1971). It locates equatorward of electron aurora in the evening hours, with the separation decreasing towards midnight. In the morning hours, electron and proton aurora overlap, and as magnetic activity increases, the electron aurora maximum may move equatorward

of the proton aurora maximum (Montbriand 1969). We believe the proton aurora has its source in the ring current, and the ring current is filled by adiabatic compression of plasma sheet protons. The extent of the proton aurora (with a ring-current source) in the morning hours is not clear. Gradient drift carries the protons to the evening side and under quiet conditions they extend at least to the dusk meridian. Occasional observations of ~ 10 keV proton precipitation near midday indicates that gradient drift may at times carry precipitation around to the noon meridian, but this does not seem to be a regular occurrence. We know of no experimental data that allows the connection of the proton aurora at dusk to the hard proton precipitation at midday, so we have dashed the connection in Fig. 17b and indicated uncertainty with a question mark.

The soft-proton precipitation from the magnetosheath gives the main zone of proton aurora on the dayside. We classify this as the main zone as it is a regular feature of the daytime precipitation pattern, whereas the zone of harder precipitation seems transitory. The azimuthal extent of this soft proton precipitation has not been established, though it clearly does not extend into the evening sector at high latitudes. Gradient drift could take these protons to the dawn sector and confuse the picture there, though for these low energies we suspect the proton lifetime could be considerably shorter than the drift time.

If a and b of Fig. 17 were superimposed, one could obtain an idea of the complexity of auroral precipitation. With two particle types and a number of source regions and precipitation processes, it is clear than any well-designed experiment (either photometric, rocket, or satellite) must measure a wide variety of parameters to obtain the complete picture.

Our Figure 17a (for electrons) is considerably different from the Hartz & Brice model, as modified recently by Hartz (1971). Hartz implies continuous (24-hour) zones of 'splash' and 'drizzle' type of precipitation, with the superposition of the magnetosheath precipitation near midday (Fig. 18). We would associate his low-intensity 'drizzle' on the nightside with our soft zone (and point out that it should extend up to higher latitudes $\sim 79°$), but on the dayside we would associate his higher-intensity drizzle with our dayside hard zone. As we envisage different source mechanisms, we would not connect these two regions. We would associate his high intensity 'splash' on the nightside with the auroral oval

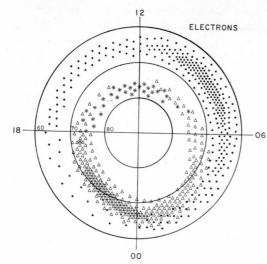

Fig. 18. Auroral precipitation patterns after Hartz (1971). Triangles indicate zones of discrete or splash precipitation, and dots indicate diffuse or drizzle precipitation. Precipitation of magnetosheath plasma is indicated by stars. Intensity is indicated by symbol density.

precipitation, and his low intensity splash on the dayside with the high-latitude soft zone, and again we see no evidence to link these regions in a 24-hour pattern, as they have separate source regions. We would prefer to connect the high-intensity nightside splash with the high-intensity dayside drizzle, since we believe the latter results from the former, via gradient drift.

Finally, both photometric and satellite data show that the dayside soft and hard zones are adjacent to each other, and not separated by a region of low or zero precipitaition as indicated in the Hartz model (Fig. 18).

In Fig. 19 we have drawn a model of the magnetospheric source regions in the noon-midnight plane. This model is similar to recent magnetospheric models (O'Brien 1967, Vasyliunas 1970b, Frank 1971a) though different from all of them in some respects. The salient features of Fig. 19 have all been discussed in the preceding text, so will not be further elaborated.

Acknowledgements: This review was supported by grant NGR 22–003–018 from the National Aeronautics and Space Administration, Airborne Sciences Office.

REFERENCES

Burch, J. L. 1968. *J. Geophys. Res. 73,* 3585.
Chase, L. M. 1969. *J. Geophys. Res. 74,* 346.
Cornwall, J. M., Coroniti, F. V. & Thorne, R. M. 1970. *J. Geophys. Res. 75,* 4699.
Eather, R. H. 1967. *Rev. Geophys. 5,* 207.
Eather, R. H. 1969. *J. Geophys. Res. 74,* 153.
Eather, R. H. & Akasofu, S.-I. 1969. *J. Geophys. Res. 74,* 4794.
Eather, R. H. & Carovillano, R. L. 1971. *Cosmic Electrodynamics 2,* 105.
Eather, R. H. & Mende, S. B. 1971. *J. Geophys. Res. 76,* 1746.
Fairfield, D. H. 1968. *J. Geophys. Res. 73,* 7329.
Frank, L. A. 1967. *J. Geophys. Res. 72,* 185.
Frank, L. A. 1970. In McCormac, B. M. (ed.). *Particles and Fields in the Magnetosphere,* p. 319. D. Reidel, Dordrecht, Holland.

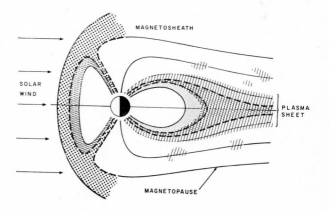

Fig. 19. Source regions in the magnetosphere for the precipitation regions depicted in Fig. 17 (noon-midnight plane).

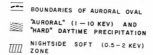

153

Frank, L. A. 1971a. *J. Geophys. Res. 76.* In press.

Frank, L. A. 1971b. *J. Geophys. Res. 76.* 2512.

Hartz, T. R. 1971. Paper presented at NATO Advanced Study Institute, Kingston, Ontario, August 1970. To be published in Proceedings, McCormac, B. M. (ed.).

Heikkila, W. F. & Winningham, J. D. 1971. *J. Geophys. 76,* 883.

Hoffman, R. A. 1971a. *J. Geophys. Res. 76.* In press.

Hoffman, R. A. 1971b. In Folkestad, Kr. (ed.). *Magnetosphere-Ionosphere Interactions,* Universitetsforlaget, Oslo.

Hoffman, R. A. & Evans, D. S. 1968. *J. Geophys. Res. 73,* 6201.

Hones, E. W. 1968. In Carovillano, R. L., McClay, J. F. & Radoski, H. R. (eds.). *Physics of the Magnetosphere.* Reidel, Dordrecht, Holland.

Hones, E. W., Akasofu, S.-I., Perreault, P., Bame, S. J. & Singer, S. 1970. *J. Geophys. Res. 75,* 7060.

Hones, E. W., Askbridge, J. R., Bame, S. J. & Singer, S. 1971. *J. Geophys. Res. 76,* 63.

Jacchia, L. G. 1964. Smithsonian Astrophys. Obs. Spec. Rep. 150.

Johnson, R. G., Sharp, R. D. & Shea, M. F. 1966. *Trans. Am. Geophys. Union 47,* 64.

Lassen, K. 1969. In McCormac, B. M. (ed.). *Auroar and Airglow.* Reinhold, New York.

Montbriand, L. E. 1969. Morphology of auroral hydrogen emission during auroral substorms. Thesis, University of Saskatchewan.

O'Brien, B. 1967. In Newman, W. S. & King, T. W. (eds.). *Solar-Terrestrial Physics,* Academic Press, London.

Sandford, B. P. 1964. *J. Atmos. Terr. Phys. 26,* 749.

Sandford, B. P. 1968. *J. Atmos. Terr. Phys. 30,* 1921.

Schield, M. A. & Frank, L. A. 1970. *J. Geophys. Res. 75,* 5401.

Sharp, R. D. & Johnson, R. G. 1969. In McCormac, B. M. (ed.). *Aurora and Airglow.* Reinhold, New York.

Sharp, R. D., Carr, D. L. & Johnson, R. G. 1969. *J. Geophys. Res. 74,* 4618.

Vasyliunas, V. M. 1968. *J. Geophys. Res. 73,* 2839.

Vasyliunas, V. M. 1970a. Review paper presented at STP Symposium, Lenningrad, U.S.S.R.

Vasyliunas, V. M. 1970b. In Skovli, G. (ed.). *The Polar Ionosphere and Magnotospheric Processes.* Gorden and Breach, New York.

Winningham, J. D. 1970. Ph. D. thesis, Texas Agricultural and Mining University.

Electric Fields in the Ionosphere and Magnetosphere

N. C. MAYNARD

Laboratory for Space Physics, NASA-Goddard Space Flight Center,
Greenbelt, Maryland 20771

Abstract: Current techniques for measuring ionospheric and magnetospheric electric fields and existing measurements are reviewed. Considerable progress in understanding electric fields has been made in the auroral regions where fields originating basically from convection patterns in the magnetosphere and modified by ionospheric interaction have been detected by both the barium ion cloud and double floating probe techniques and compared against predictions. The anti-correlation of electric fields and auroral arcs, the establishment of the auroral electrojet currents as Hall currents, the irregular nature of the electric fields, and the reversal of the electric fields between the eastward and westward electrojet regions have been some of the important observations. The existence of large fields parallel to $\vec{B}$ is doubtful, although small magnitude fields are possible. Recent barium ion cloud observations in the polar cap have indicated that the long assumed electrojet return current across the polar cap does not exist. Convection across the polar cap is anti-sunward. Measurements of DC electric fields at lower latitudes are much more sparse. They have shown some agreement and some disagreement with Sq dynamo electric field predictions. Variational effects in the electric fields have been found wherever strong fields exist. Both electrostatic and electromagnetic phenomena have been detected looking at the AC components.

1. INTRODUCTION

The existence of large-scale electric fields has long been needed for the interpretation of many geophysical phenomena. Theories involving a neutral wind-driven dynamo to drive the Sq current system were used to explain the diurnal magnetic variation data back at the beginning of the century (see Chapman & Bartels 1940). Large-scale convection fields in the magnetosphere evolved from the work of Axford & Hines (1961), to tie together magnetospheric and auroral phenomena. Only recently have actual measurements progressed to the point where comparison with theory has become possible. The purpose of this paper is to define the methods now available for measuring electric fields, to consider the results obtained from recent measurements, and to relate these measurements to the predicted sources of electric fields where possible. DC electric fields will be the primary subject with short comments on variational and AC electric fields. In order to understand the relationships to theory, a brief outline of the sources of electric fields follows.

A. *Magnetospheric electric fields*

Energy and momentum from the solar wind is transferred to the magnetosphere by interaction at the boundary of the magnetosphere. Convective motions are set up by the generated large-scale electric fields. Since the early paper of Axford & Hines (1961), many authors have looked at convection in both open and closed magnetospheric models. A review by Axford (1969) on convective processes and one by Obayashi & Nishida (1968) on the large-scale electric fields are helpful references. The source of the convective electric field depends on the model of the magnetosphere used. In a closed or shielded magnetospheric model the solar wind, as it flows past, exerts frictional forces on the magnetospheric plasma. These result in polarization fields from charge separation (see Piddington 1960, Axford 1969). In an open configuration of the magnetosphere (Dungey 1961) the electric field from the bulk motion of the solar wind can penetrate into the magnetosphere.

Regardless of the source of the electric field driving the convection, these fields will propagate down the field lines to the ionosphere. If one assumes the magnetic field lines as equipotentials, then the DC electric field is imposed on the ionosphere in accordance with the configuration of the magnetic field. Farley (1959) and Mozer (1970) have made studies on the mapping of the fields observed in the ionosphere outside the magnetic field lines. Reid (1965) has studied how magnetospheric fields of various scale lengths map down the field lines into the ionosphere. If a finite conductivity exists along the field line and potential drops occur, then one must return again to Maxwell's equations for a solution. Thus, the ionosphere can influence magnetospherically generated electric fields. It is noted that Hall currents have no loading effect on the magnetospheric field (Farley 1959, 1960, Reid 1965).

Convection patterns have been derived by looking at ground magnetic variations and building a model that would create these disturbances. Nishida (1966) has separated effects of the auroral electrojet (DP1) from the more worldwide fluctuations (DP2) and has derived current systems and electric fields producing each. As will be seen in section 3, this technique may have pitfalls in that the measured electric fields do not in general directly relate to the magnetic field variations.

Inside the plasmapause co-rotation of the plasma is generally assumed. How far out co-rotation exists is not clear. Depending on the frame of reference of the observer, there exists a small electric field from this motion. One also must remember that fields generated in the ionosphere will propagate up the field lines following the same laws.

B. *Ionospheric electric fields*

In the auroral and polar regions of the ionosphere the situation is dominated by the magnetospherically generated electric fields described previously. One must also consider localized electrostatic fields.

At lower latitudes the electric field may be dominated by the dynamo field driving the Sq current system. Maeda (1955) used geomagnetic variations and assumed conductivities to derive the electric field. He then derived the dynamo field from the wind patterns and subtracted this from the above to get the resultant electrostatic field. Fig. 1 (Fig. 5 of Obayashi & Maeda 1965) shows Maeda's resulting horizontal electrostatic field and the calculated vertical electrostatic field (note that these fields are all perpendicular to $\vec{B}$). One sees the basic current cells from the Sq pattern in the Figure with the amplitudes from 1 to 5 mv/m. Matsushita (1969) has made a more recent calculation obtaining similar but slightly different results.

These fields generated in the E-region of the ionosphere will propagate up to higher altitudes. The amount of attenuation in the propagation has been studied by Farley (1960, 1961) and Spreiter & Briggs (1961) showing that large-scale DC fields propagate up the field lines nearly unattenuated while small scale variations will be attenuated according to wavelength and to the geophysical conditions present.

Near the equator where the magnetic field lines become horizontal, the vertical fields are more prominent. Polarization fields driving the electrojet will be in evidence.

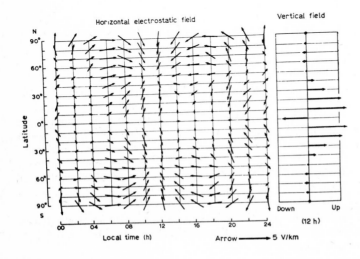

Fig. 1. Global distribution of the electrostatic field from Sq dynamo considerations from Fig. 5 of Obayashi & Maeda (1965) following the work of Maeda (1955).

2. MEASUREMENT TECHNIQUES

A. *Early experimental attempts*

The measurement of electric fields has historically lagged behind theory due to the difficulty of measuring the small geoelectric fields. An object immersed in a plasma will assume a potential such that the net current flow between the object and plasma is zero. The resultant sheath around the object often contains fields several orders of magnitude larger than the ambient fields in the medium. The early attempts at measuring electric fields suffered from trying to look at millivolt per meter fields through volt per centimeter sheath fields.

Imyanitov et al. (1964), Gdalevich (1964), and Gdalevich et al. (1965) attempted in the late 1950s and early 1960s to use the field mill technique (successfully used in atmospheric electricity measurements) of measuring the current to a surface alternately screened from the external field by a shutter. Results were obviously sheath fields of the order of volts/cm. Imyanitov et al. estimated the external field to be of the order of 100 mv/m. The use of the field mills has been abandoned until recently, when Knott has attempted to use them to detect the vehicle wake and then estimate the electric field from the configuration of the wake (Knott 1970, Fahleson et al. 1971).

A new approach was taken by Kavadas & Johnson (1964). The potential difference between two closely spaced electrodes was measured. Although the interpretation of the data was hindered by the asymmetry of the electrodes and small separation, fields of the right magnitude were detected in the auroral region from Fort Churchill. A variation of the technique was tried by Unger & Rawer (1967) but suffered from the aforementioned problems.

Subsequent experiments were proposed by Dolezalek (1964) using spherical probes on long booms and by Aggson & Heppner (1964) using long cylindrical antennas. The resulting probe technique, described in 2-B, is one of the two direct methods most commonly used for electric field measurements.

The second direct method involves following photographically the motion of clouds of barium ions (Ba$^+$) injected into the medium (Föppl et al. (1965)). This method (section 2C) is restricted to twilight conditions as the Ba$^+$ cloud must be sunlit, and the cloud is dim relative to the sky for solar depression angles of less than 6°.

Several indirect means of deriving electric fields will be discussed in section 2D.

B. *Double floating probe method*

The double floating probe technique, as defined by Aggson & Heppner (1964) and by Dolezalek (1964) and reviewed by Fahleson (1967), depends on deploying symmetrical sensors, whether cylindrical or spherical, some distance away from the vehicle. As shown by Langmuir & Mott-Smith (1926), a probe in a plasma will seek a potential that will establish a current balance between the probe and the plasma. If no current is drawn from the probe, then the potential will depend on the properties of the medium, including potential differences existing in the medium. The technique as shown schematically in Fig. 2 is to measure the floating potential of each sensor with respect to the vehicle potential and differentially substract the resultants, eliminating the vehicle potential. If no electric field exists, the probes will float at the same potential. The result may be expressed by

$$(V_A - V_S) - (V_B - V_S) = V_A - V_B =$$
$$(\vec{E} + \vec{v} \times \vec{B}) \cdot \vec{d}, \quad (1)$$

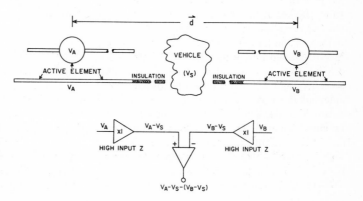

Fig. 2. Schematic representation of the double probe technique for measuring electric fields. The vector $\vec{d}$ represents the distance between the element midpoints whether the sensors are spherical or cylindrical.

where $\vec{E}$ is the electric field in the rest frame, $\vec{v}$ is the velocity of the probe system, $\vec{B}$ is the earth's magnetic field, $\vec{d}$ is the vector separation of the sensor midpoints, and V_A, V_B, V_S are the potentials of the sensors (A and B) and vehicle or spacecraft (S).

The method is subject to many potential hazards; hence care must be taken in using the technique. Fahleson (1967) and Aggson & Heppner (1964) have discussed in detail the various pitfalls, which will only be summarized here.

The most obvious problem (see equation 1) is that of Lorentz invariance. Since E is often small by comparison to $\vec{v} \times \vec{B}$ (especially true for low-latitude ionospheric measurements), the accuracy to which $\vec{v} \times \vec{B}$ is known both in magnitude and direction is a limitation on the accuracy of the measurement of $\vec{E}$. For instance a polar orbiting satellite moving at 8 km/sec perpendicular to the earth's magnetic field of 0.5 gauss will generate a 400 mv/m $\vec{v} \times \vec{B}$ field. In practice this large field limits the detection of small ambient fields in the direction of maximum $\vec{v} \times \vec{B}$.

Many potential pitfalls can be eliminated by symmetry, both in shape and material. The current balance depends on photo emission as well as the collection of ions and electrons and the current drawn by the voltmeter. Thus, any shadowing of the sensors that is not symmetrical will cause a change in the floating potential. Symmetry will allow contact potential errors to be cancelled through the differential subtraction. Variations in work functions over the material can cause asymmetric photoemission effects, thus a stable and relatively uniform work function is desired.

The input impedance to the electronics must be high so that the current drawn by the electronics will not modify the floating potential by loading the plasma. The plasma impedance varies from 10 to 100 kΩ in the lower ionosphere to greater than 10 megohms in the magnetosphere.

Two of the hardest effects to characterize are sheath overlap and wake effects. Both of these can be minimized by moving the sensors well away from the vehicle. In the case of cylindrical antennas this is done by insulating the inner portion of the rod, while for spheres the supporting boom is insulated. These problems are most critical in the distant magnetosphere at middle and high latitudes where the low plasma density results in Debye lengths of meters.

Most of the effects mentioned produce errors

that are of the order of kT, where k is the Boltzman constant and T is the plasma temperature, thus the error analysis for a magnetospheric experiment is much more critical than in the ionosphere.

Increasing the length of the baseline not only helps in minimizing errors, but also increases the sensitivity of the experiment. It can, however, reduce the frequency response to short wavelength AC signals. Equation 1 is true for AC signals only as long as the wavelength is long compared to $\vec{d}$. For electrostatic waves having wavelengths of the order or greater than the Debye length the potential difference must be divided by the wavelength ($\lambda \ll |\vec{d}|$). Spheres, as opposed to cylindrical antennas, have a simpler geometry and effectively make the measurement at a point. The use of cylindrical antennas effectively integrates effects over the length of the probe. The cylindrical antennas are easier to extend to large distances, resulting in a larger $\vec{d}$ and more signal. The greater distance also lessens the wake and shadowing problems.

The first flights using this technique were made by Aggson et al. (1967) in 1966, using cylindrical antennas, and by Mozer & Bruston (1967) in 1966 using spheres. The flight by Aggson et al. was made at middle latitudes at a time when the Sq field was very weak. The trajectory was such that $\vec{v} \times \vec{B}$ was large. The vector sum of all three components matched $\vec{v} \times \vec{B}$ to within a millivolt per meter demonstrating the technique (see Aggson 1969). Also, an analysis of whistler results from this flight agrees with the Appleton-Hartree theory (Maynard et al. 1970). The technique is applicable to both ionospheric and magnetospheric measurements with the above limitations. An extension of this technique has been used at balloon altitudes by Mozer & Serlin (1969) and Mozer & Manka (1971) allowing continuous measurements over long time periods (see section 3 B).

C. Barium release experiments

While the probe technique can provide good spatial coverage (in altitude from rockets and over all latitudes and longitudes from satellites), studies of variations in time (excluding the balloon flights) are limited. The barium release experiments provide a means for looking at temporal variation in regions of low electric field strength. (In conditions with high electric fields the clouds move more rapidly combining spatial

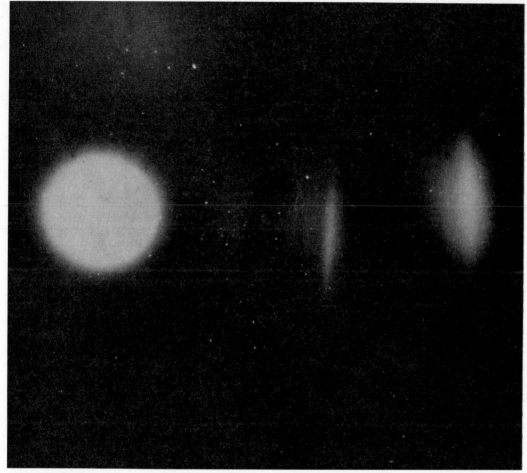

Fig. 3. A photograph of a barium release showing a neutral cloud on the left and two cigar-shaped ion clouds on the right. Note the field-aligned striations of the ion clouds.

with temporal variations.) Beginning from the study of comet tails, the idea of using an artificial ion cloud as a probe for the study of ionospheric and magnetospheric electric fields was developed by the group at Max-Planck Institute (see Föppl et al. 1965). The technique has provided much useful DC electric field data in the ionosphere and more recently in the magnetosphere.

Barium makes an ideal ion source in that the resonance lines are in the visible spectrum and the photoionization efficiencies are high. The barium is evaporated into the medium in the thermite reaction involving Ba and CUO with an excess of barium (Föppl et al. 1967), producing neutral and ion clouds. A small percentage of strontium is usually present. In the initial phase the vapor expands rapidly until it reaches equilibrium with the ambient medium. Diffusion governs further expansion of the neutral cloud. A cigar-shaped ion cloud is formed, aligned with the earth's magnetic field, and moves under the influence of the electric field and, if the cloud is at low altitudes, neutral winds, while the neutral cloud moves with the winds. Fig. 3 shows a typical neutral cloud with two well-developed ion clouds from two other releases. The ionization process involves resonance absorption resulting in spontaneous transitions to a metastable state and then photoionization from the metastable state (Haerendel & Lüst 1969).

The electric field seen by the cloud is derived from the motion of the cloud. The clouds are tracked optically from two or more sites and their position is triangulated with time using the star

159

patterns on the film. The component of the field perpendicular to the magnetic field is found from the transverse velocity of the cloud (Haerendel et al. 1967).

$$E_\perp = \left(\frac{1 + \lambda^*}{2}\right) \frac{B}{C} \left[\left(\frac{\vec{B}}{B} \times \vec{u}_\perp\right) + \right.$$
$$\left. \frac{1}{R} (\vec{u}_\perp - \vec{u}_{n\perp}) + \frac{\lambda^* - 1}{\lambda^* + 1} \left(\vec{u}_n \times \frac{\vec{B}}{B}\right)\right], \quad (2)$$

where λ^* is the ratio of the integrated Pedersen conductivities along the field lines intersecting the cloud to those outside, $u_{n\perp}$ is the transverse neutral wind velocity, $u_\perp$ is the transverse ion cloud velocity, and R is the ratio of the gyro frequency to the ion neutral collision frequency.

The effects of the second term may be kept small by keeping the release at altitudes where the collision frequency is small compared with the gyro-frequency. This condition holds above 190 to 200 km, thus in general limiting the technique to higher altitudes. The effects of the third term are controlled by the size of the release and the local conductivity. Various sizes of releases from a fraction of a kilogram up through 50 kg have been tried. The larger releases have caused a significant perturbation of the medium requiring a consideration of the third term (i.e. a 24-kg release from Fort Churchill resulted in a λ^* of 1.5) (Haerendel et al. 1969). A 2- or 3-kg release produces good observable clouds without a significant effect on the medium (see Wescott et al. 1969, Haerendel & Lüst 1969). With $R \gg 1$ and $\lambda^* \approx 1$, equation 2 reduces to

$$\vec{E}_\perp = \frac{1}{C} (\vec{B} \times \vec{u}_\perp). \quad (3)$$

The barium cloud technique was first used at mid-latitudes in small fields and later applied in the equatorial, auroral, and polar cap regions. At middle and low latitudes, the twilight requirement provides a severe restriction on local time coverage; however, in the auroral and polar cap regions the time of the year can be varied so as to include most of the local magnetic time conditions. The technique has also been applied to the magnetosphere with a release from the HEOS satellite. Here the cloud acceleration to the ambient plasma velocity must also be taken into consideration (Haerendel & Lüst, 1970).

D. *Indirect measurement techniques*

Indirect measurements in general fall into two categories. The first involves measuring drift velocities and the second involves drawing conclusions from particle pitch-angle and energy spectra.

Drift motions have been detected in two ways. The first of these was by Carpenter & Stone (1967) who interpreted changes in whistler dispersion as being caused by the motion of field-aligned ducts. They detected a westward field of 0.3 mv/m lasting for over an hour at $L = 4.5$ 28 minutes before the onset of a bay at $L = 7$. Note that since this technique is sensitive only to inward velocities, only estimates of east-west fields can be obtained. A variation on this technique proposed by Troitskaya et al. (1968) looks at the drift velocities of micropulsations.

The second technique utilizing drift motions has been the observation of nighttime equatorial electrojet irregularity motions using VHF backscatter radar (Balsley 1969). The technique is good for velocities between 50 and 360 m/sec., and the velocity is related to the east-west electric field by

$$\vec{E}y \simeq -0.88 \times 10^{-6} \vec{u}_{ey} \text{ volts/m.} \quad (4)$$

Significant findings include the reversal of the field at 0630 hours and 2030 hours local time and an increase in velocity just prior to the reversal.

Alfvén & Fälthammar (1963) have proposed that a different pitch-angle distribution will exist for electrons and protons if a parallel electric field exists along the field line. Thus, for zero electric field the ratio of the parallel to perpendicular energies of the electrons must be equivalent to that of the ions. They show that

$$E_{||} = -K \frac{dB}{ds}, \quad (5)$$

where

$$K = \frac{Wi_{||} We_\perp - We_{||} Wi_\perp}{|e| B (Wi_{||} + We_{||})}, \quad (6)$$

s is the path along $\vec{B}$ and W is the energy of the various particles denoted by the subscripts i, e, $_\perp$, and $_{||}$ referring to electrons, protons, perpendicular, and parallel. Thus, the energy ratios can differ only in a homogeneous magnetic field (where $\frac{dB}{ds} = O$).

Van Allen (1970) has drawn conclusions on the electric field in the tail from observations of solar electrons of energies greater than 50 kev by two different satellites. By establishing that the solar electron flux in the tail as observed by Explorer 35 in orbit about the moon was identical to that outside the magnetosphere, he concludes that the $|\int \vec{E} \cdot \vec{ds}|$ from a point outside the magnetosphere into the tail must be less than 1.5 kv. He points out that this does not limit the existence of higher fields in a point by point sense, but argues toward the existence of an open tail.

3. ELECTRIC FIELD MEASUREMENTS AND INTERPRETATION

A. *Low and middle latitudes*

Due to the small magnitude of the fields at low and middle latitudes, few measurements have been made. Since one is in general looking for one or two millivolts per meter, the desired field is near the accuracy of probe measurements, especially when $\vec{v} \times \vec{B}$ may be as large as 50 to 100 mv/m. As previously noted in 2B, Aggson et al. (1967) chose a trajectory with a large $\vec{v} \times \vec{B}$ to check the technique. The early measurements by the Max-Planck group with barium clouds were in the Sahara desert (Haerendel et al. 1967, Haerendel & Lüst 1968). Rieger (1970) has taken these measurements and added to them more recent equatorial and mid-latitude release data.

The releases reported by Rieger (1970) cover magnetic latitudes 53°, 36°, 26°, 0°, and − 43°. The fields obtained varied from 0.3 to 4.0 mv/m. All of the measurements were by necessity in the twilight regions on the edge of the dynamo current cells as seen in Chapman & Bartels (1940). Rieger compared his directions with those from theoretical calculations of Maeda (1955) and Matsushita (1969) and found better agreement with Maeda's calculations. Note that the assumption was made from Spreiter & Briggs's (1961) calculations that the dynamo field at 110 km would be communicated up the field line without appreciable attenuation to the altitudes of the Ba$^+$ clouds (150 to 300 km).

Measurements with Ba$^+$ at the equator present a different problem in that F-region field lines terminate outside the electrojet. The perpendicular components there are east-west and vertical. Rieger's measurements showed an eastward field in the evening ($\sim$ 1800 hours local) and a westward field ($\sim$ 0530 hours local) in the morning with values of 0.45 to 2.6 mv/m. Balsley (1969) has shown the reversal in the east-west field from drift motion measurements to be a few hours after sunset (section 2D) and in directional agreement with Rieger's results. It is noted that the vertical fields (upward, evening; downward, morning), corresponding to a 'north-south' field if propagated down the field line, were larger than the horizontal.

Rieger's conclusion is that strong evidence exists for dynamo-generated fields at evening twilight at mid-latitudes. At the equator he concludes the current is from polarization fields.

Moving up to latitudes corresponding to the plasmapause, Gurnett (1970) and Cauffman & Gurnett (1971), using INJUN–5 double probe data, impedance data, and electron density data, have been able to define the plasmapause unambiguously on eight occasions on the night side. On five of these, they have noted a 10 to 20 mv/m change in the electric field and conclude that it indicates a change in the plasma convection at the plasmapause. It is noted that these fields are at the limit of resolution of the experiment and are seen only part of the time on the nightside; hence, the general case is still ambiguous. It is evident that the plasmapause is not in general the boundary for strong convection as proposed by Brice (1967) but this region exists nearer the auroral shells (Heppner 1969).

B. *Auroral regions*

Many measurements have been made in the auroral regions with both the double probe and barium ion cloud techniques. The results show good agreement on some points and disagreement on others. The subject of electric fields parallel to $\vec{B}$ has resulted in much controversy and will be looked at in section 3-C. The measurement of perpendicular electric fields has resulted in much insight into convective patterns.

No attempt will be made to draw an overall convection pattern as analyzed data is still somewhat sparse. General comments will be injected where appropriate. Some general conclusions can be made about auroral fields from the available data; these are summarized in Table I with reference to concurring and dissenting views. Basically both double probe and ion cloud measurements generally agree that the magnitude of the field varies from near or less than 10 mv/m to over 130 mv/m, the typical values being in the 30- to 50-mv/m range, and that the magnitude and direction is very variable over short distances and time. Where directional information has been obtained, the field has been predominently southward (northern hemisphere) during negative bays and northward during positive bays. The relative magnitude of the east-west component has in general been small for the barium measurements while Mozer & Fahleson (1970) have found stronger east-west components using the probe tech-

Table I. Conclusions from auroral zone measurements

Conclusion	Concurring views	Dissenting views
1. General electric field magnitude of from 10 mv/m up to over 130 mv/m	All	
2. The field magnitude is very variable over short distances and time	All	
3. Both the eastward and westward electrojets are Hall currents	Wescott et al. 1969 Wescott et al. 1970 Haerendel & Lüst 1970 Potter 1970	
4. The field in an auroral form is reduced in magnitude	Aggson 1969 Potter & Cahill 1969 Wescott et al. 1969 Wescott et al. 1970	Mozer & Fahleson 1970
5. E cannot be simply related to ΔB	Haerendel et al. 1969 Haerendel & Lüst 1970 Wescott et al. 1969 Wescott et al. 1970	
6. No systematic variations of amplitude with altitude	Potter 1970	Mozer & Fahleson 1970
7. Parallel fields are generally orders of magnitude less than perpendicular fields	Föppl et al. 1967 Mende 1967 Potter 1970 Wescott et al. 1970	Mozer & Bruston 1967 Mozer & Fahleson 1970 Cauffman & Gurnett 1971 (?)
8. Field reversal in direction on the 9 pole side of the auroral electrojets	Haerendel et al. 1969 Wescott et al. 1969 (pos. to neg.bay) Cauffman & Gurnett 1971	
9. Conjugacy of variational effects	Gurnett 1970 Maynard & Heppner 1970	

nique. The nature of the bay activity from the magnetograms and the measured electric field prescribes that the currents causing the magnetic perturbations are Hall currents. A composite of Ba⁺ cloud results plotted in magnetic latitude and magnetic local time is shown in Fig. 4 (polar cap

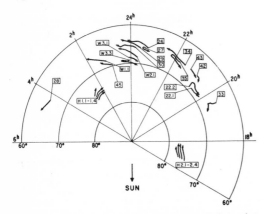

Fig. 4. A magnetic latitude-magnetic local time plot of the paths of many Ba⁺ clouds (after Haerendel & Lüst 1970). The numbers preceded by W refer to Wescott et al. (1969), those by H refer to Heppner et al. (1971a) and the others the work of the Max-Planck group (see above reference).

results from Heppner et al. (1971a) have been added to Fig. 2 of Haerendel & Lüst (1970)). The general features of eastward and westward flow in, respectively, the morning and evening auroral belt, and the antisolar flow across the polar cap are evident. More recent (unpublished) data from a large number of flights provide additional confirmation of the general features.

The large variability in magnitude, both spatial and temporal, limits direct comparisons with ground magnetogram data primarily to vector directions. Fig. 5, taken from the Ba⁺ work of Wescott et al. (1969) is illustrative of the variability in magnitude. Obviously the point to point conductivity must be known to calculate electric fields. Thus, attempts to derive electric field configurations from ground data (e.g. Bullen 1968) can at best produce qualitative results about gross convection patterns.

An important question is what happens to the field inside an auroral form. Aggson (1969) deduced from double probe experiments that the field in an arc was greatly reduced. From that he eliminated the Swift (1963) dynamo model of the electrojet and two models of Bostrom (1967) involving field-aligned currents, both requiring

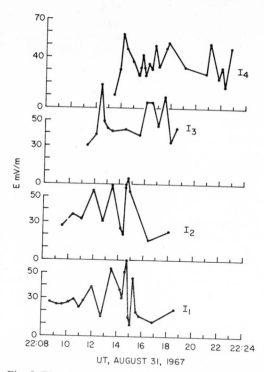

Fig. 5. The electric field magnitude perpendicular to $\vec{B}$ derived from four ion cloud motions (Fig. 3 from Wescott et al. 1969).

equal or greater fields within the arc. The resultant picture, similar to that of Piddington (1964), was one of the ionosphere Pederson conductivity loading the magnetospheric dynamo. Thus, the magnetosphere was considered as a current source. The observational evidence was added to by Wescott et al. (1969, 1970) and Potter & Cahill (1969). Recently, however, Mozer & Fahleson (1970) have published data which contradict this, concluding that the field remains constant or increases crossing the boundary of an arc. Thus, at least in specific cases, the results are still controversial.

An interesting region has been the transition from positive to negative bays. Several Ba+ releases have seen field reversals in this region. In the flight of Wescott et al. (1969) the initial cloud moved westward in response to the positive bay. However, the other clouds, released more to the north, reversed direction several times coincident with changes in magnetic activity (see W 3.3 in Fig.4). These were apparently in the region between positive and negative bay activity (see model by Heppner (1967) showing overlapping positive and negative bay regions). Similar reversals occur

on the pole side of the auroral region. Haerendel et al. (1969) observed a reversal on a flight from Fort Churchill in which the aurora was located to the south (launched at 0200 hours local time). Cauffman & Gurnett (1971) using a double probe on INJUN–5, have seen reversals of the field on the polar cap side of the auroral zone. Their basic pattern is for sunward convection on the low-latitude side and anti-sunward convection on the high-latitude side. Double probe data from OGO–6 shows this reversal to be a typical characteristic, but with the magnitude and the space over which it occurs quite variable (see also section 3 D).

Perturbations of the field in one hemisphere should also occur in the other hemisphere at the conjugate point. Auroral conjugacy has been established by Belon et al. (1969) with simultaneous airplane flights in conjugate locations using all-sky cameras and image orthicon TV systems. During some orbits, a polar orbiting satellite will pass through regions which are approximately conjugate. Gurnett (1970) has found good correlations between hemispheres on a large-scale oscillatory structure. It must be noted that for this interpretation to be made the structure must be relatively stable over the time scale of the satellite traversal from one pole to the other. Looking at small scale irregularities, Maynard & Heppner (1970) found conjugate agreement in the point of onset of the irregularities. More will be said on variational fields in section 3 E.

The balloon measurements of Mozer & Serlin (1969) and Mozer & Manka (1971) have utilized the double probe technique at balloon altitudes to attempt to measure ionospheric and magnetospheric electric fields. They claim that the results represent several hundred kilometer averages of the horizontal ionospheric electric field. Results, especially those of Mozer & Manka (1971), have tended to reproduce the gross features as seen by in situ measurements including lower fields near plasmapause latitudes, the reversal near polar cap regions, and the basic gross time dependence of the north-south component. However, several problems exist. The magnitude of their east-west component is quite often a large fraction of, or greater than, the north-south component, which is generally not the case in the in situ measurements. Most of the aforementioned Ba+ experiments have measured much larger north-south electric fields than east-west fields. One must remember that atmospheric fields are large and variable and mainly vertical. A small atmospheric variation could be equivalent to the measured result. Measurements over a wide latitude range on a given day are necessarily made under greatly differing atmospheric conditions.

C. *The question of parallel fields*

The existence of electric fields parallel to $\vec{B}$ in the auroral zone has long been a source of controversy. As seen from Table I, it is this point that has evoked the most disagreement. Parallel fields have been sought by theorists as a convenient means of auroral particle acceleration (see Alfvén & Fälthammer 1963, Persson 1966, 1967).

Mozer & Bruston (1967) and later Mozer & Fahleson (1970) have taken probe measurements from a flight that had a large precession cone and have deduced that a parallel field of 20 mv/m existed over the first part of the flight. The method requires the assumption of a constant field along $\vec{B}$ for a period longer than a precession period. The highly variable nature of the fields as observed by other experiments makes this assumption questionable. It was noted by Mozer & Fahleson (1970) that a parallel electric field strength of 20 mv/m would require that the conductivity along $\vec{B}$ be reduced by four orders of magnitude, suggesting wave particle interactions as the mechanism (Coroniti 1968). Mozer & Fahleson show a perpendicular field increasing with altitude during the period where they deduce the parallel field. This is necessary to maintain a curl-free electric field in the steady state condition. By comparison, Potter (1970) sees no systematic variation with altitude of the perpendicular field and deduces that no parallel fields of significant magnitude existed. Also, multiple releases of Ba$^+$ clouds over the 200–300 km altitude range have not indicated any systematic changes in E as a function of altitude.

Mende (1968) looked at the density distribution of Ba$^+$ clouds. Considering gravity and polarization of the cloud he concluded, from the absence of any field-aligned cloud distortion, that the field along B in the ionosphere must be less than 60 μv/m (the field within the cloud being up to 10 times less, or 6 μv/m). However, Mende neglected ambipolar diffusion. Scholer & Haerendel (1971) have recently repeated the calculations taking into account ambipolar diffusion and have reached a similar conclusion to Mende. Föppl et al. (1968) and Wescott et al. (1969) both reported that no unusual vertical distortion of the clouds have been observed and thus conclude that parallel electric fields are several orders of magnitude less than the perpendicular fields. Mozer, in a discussion led by Fälthammer (1969), argued that the possibility of anomalous resistivity in a turbulent plasma could affect the results.

If an auroral form acts as a load on the convection field, as discussed earlier, then a parallel field may exist at higher altitudes or the convection pattern in the magnetosphere may be very irregular. If a parallel electric field does exist then the magnitude may be very small as the drop can be spread out over the entire magnetic field line. At this conference Hultqvist reported on parallel fields derived from differences in pitch-angle measurements (see section 2 D), which would be small in magnitude if spread out along the field line. Cauffman & Gurnett (1971) have attempted to deduce a small parallel field from the differences in variations in the field between INJUN–5 apogee and perigee data (note that the measurements were of necessity made at different times).

It would appear that the evidence is weighed towards small or nonexistent steady state fields along $\vec{B}$. This does not preclude electrostatic waves and short duration parallel electric fields.

D. *Polar cap measurements*

The question of where the return current from the auroral electrojet flows, led people to postulate a constant ionospheric Hall current across the polar cap consistent with the magnetic variations observed on the ground. One would thus expect an electric field in the direction of $\vec{\Delta H}$ (the change in the horizontal component of $\vec{B}$) or, if the Pederson conductivity is large, an electric field vector displaced from $\vec{\Delta H}$ in the direction of the current.

Wescott et al. (1970) and Heppner et al. (1971 a, b) found using Ba$^+$ cloud data from three flights (12 releases) in the polar cap that the convection velocity was away from the sun resulting in an electric field pointing toward the evening sector. The direction of the electric field forbade the explanation of the total ground magnetic variations in terms of Hall or Pederson currents. The same type of discrepancy showed up in the Ba$^+$ release from HEOS in the magnetospheric tail at 12.5 Re, 42° mag. lat., by Haerendel & Lüst (1970).

The polar cap field, at locations 6 to 10° from the northernmost aurora, was found by Heppner et al. (1971 a, b) to be more uniform in space and

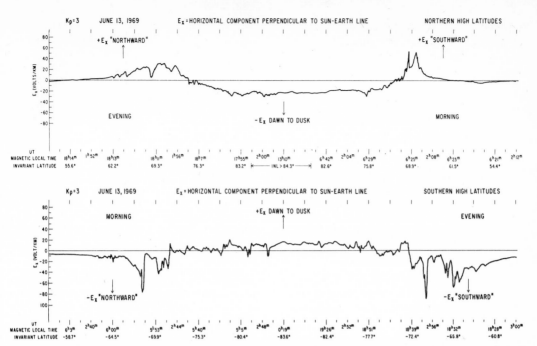

Fig. 6. The magnitude of the horizontal electric field perpendicular to the earth-sun line for an orbit of OGO-6 after subtraction of $\vec{v} \times \vec{B}$. The northern hemisphere pass went nearly over the magnetic pole. It is believed that the southern hemisphere curve should be shifted upward by 5 to 10 mv/m from a systematic trajectory error in the $\vec{v} \times \vec{B}$ subtraction.

time than the auroral zone electric fields. Small-scale changes were still very evident. The magnitudes were in the range of 20 to 40 mv/m. No significant differences were detected between the dawn and dusk magnitudes. The paths of the clouds from flights 1 and 2 have been plotted in Fig. 4 for directional comparisons to the auroral zone measurements. Note that the general pattern of electric field reversal previously mentioned in section 3 B is followed by the cloud paths. The electric field vectors were directed from 40° to 80° from the earth-sun line at 0200–0300 hours magnetic local time and 80° to 120° at 1700–1800 hours magnetic local time.

Satellite data from OGO–6 has shown a generally stable field across the polar cap of 10 to 40 mv/m with the same basic orientation as seen with barium releases. The exception to this is in the morning side cusp region which Axford & Hines (1961) called the 'zone of confusion'. An example of a polar pass is shown in Fig. 6 showing the field reversals on the poleward side of the auroral zone and the uniform polar cap field. It must be remembered that since only one component is measured, the total horizontal field is still

undetermined. However, OGO–6 was oriented such that it always measured the component perpendicular to the earth-sun line which from the Ba+ releases should be the major component.

Different results are obtained by Cauffman & Gurnett (1971) and Frank & Gurnett (1971), who state that the general polar cap field is small and that polar cap convection exists mainly near the auroral zone. In weighing these results one must remember the high threshold value for the INJUN –5 data and the possible ambiguities in $\vec{v} \times \vec{B}$ and direction (affecting the vector subtraction). It is noted that both moderately strong and near zero fields have been seen by both experiments, the question being that of the general case. The Ba+ data supports the OGO–6 results.

The fact that the polar cap field is in the wrong direction for an ionospheric return current interpretation led Heppner et al. (1971 a, b) to postulate that little or no current exists and that the magnetic deflection over the polar cap is from two regions of net field-aligned current completing the electrojet circuit. Fig. 7 shows their general ionospheric pattern of current flow and the regions of net field-aligned current flow, an inward cur-

165

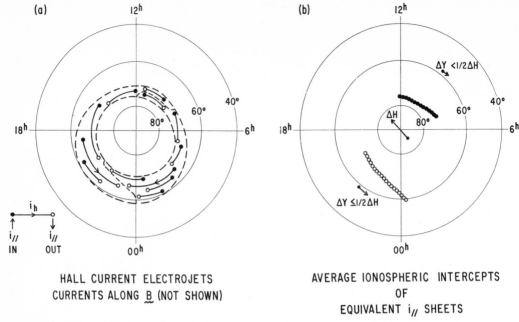

(a)
12ʰ

40°
60°
80°
18ʰ
6ʰ

iₕ
i∥   i∥
IN   OUT
00ʰ

HALL CURRENT ELECTROJETS
CURRENTS ALONG B̲ (NOT SHOWN)

(b)
12ʰ

ΔY <1/2ΔH
40°
ΔH   60°
80°
18ʰ
6ʰ

ΔY ≤1/2ΔH

00ʰ

AVERAGE IONOSPHERIC INTERCEPTS
OF
EQUIVALENT i∥ SHEETS

Fig. 7. Illustration of the distribution of Hall current electrojets terminated by field aligned currents and the region of net field-aligned currents used by Heppner et al. to explain the polar cap data (Fig. 14 of Heppner et al. 1971a).

rent in the morning sector and an outward current in the region between the positive and negative bay electrojets. The closure of the system is in the magnetospheric equatorial plane consistent with observed asymmetric ring current effects.

E. *Variational effects and AC electric fields*

One of the most striking features in all Ba^+ cloud measurements has been the striations of the ion clouds (see Fig. 3). They have been observed in large and small releases and at mid-latitudes (developing at a much slower rate) as well as in the auroral and polar cap regions. In the auroral regions it is often hard to visually distinguish them from rayed aurora. Many studies have been done attributing the origin of the striations to instabilities, the favorite being the $\vec{E} \times \vec{B}$ instability (see Simon 1963). More important to the physics of the ionosphere is the question of whether the Ba^+ ions cause the instability or whether they merely trace out a pattern of variations that commonly exists. Wescott et al. (1969) believe the latter to be the case for the smaller releases normally used for geophysical experiments.

Evidence of a highly variable spatial structure

of the fields is seen on a large scale in the satellite results of Cauffman & Gurnett (1971) (defined as high-latitude noise) and of OGO-6. On a finer scale, Maynard & Heppner (1970) found that small-scale irregularities exist wherever large convective electric fields exist. This variational structure, resulting in an AC signal of less than 50 Hz, reported by Maynard & Heppner (1970) from OGO-6 and OV1-10 data and by Heppner (1969) from OV1-10 data, was found to basically follow the variations of the auroral zone with Kp. These fields were also in general present over much of the polar cap. Recently Holtet et al. (1971) have found noise bursts from near DC up to 1.5 kHz in the 100- to 120-km region on a flight into an auroral glow.

Although AC fields will not be treated in detail here, mention should be made of a few general results. ELF and VLF electric fields have in many cases confirmed and added to results obtained previously looking at the magnetic component of electromagnetic waves (e.g. the work of Gurnett and co-workers). A significant new tool is the measurement of the Poynting vector by Mosier & Gurnett (1969) and Mosier (1971), which has helped define the source location of several VLF phenomena. Electric field experiments have also led to the detection of electrostatic waves and their effects (e.g. Scarf et al. 1968).

Acknowledgements: The OGO–6 DC electric field conclusions given here were part of a paper presented at the Spring AGU Meeting, Washington, DC., April 1971, by J. P. Heppner. T. L. Aggson and the author were also experimenters. A comprehensive paper on these results will be published elsewhere.

The author wishes to thank Dr. Heppner for helpful discussions during the assembly of this material.

REFERENCES

Aggson, T. L. 1969. In McCormac, B. M. & Omholt, A. (eds.). *Atmospheric Emissions*, p. 305, Reinhold, New York.
Aggson, T. L. & Heppner, J. P. 1964. NASA-GSFC proposal submitted July 1964.
Aggson, T. L., Heppner, J. P. & Maynard, N. C. 1967. *Trans. Am. Geophys. Union 48*, 156.
Alfvén, H. & Fälthammar, C.-G. 1963. *Cosmical Electrodynamics*, p. 162, Clarenden Press, Oxford.
Axford, W. I. 1969. In Williams, D. J. & Mead, G. D. (eds.). *Magnetospheric Physics*, p. 421, Am. Geophys. Union, Washington, D. C.
Axford, W. I. & Hines, C. O. 1961. *Can. J. Phys. 39*, 1433.
Balsley, B. B. 1969. *J. Atmos. Terr. Phys. 31*, 475.
Belon, A. E., Maggs, J. E. Davis, T. N., Mather, K. B., Glass, N. W. & Hughes, G. F. 1969. *J. Geophys. Res. 74*, 1.
Bostrum, R. 1967. In McCormac, B. M. (ed.). *Aurora and Airglow*, p. 293, Reinhold, New York.
Brice, N. M. 1967. *J. Geophys. Res. 72*, 5193.
Bullen, J. M. 1968. *J. Atm. Terr. Phys. 30*, 527.
Carpenter, D. L. & Stone, K. 1967. *Planet. Space Sci. 15*, 395.
Cauffman, D. P. & Gurnett, D. A. 1971. *J. Geophys. Res. 76*, 6014.
Chapman, S. & Bartels, J. 1940. *Geomagnetism, Vol. 1*, chapter VII, Clarendon Press, Oxford.
Coroniti, F. V. 1968. In Coroniti, S. C. & Hughes, J. (eds.). *Planetary Electrodynamics*, p. 309, Gorden & Breach, New York.
Dolezalek, H. 1964. *AFCRL-678* Air Force Cambridge, Labs., Bedford, Mass. (see also *Z. Geophys. 32*, 318).
Dungey, J. W. 1961. *Phys. Rev. Letters 6*, 47.
Fälthammar, C.-G. 1969. In Coroniti, S. C. & Hughes, J. (eds.). *Planetary Electrodynamics*, p. 437, Gorden & Breach, New York.
Fahleson, U. V. 1967. *Space Sci. Rev. 7*, 238.
Fahleson, U. V. 1968. In Coroniti, S. C. & Hughes, J. (eds.). *Planetary Electrodynamics*, p. 413, Gorden & Breach, New York.
Fahleson, U. V., Fälthammer, C.-G., Pedersen, A., Knott, K., Brommundt, G., Schumann, G., Haerendel, G. & Rieger, E. 1971. *Radio Science 6*, 233.
Farley, D. T., Jr. 1959. *J. Geophys. Res. 64*, 1225.
Farley, D. T., Jr. 1960. *J. Geophys. Res. 65*, 869.
Farley, D. T., Jr. 1961. *J. Geophys. Res. 66*, 3956.

Föppl, H., Haerendel, G., Loidl, J., Lüst, R., Melzner, F., Meyer, B., Neuss, H. & Rieger, E. 1965. *Planet. Space Sci. 13*, 95.
Föppl, H., Haerendel, G., Haser, L., Loidl, J., Lütjens, P., Lüst, R., Melzner, F., Meyer, B., Neuss, H. & Rieger, E. 1967. *Planet. Space Sci. 15*, 357.
Föppl, H., Haerendel, G., Haser, L., Lüst. R., Melzner, F., Meyer, B., Neuss, H., Rabben, H., Rieger, E., Stöcker, J. & Stoffregen, E. 1968. *J. Geophys. Res. 73*, 21.
Frank, L. A. & Gurnett, D. A. 1971. *J. Geophys. Res. 76*, 6829.
Gdalevich, G. L. 1964. *Space Research IV*, p. 452, North-Holland, Amsterdam.
Gdalevich, G. L., Imyanitov, I. M. & Shvarts, Y. M. 1965. *Kosmicheskie Issledovania 3*, 102.
Gurnett, D. A. 1970. In McCormac, B. M. (ed.). *Particles and Fields in the Magnetosphere*, p. 239, Reidel, Dordecht.
Haerendel, G. & Lüst, R. 1968. In McCormac, B. M. (ed.). *Earth's Particles and Fields*, p. 271, Reinhold, New York.
Haerendel, G. & Lüst, R. 1969. In Coroniti, S. C. & Hughes, J. (eds.). *Planetary Electrodynamics Vol. 2*, p. 381, Gorden & Breach, New York.
Haerendel, G. & Lüst, R. 1970. In McCormac, B. M. (ed.). *Particles and Fields in the Magnetosphere*, p. 213, Reidel, Dordrecht.
Haerendel, G., Lüst, R. & Rieger, E. 1967. *Planet. Space Sci. 15*, 1.
Haerendel, G., Lüst, R., Rieger, E., Völk, H. 1969. In McCormac, B. M. & Omholt, A. (eds.). *Atmospheric Emissions*, p. 293, Reinhold, New York.
Heppner, J. P. 1967. In McCormac, B. M. (ed.). *Aurora and Airglow*, p. 75, Reinhold, New York.
Heppner, J. P. 1969. In McCormac, B. M. & Omholt, A. (eds.). *Atmospheric Emissions*, p. 251, Reinhold, New York.
Heppner, J. P., Stolarik, J. D. & Wescott, E. M. 1971 a. *J. Geophys. Res. 76*, 6028.
Heppner, J. P., Stolarik, J. D. & Wescott, E. M. 1971 b. In McCormac, B. M. (ed.). *The Radiating Atmosphere*, p. 407. Reidel, Dordrecht.
Holtet, J., Egeland, A. & Maynard, N. C. 1971. In McCormac, B. M. (ed.). *The Radiating Atmosphere*, p. 345. Reidel, Dordrecht.
Imyanitov, I. M., Gdalevich, G. L. & Shvarts, Ya. M. 1964. *Artificial Earth Satellites 17*, 66.
Kavadas, A. & Johnson, D. 1964. *Space Research IV*, p. 365, North-Holland, Amsterdam.
Knott, K. 1970. *Space Research X*, p. 773, North-Holland, Amsterdam.
Langmuir, I. & Mott-Smith, H. M. 1926. *Phys. Rev. 28*, 727. (Reprinted in Suits, G. (ed.). *The collected Works of Irving Langmuir Vol. 4*, p. 99, Pergamon Press, 1961).
Maeda, H. 1955. *J. Geomag. Geoelect. 7*, 121.
Matsushita, S. 1969. *Radio Science 4*, 771.
Maynard, N. C. & Heppner, J. P. 1970. In McCormac, B. M. (ed.). *Particles and Fields in the Magnetosphere*, p. 247, Reidel, Dordrecht, 247.
Maynard, N. C., Aggson, T. L. & Heppner, J. P. 1970. *Radio Science 5*, 1049.
Mende, S. B. 1968. *J. Geophys. Res. 73*, 991.
Mosier, S. R. 1971. *J. Geophys. Res. 76*, 1713.
Mosier, S. R. & Gurnett, D. A. 1969. *J. Geophys. Res. 74*, 5675.

Mozer, F. S. 1970. *Planet. Space Sci. 18*, 259.

Mozer, F. S. & Bruston, P., 1967. *J. Geophys. Res. 72*, 1109.

Mozer, F. S. & Fahleson, U. V. 1970. *Planet. Space Sci. 18*, 1563.

Mozer, F. S. & Manka, R. H. 1971. *J. Geophys. Res. 76*, 1697.

Mozer, F. S. & Serlin, R. 1969. *J. Geophys. Res. 74*, 4739.

Nishida, A. 1966. *J. Geophys. Res. 71*, 5669.

Obayashi, T. & Maeda, K.-I. 1965. In Coroniti, S. C. (ed.). *Problems of Atmospheric and Space Electricity*, p. 532, Elsevier, New York.

Obayashi, T. & Nishida, A. 1968. *Space Sci. Rev. 8*, 3.

Persson, H. 1966. *Phys. Fluids 9*, 1090.

Persson, H. 1967. *Space Sci. Rev. 7*, 228.

Piddington, J. H. 1960. *J. Geophys. Res. 65*, 93.

Piddington, J. H. 1964. In Matsushita, S. & Campbell, W. (eds.). *Physics of Geomagnetic Phenomena, Vol. 2*, p. 1203, Academic Press, New York.

Potter, W. E. 1970. *J. Geophys. Res. 75*, 5415.

Potter, W. E. & Cahill, L. J., Jr. 1969. *J. Geophys. Res. 74*, 5159.

Reid, G. C. 1965. *Radio Science 69D*, 827.

Rieger, E. 1970. *Max-Planck Institute Report* MPI/ PAE-Extraterr. 49/70.

Scarf, F. L., Crook, G. M. & Fredericks, R. W. 1968. *J. Geophys. Res. 73, 1723*.

Scholer, M. & Haerendel, G. 1971. *Planet. Space Sci. 19*. In Press.

Simon, A. 1963. *Phys. Fluids 6*, 382.

Spreiter, J. R. & Briggs, B. R. 1961. *J. Geophys. Res. 66*, 1731.

Swift, D. W. 1963. *J. Geophys. Res. 68*, 2131.

Troitskaya, V. A., Shchepetnov. R. V. & Gul'yelmi, A. V. 1968. *Geomag. and Aeronomy 8*, 634.

Unger, L. & Rawer, K. 1967. *Space Research VIII*, p. 313, North-Holland, Amsterdam.

Van Allen, J. A. 1970. *J. Geophys. Res. 75*, 29.

Wescott, E. M., Stolarik, J. D. & Heppner, J. P. 1969. *J. Geophys. Res. 74*, 3469.

Wescott, E. M., Stolarik, J. D. & Heppner, J. P. 1970. In McCormac, B. M. (ed.). *Particles and Fields in the Magnetosphere*, p. 229, Reidel, Dordrecht.

The Plasmapause as Measured in Positive Ions

G. W. SHARP, C. R. CHAPPELL AND K. K. HARRIS

Lockheed Palo Alto Research Laboratories, 3251 Hanover Street, Palo Alto,
California 94304

Abstract: Extensions of the existing theory of magnetospheric convection are
used to describe the dynamics of the plasmasphere and the variation in the
plasmapause location. The equatorial local time plane is divided into three separate and physically distinct regions, the bulge region, the nightside region, and
the dayside region, corresponding to local times of 1500 hrs to 2200 hrs, 2200
hrs to 0600 hrs, and 0600 hrs to 1500 hrs, respectively. The implications of both
a constant convection electric field and a varying convection electric field are
given for each of the three regions. The characteristics predicted by the model
in the bulge region are: presence of the bulge at dusk, $1/R^4$ radial dependence of
plasma concentration, and large fluctuations in plasma density at the plasmapause and plasma detachment. In the nightside region the predicted characteristics are: rapid response to magnetic activity changes, formative region for
plasmasphere ripples, and the formative region for the dayside plasmapause
location. The model also predicts the dayside plasmasphere characteristics, such
as the slow response to magnetic activity changes, and filling of the plasmasphere from the ionosphere, including the formation of a 'double plasmapause'.

The predicted features of the plasmasphere are compared with measurements
made from the light ion mass spectrometer on OGO-5. Excellent qualitative
agreement exists between the measured results and the predicted characteristics.

1. INTRODUCTION

From the early whistler measurements of Carpenter (1963) and the direct measurements from
satellites of a host of experimentors (Gringauz
et al. 1960, Taylor et al. 1965, 1968, Brinton et al.
1968, Binsack 1967, Hagg (1967)), the picture of
the plasmasphere as a cold dense plasma envelop-
ing the earth began to emerge. Several of the
characteristics of this plasma envelope were observed. The existence of a well-defined outer
boundary, the plasmapause, was detected. The
asymmetric shape of the envelope with a bulge
occurring in the dusk sector of the equatorial
plane was noted. More recent measurements and
analysis, notably by Harris et al. (1970), Chappell
et al. (1970a, b) and others, have begun to reveal
more of the plasmasphere characteristics. A consistent picture of the plasmasphere and its dynamics is beginning to be developed.

The data for this study were obtained by the
Lockheed light ion mass spectrometer which was
flown on the OGO–V satellite. The data cover the
period of time from March 1968 through January
1969. The spectrometer measured concentrations
of ambient H^+, He^+, and $(O^+ + N^+)$ in a range
of $< .1$ to $> 10^4$ ions/cm³ from an initial perigee
height of 300 km through an apogee height of

about 23 earth radii. Because of a failure in instrument logic during the flight, the data after
May 1968 contain no H^+ concentrations greater
than about 200 ions/cm³. However, even this reduced range of concentration is sufficient to measure plasmapause structure.

During the period covered by the present data,
a complete local time coverage of the plasmasphere was obtained with the density profiles measured at geomagnetic latitudes of about 45° or less.
H^+ ions are the major component of the positive

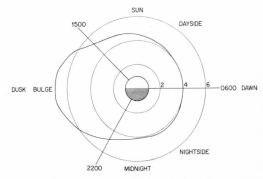

Fig. 1. The average position of the plasmapause
location measured from OGO-5. The local time vs.
L plot for the equatorial plane is divided into three
regions: nightside, dayside, and bulge.

ions of the plasmasphere and a composite grouping of their profiles is descriptive of the plasmasphere morphology. The average plasmapause position is shown in L-local time coordinates in Fig. 1. It is convenient to partition the local time into three distinct regions: 2200 LT to 0600 LT, 0600 LT to 1500 LT and 1500 LT to 2200 LT. These regions will be referred to as the nightside region, the dayside region, and the bulge region, respectively. The average plasmapause position shown here is derived from about 150 density profiles measured by OGO–V. The spread in the plasmapause positions as deduced from the density profiles is greatest around the bulge region and smallest in the nightside region.

2. THE CONVECTION MODEL

Most characteristics of the observed density profiles can be explained qualitatively using an extension of the existing convection model of the plasmasphere suggested by Axford & Hines (1961), Carpenter (1962), Nishida (1966), and Brice (1967). The original convection model explained the steep gradient in the plasma density profile, i.e. the plasmapause, as the boundary between flux tubes which corotate with the earth and flux tubes which have their motion dominated by a convection electric field. The former flux tubes always remain closed, thereby holding their plasma, while these latter flux tubes are convected to the magnetopause where they lose their plasma. The

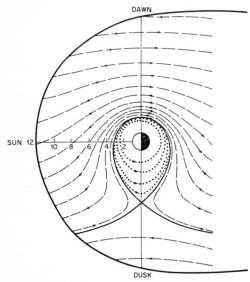

Fig. 2. Convection diagram in local time vs. L for the equatorial plane.

origin of the convection electric field is probably in the solar wind.

The basic model, which is explained in detail in the works of Nishida & Brice, is represented by an equatorial flow diagram such as that calculated by Kavanagh et al. (1968) and shown in Fig. 2. In this diagram the dotted flow patterns inside of the solid line represent the paths of flux tubes which approximately corotate with the earth. The dashed lines outside of the solid line show the flow paths of flux tubes whose motion is dominated by convection. The closed part of the solid line represents the location of the plasmapause. From this flow diagram it can be seen that a *bulge* on the dusk side is formed in general agreement with observation. The shape and location of this plasmapause boundary and the directions of the flow lines should be considered only in a qualitative manner. Other effects such as ionospheric conductivity are not included in the model. These effects may distort the precise picture of the plasmapause and create a much more complex picture from the smooth flow diagram presented by the model.

The flow diagram presented in Fig. 2 represents a steady-state situation where the convection electric field remains uniform. This uniform convection electric field can be thought of as representative of a period of steady magnetic activity. The effect of varying magnetic activity on this convection diagram will be considered below.

Consider first the basic flow pattern of the flux tubes which are *inside* the plasmapause for a steady convection electric field. Fig. 3 shows a more detailed view of this region. The spacing between dots on each of the flow paths represents the distance a flux tube will drift in one hour, and the arrows show the direction of drift. Consider a typical density profile shown in Region A, the dawn sector (Chappell et al. 1970b and OGO–V data to be published). This profile is characterized by a steep drop in density of two to three orders of magnitude at about L = 3.5. If the group of flux tubes which make up this Region A profile are allowed to flow to the dusk meridian according to the theoretical paths shown in the figure, the Region B (the dusk sector) profile will result.

Inside of about L = 2.5 the motion is very nearly that of corotation. However, the flux tubes which cross the dawn meridian between L $\cong$ 2.5 and 3.5 are spread through L values of about 2.5 to 6.5 at the dusk meridian as a consequence of the E × B drift of the plasma. This expansion of the plasmasphere results in the $1/R^4$ density de-

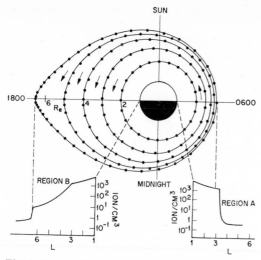

Fig. 3. Convection diagram for the region inside of the plasmapause boundary. Typical concentration profiles as a function of L are shown.

crease between roughly L = 2.5 and 6.5 that is shown in the Region B profile. This density decrease – proportional to $1/R^4$ – comes from the increase in flux tube volume which results as the flux tube drifts to larger L values. The steep gradient at L = 3.5 at dawn is mapped to L = 6.5 at dusk as shown.

As these flux tubes drift from dawn to dusk, filling from the ionosphere can also take place. Filling from the ionosphere is assumed constant and uniform across the base of the flux tube. Since the volume of a flux tube is proportional to R^4, the resulting equatorial density profile from ionospheric filling will exhibit a $1/R^4$ dependence. Therefore, as the flux tubes drift through the bulge region, the tube expansion and the filling from the ionosphere will both create a $1/R^4$ profile between the region of true corotation ($\sim L = 2.5$) and the steep gradient.

The flux tubes in the bulge region do not strictly corotate but drift at different speeds, as shown by the spacings between the dots. A thermal particle which drifts along the path of $R_E = 6.5$ at dusk from noon to midnight takes almost twice as long as a particle which drifts from noon to midnight along the path of $R_E = 3$ at dusk. The differential rotation will distort the simple $1/R^4$ profile in the region near the plasmapause. Since the flux tubes at greater distances drift more slowly than those at the smaller distances, they will experience greater filling from the ionosphere. To describe the exact profile, therefore, this and

perhaps other effects should be included. This serves to reemphasize that the simple flow pattern will provide only a qualitative picture of the plasmasphere.

In quiet times when the convection field is very small or is absent and the plasmasphere is very full of plasma, the teardrop shape may become more circular and corotation may dominate the drift even in the bulge region of the plasmasphere. In extremely quiet times, this circular-shaped plasmapause may be located almost as far out as the magnetopause.

3. CHANGES IN PLASMAPAUSE PROFILES DUE TO NON-UNIFORM CONVECTION

In order to describe plasmasphere dynamics, the more realistic approach of a non-uniform convection electric field within the magnetosphere must be adopted – one which on the average increases during magnetically disturbed times and decreases during magnetically quiet times. Upon combining the effect of this varying convection field with the effects of filling of the plasmasphere from the ionosphere on the dayside, the total picture of the plasmasphere will emerge. First consider the effect that a varying convection electric field has on the equatorial flow diagram of the flux tubes. If the convection electric field is not steady but varies with changing activity, the con-

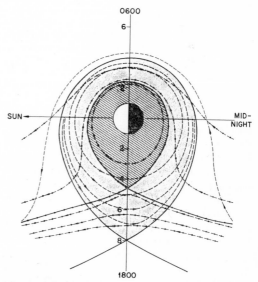

Fig. 4. Superposition of two convection diagrams corresponding to two different values for the convection electric field.

171

vection diagram of Fig. 3 will be changed as shown in Fig. 4. In this Figure two equatorial flow diagrams representing two different values of the crosstail electric field are superimposed. These two values are .2 mV/m and .6 mV/m, in agreement with estimates made by Kavanagh et al. 1968, and others. The diagram representing the .2 mV/m field is given by the outer solid line and the dashed flow lines. The region of corotation is shown by the entire grey area (including lined area). This field represents quiet magnetic activity, and allows flow of closed flux tubes out to L = 8 in the dusk meridian. The .6 mV/m field is represented by the inner dotted solid line surrounding the lined area with the dotted dashes showing flow lines. This field can support flow of closed flux tubes only within the lined area which extends only to L = 4.5 at dusk, with convective flow dominating outside that point. This stronger field value represents periods of high magnetic activity.

Three interesting effects are observed from this diagram. First, the boundary between always closed flux tubes and occasionally open flux tubes (the plasmapause) occurs at smaller L-values for increasing values of convection field (or magnetic activity). Second, an increase in convection electric field (or increasing activity) drives the plasmapause to lower L-values on the nightside and *not* the dayside. Third, a reversal in flow direction can occur in the bulge region during increasing activity.

4. DAYSIDE FILLING DURING VARIOUS DEGREES OF MAGNETIC ACTIVITY

The results of Fig. 4 are sketched in Fig. 5, which shows the plasmasphere boundaries in relation to the overall magnetosphere convection pattern. Region A surrounded by boundary *a* represents the plasmapause during magnetically active times. Region A plus Region B surrounded by boundary *b* represents the plasmasphere during quiet magnetic periods. Region C represents the normal plasma trough region of the magnetosphere.

During the day (i.e. the time that the E-region at the foot of a particular flux tube is sunlit) there is filling of the plasmasphere from the ionosphere in Regions A, B, and C. The rate at which this filling takes place is influenced by several things, such as equatorial plasma pressure, F-region ionospheric concentrations (location of high-latitude ion trough), the presence of precipitating particles at high latitudes, etc. The filling rate may

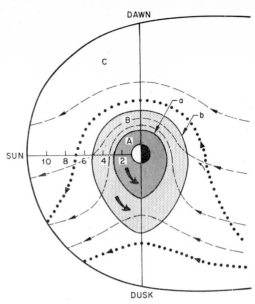

Fig. 5. Schematic diagram for superposition of two convection diagrams corresponding to two different values for the convection electric field.

therefore vary in each of the three regions shown. An estimate of this filling rate in Region B has been made by Park (1970) who found that this region could fill from essentially empty conditions to the densities of the outer portion of Region A (several hundred ions/cm^3) in about five days. This corresponds to an upward flux in the daytime of about 3×10^8 ions/cm^3 combined with a downward flux at night of 1.8×10^8 ions/cm^3. The upward flux is close to the polar wind fluxes of Banks & Holzer (1969). The downward flux of 1.8×10^8 ions/cm^3 at night is that which is required to support the nighttime F-region.

The equatorial ion density build-up in the trough region as a function of local time can be estimated by assuming a constant upward flux on the dayside. Fig. 6 shows the estimated increase in H$^+$ density at the equator for various L-shells (L = 4 → L = 8) for an upward flux of 3×10^8 ions/cm^2-sec at 1000 km, starting at 0500 LT. A collisionless distribution of ionization along the field line has been assumed. All three regions, A, B, and C, should fill on a day-by-day basis. After a period of quiet magnetic activity, Regions A and B are full of plasma and the plasmapause occurs approximately at boundary *b*. As the flux tubes rotate from dawn to dusk, the tubes in Regions A, B, and C are filled. In Region C the plasma pressure is low and the filling rate may

172

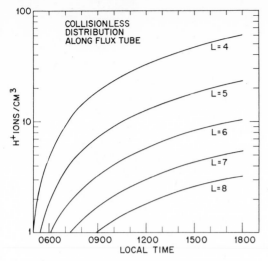

Fig. 6. Ion density build-up along flux tubes as a function of local time for an assumed upward flux of 3×10^8 ions/cm² sec at 1000 km.

approach polar wind fluxes. At ∼ 1500–1600 LT, the flux tubes in Region C are convected sunward and out of the magnetosphere, and the accumulated plasma is lost (through open flux tubes). Regions A and B retain the plasma (since the flux tubes remain closed) and part of this plasma is available to supply the nightside ionosphere. Filling and loss will continue in this manner as long as there is no change in magnetic activity.

On days of steady high magnetic activity the filling and loss will be similar to the above example except that only the plasma inside boundary *a* will be retained and the accumulated plasma in both Regions B and C will be lost through convection to the magnetopause in the afternoon dusk sector.

It is possible to get double levels of filling, which results in two steep gradients in the plasmapause profile. Consider a quiet day following a period of several days at high magnetic activity. The days of enhanced magnetic activity will have established the plasmasphere in Region A inside boundary *a*. This plasmasphere will exhibit a steep gradient at boundary *a*. If the activity then becomes quiet, Regions A, B, and C will experience dayside filling as before, with the plasma inside both Regions A and B being retained while that of Region C will be lost. This chain of circumstances will result in two steep gradients in plasma concentration, i.e. a double plasmapause, the original one at boundary *a* and a new one at boundary *b*, resulting from filling and plasma retention in Region B. Fig. 6 showed that the level of filling for one day is about 20–30 ions/cm³ at the equator. After one day, a double level of concentration will be expected, with Region A full at several hundred ions/cm³ and Region B only partially full at about 20 ions/cm³.

5. REACTION OF NIGHTSIDE PLASMASPHERE TO VARYING CONVECTION

Changes in plasmapause position in the nightside are also predicted from the varying convection electric field. As the convection field increases, the flux tubes in the midnight to dawn sector are driven to lower L-values (Carpenter & Stone 1967) as shown in the left diagram of Fig. 7. This inward motion does not occur on the dayside. During times of decreasing activity, the bulge region is allowed to corotate into the nightside region thereby increasing the L-value of the plasmapause. This movement is indicated in Fig. 7 in the dia-

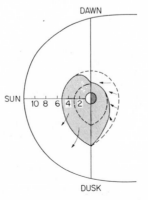

NIGHTSIDE DECREASE

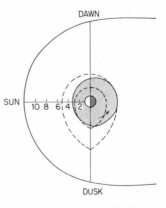

NIGHTSIDE INCREASE

Fig. 7. Schematic diagram showing changes in the position of the plasmapause on the nightside for increasing and decreasing convection electric fields.

173

gram on the right. This increase in plasmapause radius cannot take place rapidly in the dayside because the bulge region would have to corotate for more than 12 hours before reaching the dayside sector. Hence one expects the nightside sector to react more quickly to changes in magnetic activity than the dayside sector.

6. THE DAYSIDE PLASMAPAUSE

Carpenter (private communication) has suggested that the characteristics and position of the plasmapause on the dayside are dependent on the sequence of magnetic activity changes which occurred as this particular sector of the plasmasphere corotated previously through the nightside region where convection effects are important. This idea is illustrated in Fig. 8, which shows the convection effects influencing the plasmapause location in the sector of interest during its corotation through the formative nightside region.

A special case of the inward convection in the formative region near midnight is the formation of an indentation or 'ripple' in the surface of the plasmasphere. This ripple can result from a localized onset of a convection field in the midnight sector. This localized field would cause an inward convection of a small portion of the plasmasphere surface, as illustrated in Fig. 9. Evidence of these localized increases in the convection electric field has been reported by DeForest & McIlwain (1970). Once the longitudinal ripple has been formed near midnight, it corotates into the dayside sector. This ripple in the plasmasphere should then be observed in the dayside features of the plasmasphere.

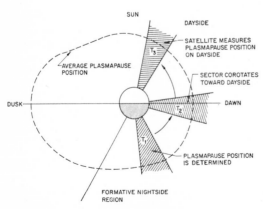

Fig. 8. Schematic diagram showing the formation of the dayside plasmapause location.

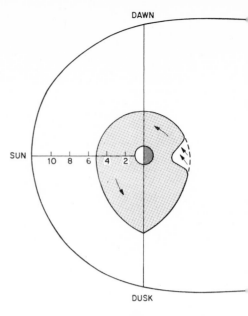

RIPPLE FORMATION AT MIDNIGHT

Fig. 9. Schematic diagram showing the formation a 'ripple' in the surface of the plasmasphere.

7. DETACHMENT OF PLASMA

It was observed that an increase in the convection electric field could reverse the flow of plasma the bulge region of the plasmasphere. This effect is illustrated in Fig. 10. The pre-storm left-hand part of the Figure shows the plasmasphere during a period of low magnetic activity. It is full out boundary b. During the storm the convection electric field increases and the plasma in the bulge region which *was* corotating in the quiet situation will *now* be detached from the main flow of the plasmasphere and will be convected sunward as shown in the right-hand part of the Figure. From the flow diagram for varying magnetic fields, Fig. 4, it can be deduced that the dayside plasma which had built up to Region B will also be peeled away and convected out to the magnetopause. The nightside flux tubes are driven to lower L-values as discussed previously. The net effect of the storm is to reduce greatly the total plasma content of the plasmasphere and it is only through dayside filling after a return to quiet conditions that the plasmasphere can recover.

If the magnetic activity fluctuates rather than going in one jump from quiet to disturbed, one would expect the bulge region to contain fluctuations in the density profile rather than a single steep gradient. These density fluctuations would

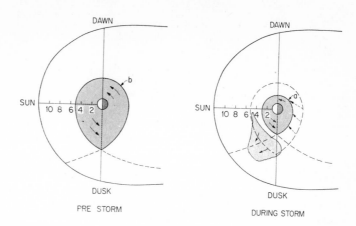

Fig. 10. Schematic diagram showing the process of plasma detachment.

DAWN

SUN 10 8 6 4 2 b

DUSK

PRE STORM

DAWN

SUN 10 8 6 4 2 a

DUSK

DURING STORM

be caused by the repeated switching from corotation to convective flow combined with the differential flow speeds in the bulge region.

8. SUMMARY OF PLASMASPHERE CHARACTERISTICS PREDICTED BY THE MAGNETOSPHERIC CONVECTION MODEL

The magnetospheric convection model may be employed to predict several characteristic features of the plasmasphere. These characteristics have been discussed above. The plasmasphere, described in terms of the equatorial plane representation, is conveniently divided into three regions: the bulge region, the nightside region, and the dayside region. Each region was found to display certain characteristics distinct from the characteristics of the other regions. These characteristics are enumerated as follows:

The bulge region:

- presence of the bulge at dusk
- $1/R^4$ radial dependence of plasma concentration
- large fluctuation in plasma density at the plasmapause
- plasma detachment

The nightside region:

- rapid response to magnetic activity changes
- formative region for plasmasphere ripples
- formative region for dayside plasmapause

The dayside region:

- slow response to magnetic activity changes
- plasmapause position formed on nightside sector

- characteristic filling of plasmasphere from the ionosphere, formative region of double plasmapause.

9. MEASUREMENTS OF ION CONCENTRATION IN THE PLASMASPHERE AND PLASMA TROUGH

Recall that Fig. 1 was the average location of the plasmapause when plotted in local time-L coordinates. These data were obtained from density profiles and represent the average of over 150 passes through the plasmasphere. The bulge region in the dusk sector is clearly evident from the data. The gross features of the plasmasphere shape are in good agreement with the convection model, Fig. 2.

10. MEASUREMENTS IN THE BULGE REGION

In almost all cases the density profiles through the bulge region exhibit a $1/R^4$ dependence with radial distance and have a steep density gradient at the outer edge of the bulge. A typical example is shown in Fig. 11. The plasmapause in the bulge region is located between approximately $L = 4$ and $L = 9$ and is generally found at increasingly larger L-values as the magnetic activity decreases. The bulge region of the plasmasphere is found to be filled out to large L-values during quiet magnetic periods. During periods of moderate to high magnetic activity, the plasma in the bulge region appears to be 'peeled away' from the outer parts of the plasmasphere. During extended large magnetic storms, the 'peeling' process can drastically deplete the plasma population of the bulge region.

175

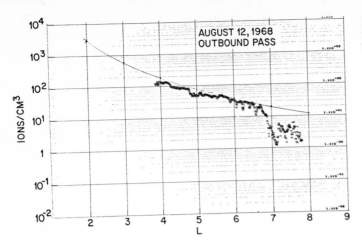

Fig. 11. An example of the measured ion concentration profile in the bulge region.

Examples of this filling and peeling away are shown in Fig. 12 by a sequence of passes which occurred before, during, and after a magnetic storm. These passes were taken in the local time region 1620 LT–1720 LT. A $1/R^4$ profile normalized to 3×10^3 at $L = 2$ has been put in as a reference line with which to compare the changing density levels.

The first pass, on August 12, follows a two-and-a-half-day period of generally low activity

($K_p \cong 1^+$). The plasmasphere displays the $1/R^4$ profile inside the steep gradient. The flux tubes making up this profile are relatively full following this quiet period. The second pass, on August 15, follows one and three quarter days of moderate to high activity ($K_p \cong 4$). The plasmapause position has moved inward from about $L = 6.8$ to $L \cong 5.5$ and most of the plasma outside of 5.5 appears to have escaped. The part of the profile inside the steep plasma density gradient appears

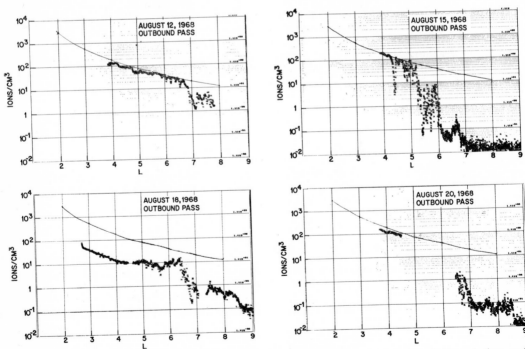

Fig. 12. Four ion density profiles from consecutive passes through the bulge region, before, during, and following a magnetic storm.

176

still to follow the $1/R^4$ profile. Some very erratic fluctuations in density are observed near the plasmapause. The next two and a half days contain high magnetic activity with K_p as high as 6. The pass on August 18 which follows this highly active period shows a depletion of the ions in this local time region. The profile inside the steep gradient still resembles the $1/R^4$ shape but is depleted by roughly one order of magnitude in absolute level. It appears in this pass that the plasmasphere has lost much of its plasma during the period of high activity. The next pass, on August 20, follows a two-and-a-half day period of moderate to low activity. This profile, which unfortunately contains a data gap, shows the plasmasphere recovery after a storm. This recovery is characterized by a filling of the plasmasphere during the quiet magnetic period with the concentration again approaching the original level.

11. DENSITY FLUCTUATIONS AND PLASMA DETACHMENT IN THE BULGE REGION

Another general characteristic of the bulge region which was evident in the above sequence of passes is the presence of large density fluctuations at or just outside of the plasmapause (Fig. 13). In these cases the fluctuations were found to accompany or immediately follow periods of moderate to high magnetic activity. They were found to be characteristic of crossings made after moderate to high magnetic activity which varied rather than remaining steady such as during a period of substorms. These large fluctuations would be expected in the bulge region from the model as described above during times of rapidly changing magnetic activity.

An example of detachment of plasma is shown in Fig. 14. This pass, made at 1300–1600 LT,

Fig. 13. An example of the large plasma fluctuations observed outside the plasmapause in the bulge region.

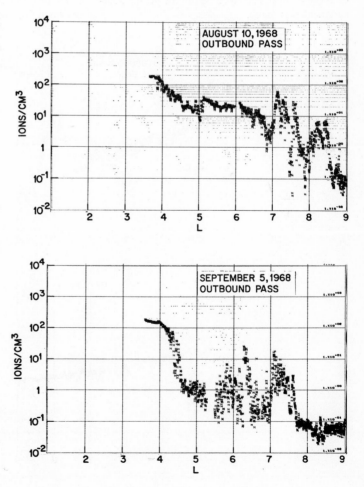

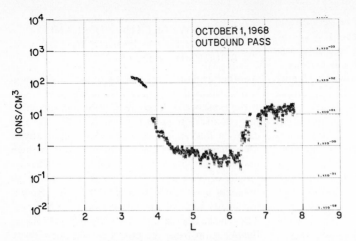

Fig. 14. An ion density profile showing a region of detached plasma.

shows a large mass of plasma separated from the main body of the plasmasphere. Characteristically, as in this case, the activity was low for a period of about a day and then high for a period of about 15 hours or more before the profile measurement was made.

Another example of detached plasma is shown in the upper curve of Fig. 15, the lower curve being an example of filling during the dayside corotation of the plasmasphere.

To examine the occurrence pattern of these detached plasma regions, an L-local time plot was

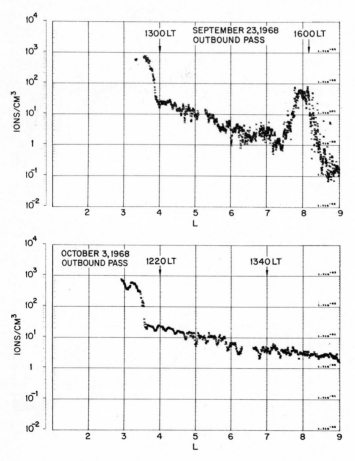

Fig. 15. An ion density profile showing a region of detached plasma (upper curve) and an example of ions filling in the trough following a magnetic storm (lower curve).

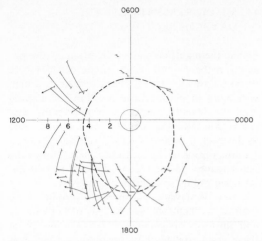

Fig. 16. Distribution of passes of OGO-5 in the local time vs. L coordinates of the equatorial plane in which plasma was observed.

made of each OGO–V pass containing detached plasma. This plot is shown in Fig. 16. It includes fluctuation regions out to L = 9. The Figure also contains a sketch of the average plasmapause position (dash line) for comparison purposes.

In this Figure only those detached fluctuation regions are considered in which the density level exceeds 10 ions/ cm³ at some point. The 10 ions/ cm³ criterion was chosen to delineate between density fluctuations that represent only small variations in the trough density and fluctuations that represent manifestation of plasma which originated in or near the plasmasphere and then became detached. Of a total of 202 plasma trough crossings, there are 49 cases of detached plasma that have densities exceeding 10 ions/cm³. Forty-one cases, or 84% of the occurrences, are found in the 0600 → 1920 LT region. Of these dayside cases, 31, or 76%, are located in the afternoon-dusk sector (1240 → 1920 LT). Approximately 70% of the total number of detached plasma cases occur following periods of moderate to high magnetic activity ($K_p \geq 3^-$ in the previous 24 hours). The local time coverage of the plasma trough by the OGO–V vehicle is uniform since the orbits examined represent nearly one complete year of data. When detached regions of plasma occur, they appear to be concentrated in the afternoon-dusk sector with very few detached regions occurring in the nightside sector. This is consistent with the flow diagrams in the convection model.

12. MEASUREMENTS IN THE NIGHTSIDE SECTOR

The plasmapause position in this nightside region is very closely correlated with the average magnetic activity over the preceding two- to six-hour period (Chappell et al. 1970a). The predictable decrease in plasmasphere radius with increasing activity is shown in Fig. 17. This Figure represents a composite of about 20 passes through this local time region. The decrease in plasmasphere radius is accompanied by an increased steepness in the concentration gradient at the plasmapause, with the total concentration levels inside and outside the plasmapause remaining approximately the same at 10³ ions/cm³ and ∼ 1 ion/cm³ respectively. Carpenter & Stone (1967) have shown the presence of flux tube convection events in this nightside region. These events are characterized by the radially inward motion of the whistler ducts during a simultaneously observed magnetic bay event. The presence of convection effects in this nightside region results in the nightside region's ability to react rather quickly (two to six hours) to changes in magnetic activity level.

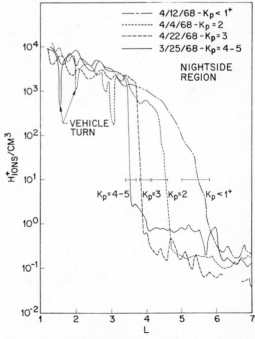

Fig. 17. The average position of the nightside plasmapause as a function of K_p.

13. PLASMASPHERE RIPPLE FORMATION

The planetary magnetic index K_p appears to be sufficient to describe the relation between the average plasmapause position and the magnetic activity as described in Fig. 17. However, for smaller more localized convection events the K_p magnetic index does not suffice. These more localized effects must be analyzed using an index more specific than K_p which involves planetary averaging. Fig. 18 shows a typical case of a density profile in which a convection event appears to have taken place. The profile between $L = 2.8$ and $L = 3.3$ shows a dramatic drop in ion concentration to values not unlike those observed immediately outside the plasmapause. Upon considering the orbit of this particular pass, it appears that the vehicle path was near grazing incidence to the plasmasphere. The density profile indicates that between $L = 2.8$ and $L = 3.3$ the vehicle exited the plasmasphere by passing through a local indentation of the plasmasphere. This effect may very well be an example of a local convection event, i.e. a ripple in the plasmasphere surface described earlier by the convection model. Several of these cases have been studied by following the individual magnetograms of stations in the longitudinal sector in which the profile was measured. In two of the cases examined the ripple occurrence was associated with a large convection event as shown by the H component of the magnetogram. The event took place as the section of the plasmasphere corotated past the midnight sector. Further studies are being undertaken to establish more statistics on correlations of this type.

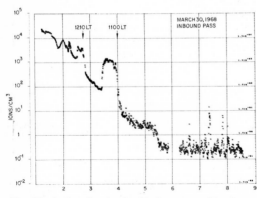

Fig. 18. An ion density profile from an orbit of near grazing incidence to the plasmasphere showing the penetration of a plasmasphere ripple.

14. MEASUREMENTS ON THE DAYSIDE SECTOR

Unlike the nightside region, the plasmapause position in the dayside sector of the plasmasphere (0600 LT to 1500 LT) is characterized by a high variability in plasmapause position for a given level of magnetic activity. The profiles in this dayside region cannot be precisely grouped according to the level of magnetic activity during the two to six hours prior to the measurement, although the plasmapause position does show a general decrease in radius with increasing activity.

Cases of dayside plasmapause profiles were examined which followed periods of both steady and unsteady magnetic activity. During 26 of these cases, the level of magnetic activity was steady from the time that the measured section corotated through the nightside region until the time of the dayside measurement. In 23 of the 26 cases the plasmapause was located in the position that would be expected if plasmapause formation had taken place on the nightside, i.e. the plasmapause showed the same predictable decrease with increasing magnetic activity as had been found on the nightside (Fig. 17). Of the remaining cases, two were not definite and only one case showed the plasmapause in an unexpected position. The magnetic activity was unsteady in 15 cases, that is the level of activity changed in value between the time that the measured section corotated through the nightside region and the time that it was measured in the dayside. Of these 15 cases, 10 showed the plasmapause in the position predicted by the activity level during the nightside transit and only one case fits the activity level that existed after the sector reached the dayside, i.e. after it passed dawn. In the remaining four cases the activity fluctuated rapidly and a judgement could not be made.

These statistics seem to indicate that the plasmapause position of a particular sector of the dayside plasmasphere is determined not by the magnetic activity level immediately preceding the profile measurement but by the level of activity which existed during the corotation of this sector through the formative nightside region. It also appears that once the sector has rotated past dawn, it is difficult to change the plasmapause location.

An excellent example of the inability of the dayside profile to react quickly to an increase in the magnetic activity level is shown in Fig. 19. This Figure shows an inbound pass through the nightside ~ 2200 LT and an outbound pass

180

Fig. 19. An example of the quick response of the nightside and the slow response of the dayside to a convection event.

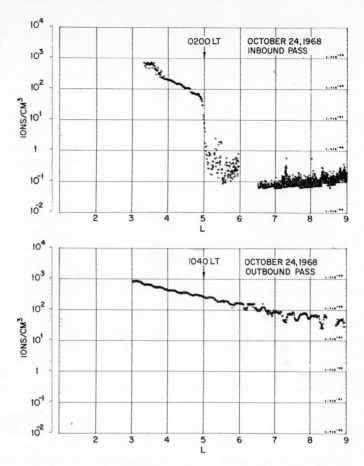

through the dayside ~ 1100 LT. Before the pass began, the magnetic activity had been quiet for a period of four days ($K_p < 1^+$). This quiet period had allowed the plasmasphere to be filled out to very high-L-values (probably close to the magnetopause in the dayside). Just at the time of the inbound pass the magnetic activity increased to $K_p = 3^-$. The inbound profile shows that the nightside of the plasmasphere reacted immediately to this increased activity (plasmapause at $L = 5$) while the dayside profile shows no change from the previous quiet time profile. In this case the shape of the dayside profile is characteristic of the activity level during its transit of the nightside at an earlier time and not of the activity level just before the profile measurements.

15. DAYSIDE FILLING

The ion density build-up in the trough region on the dayside sector is much more apparent following periods of high magnetic activity. During these periods the plasmapause will be moved to lower L-shells and the ambient ion content of the plasma trough will be greatly reduced by enhanced convection effects. It has been estimated by Park (1970) that a recovery period of five days is required to return the plasma in the depleted trough region to its average density following a magnetic storm. The estimate is in good agreement with results obtained from the Light Ion Mass Spectrometer on OGO–5. From these OGO–5 measurements it appears that the plasmasphere 'recovers' after two orbital periods, which is approximately five days.

Fig. 20 shows the measured density at $L = 5$ (outside the plasmapause) in the plasma trough at different local times following disturbed magnetic periods of duration one or more days. These densities are plotted vs. local time and show the build-up of ionization following the storm periods. The average K_p during the disturbance was 3^+. For purposes of comparison, three theoretical curves are also included. Curve A shows the ex-

181

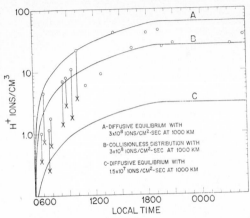

Fig. 20. Ion concentration measurements at L = 5 as a function of local time.

pected build-up of ionization in the equatorial plane on an L = 5 field line. This curve assumes a flux tube filling with a constant upward flux of 3 × 10⁸ ions/cm²-sec at 1000 km. It also assumes that a diffusive equilibrium distribution of ionization exists along the field line. Curve B shows the results using a similar value of constant upward flux with a collisionless distribution of ionization along the field line. Curve C assumes a diffusive equilibrium distribution but uses a value of 1.5 × 10⁷ ions/cm²-sec for the upward flux. This latter value is taken from Hansen & Ortenburger (1961).

The actual data points in Fig. 20 have been adjusted in the following way. The OGO–V measurements at L = 5 were made at magnetic latitudes between 29° and 49°. Values measured at these latitudes must be adjusted to equatorial

densities in order to compare them with the curves shown. To make this adjustment, some assumptions must be made about the distribution of ionization along the field line. Angerami & Carpenter (1966) found that whistler data taken from regions of filling outside the main plasmapause could be most satisfactorially explained if a collisionless distribution along the field line was invoked. Banks et al. (1971) agree with this distribution in the initial phases of the flux tube filling. However, as the filling continues they find that a shock front is formed near the equatorial plane which propagates down the flux tube toward the ionosphere. The distribution behind the shock front (between the shock front and the equatorial plane) is that of diffusive equilibrium. Their calculations show that the shock front should propagate to the magnetic latitudes of the OGO–V measurements at L = 5 in about five hours (Banks, private communication). Therefore, a diffusive equilibrium distribution is assumed between 45° and the equatorial plane after the first five hours of filling (i.e. after 1000 LT) and those data points are adjusted accordingly. During the first five hours (before 1000 LT), two sets of points are shown – the equatorial density calculated from a diffusive equilibrium distribution (O) and the equatorial density calculated from a collisionless distribution (X) – and are connected by a solid line for easy identification. The true distribution at these early times is probably some hybrid combination of these two.

These data seem to show good agreement with the ionization build-up that is calculated using a flux of near 3 × 10⁸ ions/cm²-sec as predicted

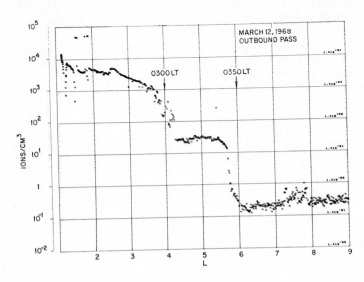

Fig. 21. An ion density profile showing the presence of a double plasmapause.

182

by Banks et al. (1971) and deduced from whistler observations by Park (1970). The increase in equatorial density appears to lag behind the predicted value during the first few hours but then approaches the expected level being bracketed by the collisionless and diffusive equilibrium distribution curves for a flux level of 3×10^8 ions/cm²-sec.

The evidence for filling in the plasma trough is given in Fig. 21. Two very distinct ion density gradients are observed, one at $L = 4.2$ and another at $L = 5.8$. This double knee in the ion density profile is undoubtedly a manifestation of the double plasmapause predicted by the convection model, the inner plasmapause corresponding to the location of the plasmapause immediately after a magnetic storm, and the outer plasmapause occurring after a period of quiet magnetic activity. During the quiet period the ion concentration in the region that was formerly the trough region continues to increase forming a new plasmapause at the $L = 5.8$ location.

16. CONCLUSIONS

The examples presented show the qualitative agreement between the characteristics of the observed plasmasphere profiles and the profiles predicted by a magnetospheric convection model which employs a non-uniform convection electric field to explain the plasmasphere dynamics. The general agreement is good but one must not expect to explain every individual profile utilizing the convection model, for there can be many small variations in the magnetic activity and different sequences of activity changes which can confuse the issue and make exact prediction difficult. This excellent agreement, however, is evidence in support of the concept of magnetospheric convection which appears to be an excellent model for explaining not only the dynamics of the plasmasphere but also the overall dynamics of the magnetosphere.

Acknowledgements: The authors are grateful to Drs. D. L. Carpenter, C. G. Park, and P. M. Banks for many helpful discussions. This work was performed under NASA Contract NAS 5-9092.

REFERENCES

Angerami, J. J. & Carpenter, D. L. 1966. *J. Geophys. Res. 71*, 711.
Axford, W. I. & Hines, C. O. 1961. *Can. J. Phys. 39*, 1433.
Banks, P. M. & Holzer, T. E. 1969. *J. Geophys. Res. 74*, 6317.
Banks, P. M., Nagy, A. F. & Axford, W. I. 1971. *Planet. Space Sci.* In press.
Binsack, J. H. 1967. *J. Geophys. Res. 72*, 5231.
Brice, Neil, M. 1967. *J. Geophys. Res. 72*, 5193.
Brinton, H. C., Pickett, R. A. & Taylor, H. A., Jr., 1968. *Planetary Space Sci. 16*, 899.
Carpenter, D. L. 1962. *Stanford Univ. Radio Sci. Lab. Rept.* SEL-62-059.
Carpenter, D. L. 1963. *J. Geophys. Res. 68*, 1675.
Carpenter, D. L. & Stone, K. 1967. *Planet. Space Sci. 15*, 395.
Chappell, C. R., Harris, K. K. & Sharp, G. W. 1970a. *J. Geophys. Res. 75*, 50–56.
Chappell, C. R., Harris, K. K. & Sharp, G. W. 1970b. *J. Geophys. Res. 75*, 3848.
DeForest, S. E. & McIlwain, C. E. 1970. University of California, San Diego, Space Physics Group, Rept. UCSD-SP-70-04.
Gringanz, K. I., Bezrukikh, V. V., Ozerov, V. D. & Rybehinsky, R. Y. 1960. *Phys. Dokl. 5*, 361.
Hagg, E. L. 1967. *Can. J. Phys. 45*, 27.
Hansen, W. B. & Ortenburger, I. B. 1961. *J. Geophys. Res.* 1425.
Harris, K. K., Sharp, G. W. & Chappell, C. R. 1970. *J. Geophys. Res. 75*, 219–224.
Kavanagh, L. D., Jr., Freeman, J. W., Jr. & Chen, A. J. 1968. *J. Geophys. Res. 73*, 5511.
Nishida, A. 1966. *J. Geophys. Res. 71*, 5669.
Park, C. G. 1970. *J. Geophys. Res. 75*, 4249.
Taylor, H. A., Jr., Brinton, H. C. & Smith, C. R. 1965. *J. Geophys. Res. 70*, 5769.
Taylor, J. A., Jr., Brinton, H. C. & Pharo, M. W. III, 1968. *J. Geophys. Res. 73*, 961.

Storm Time Instabilities of the Ring Current

R. M. THORNE

Department of Meteorology, University of California at Los Angeles

Abstract: The resonant cyclotron instability between radiation belt protons and ion-cyclotron waves can account for many observed features of the magnetospheric ring current. Analogous results apply to the electron-whistler interaction although the former are not considered to be important for ring current energetics. Particles with energy exceeding 100 keV are readily destabilized throughout the entire magnetosphere and their fluxes are consequently limited to the stably trapped levels described by Kennel & Petschek. However, at the dominant ring current energies between 10 and 100 keV, a broad zone of stability exists in the region just outside the plasmapause. Particles injected into this *outer zone* during substorms may remain trapped for many drift orbits allowing an intense ring current to develop. In direct contrast, this stable ring current zone is bounded by regions of rapid precipitational loss within the plasmasphere and at large radial distance in the auroral zone.

During geomagnetic storms much of the ring current energy is dissipated into ion-cyclotron turbulence in a narrow zone just within the plasmapause. Throughout, the main phase proton lifetimes approach the strong diffusion limit of one hour in agreement with the observations of Frank. Protons injected from the magnetospheric tail are removed before they can drift to the dayside of the magnetosphere thus producing a strongly asymmetric ring current.

After the cessation of substorm associated injection events, the protons form a symmetric ring current and their subsequent removal is controlled by the outward expansion of the plasmapause. During this rapid phase of the storm recovery, the intense zone of ion-cyclotron turbulence provides the energy source to excite SAR arcs along the expanding plasmapause. Further decay takes place on a charge exchange time scale of a few days.

Relativistic electrons and high-energy protons will also be subject to rapid parasitic pitch-angle scattering through resonant cyclotron interactions with the intense ring current generated ion-cyclotron turbulence. Precipitation of such particles near the strong diffusion limit is therefore expected to occur in association with low-energy proton dumping and SAR arc generation just inside the plasmapause.

1. INTRODUCTION

The most pronounced signature of a geomagnetic storm is a global depression of the earth's horizontal magnetic field. This main-phase decrease, which takes about 12 hours to develop, is caused by the injection of energetic plasma into the region of trapping within the Earth's radiation belts. Because of the general inhomogeneities of the geomagnetic field, the injected energetic particles are induced to drift azimuthally; protons to the west and electrons to the east. This results in a large-scale ring current encircling the Earth, which produces the field depression observed at the Earth's surface. My subsequent discussion will concentrate on recent advances in our understanding of the ring current and its association with other storm-time phenomena.

Let us first delve back into history and consider the information available from ground-based observations. Early theoretical models showed that the field depression ΔB measured at low latitudes on the ground depends almost entirely on the total energy content ε_T of the injected plasma (Dessler & Parker 1959, Sckopke 1966):

$$\frac{\Delta B}{B_0} = -\frac{2}{3}\frac{\varepsilon_T}{\varepsilon_M}.$$

Here B_0 (≈ 0.3 gauss) is the equatorial geomagnetic field and ε_M ($\approx 10^{25}$ ergs) is the total geomagnetic energy contained above the Earth's surface. ΔB is independent of the type of the injected charged particles, their individual energies or their spatial distribution within the magnetosphere.

It is therefore clear that ground-based observations give no clue on three important counts:

185

the location, the species, and the mean energy of ring current particles. In what follows I will describe how these and other general properties of the ring current can be understood from a non-adiabatic viewpoint. In a previous talk at this symposium Atkinson has discussed the impulsive injection of ring current plasma during substorms. My presentation will complement his by concentrating on resonant wave-particle interactions which cause the particles to be scattered in pitch angle towards the atmospheric loss cone and thus be removed from the region of trapping. In particular this treatment allows us to predict which particles should dominate the ring current energetics and where they are able to remain trapped long to produce a symmetric ring current belt.

With the advent of satellite technology it became feasible to undertake a systematic search for the hypothetical ring current particles. Early geiger tube measurements, which were confined to very high energies, soon showed that the ring current must be composed of much lower energy particles than was initially anticipated. The Iowa group therefore undertook the task of building a low-energy electrostatic analyser which culminated in Frank's first (and incidentally as yet our only) overall picture of the particles responsible for a small geomagnetic storm (Frank 1967). Frank found that the dominant ring current energies lay near a few tens of keV and that these particles were confined to the outer radiation zone at distances generally exceeding 3 Earth radii. He furthermore discovered that protons were the dominant contributors (in terms of total energy content) to this particular storm.

Ground-based magnetograms also show that there are *three* distinct time scales associated with the removal of injected plasma. During the storm main phase, plasma is successively injected and removed from the radiation belts on a time scale of an hour or so. A pronounced ring current develops only if the substorm repetition rate is rapid enough to compete with losses (Akasofu 1968). The ring current has an appreciable assymetric component throughout the entire half- to one-day main phase development. Following the main phase, substorm activity subsides and the ring current becomes symmetric. Two distinct decay rates can be identified: a rapid recovery lasting half to one day, followed by a slow asymptotic approach to prestorm conditions over several days.

Soon after the in situ discovery of ring current protons, Swisher & Frank (1968) attempted to describe the storm recovery as due to charge exchange loss with neutral hydrogen (Dessler et al. 1961). Clearly this process is not rapid enough to account for the substorm recovery on a time scale of an hour. Furthermore, we now have two separate experimental observations, which rules out charge exchange as the dominant loss process of the overall storm recovery following the main phase.

a) On the same OGO–3 satellite where Frank detected ring current protons, Taylor et al. (1968) measured light ion densities. These two sets of observations have recently been combined by Russell & Thorne (1970) to demonstrate the striking correlation shown in Fig. 1. Notice that the ring current protons are excluded from the high-

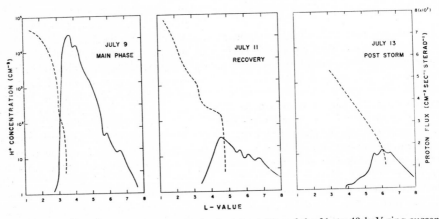

Fig. 1. Simultaneous measurements obtained on the Ogo 3 satellite of the 31- to 49-keV ring current proton fluxes (solid lines; Frank 1967) and the thermal hydrogen profile (dashed lines; Taylor et al. 1968) are shown for three phases of the July 1966 geomagnetic storm.

density plasmasphere and that the sharp inner edge of the ring current is essentially coincident with the plasmapause at each phase of the July 1966 storm. Furthermore, the ring current appears to be erroded away at its inner edge as the plasmapause expands outward during the storm recovery. Such control is clearly not accounted for by a charge exchange loss.

b) One further fact pertinent to understanding the recovery phase of a storm has recently been given by Frank (1970). He has demonstrated that protons injected into the dusk to midnight quadrant are removed from the region of trapping before they can drift westwards to local noon. This places an upper limit of a few hours on the proton lifetimes which is also clearly not compatible with charge exchange.

The coincidence of the plasmapause and the inner edge of the ring current during main phase is not in itself conclusive evidence for a proton loss mechanism at the plasmapause, at least during main phase. The most efficient proton source is probably magnetospheric convection (Axford & Hines 1961, Axford et al. 1965). If the plasmapause is the boundary of innermost penetration of convective flow (Nishida 1966, Brice 1967), the spatial coincidence of the plasmapause and the inner edge of the ring current during main phase would not be surprising. It is difficult, however, to explain this spatial coincidence during the recovery phase by a convection model alone. Convection could act as a sink when the plasmapause expands outward during the recovery phase, by causing protons to flow outward to the magnetospheric boundary, but this effect would require flow velocities at least of the order of diamagnetic drift velocities (about 10 km/sec) or greater. It then becomes difficult to see how the symmetric ring current (established by drifting) could form during main phase in the face of such large flow velocities. These uncertainties lead us to consider loss mechanisms other than convective transport.

Cornwall et al. (1970) have recently suggested turbulent loss process for the ring current decay and our subsequent discussion will concentrate on this. The energetic protons can be pitch-angle scattered into the atmospheric loss cone, whereupon they are removed by collisions, by resonant interactions with ion-cyclotron turbulence (Cornwall 1965, 1966, Kennel & Petschek 1966). The actual location of maximum wave growth and hence turbulent dissipation of the ring current is controlled by the energy of the protons and the ambient plasma conditions. One finds that there is a threshold energy for the protons which take part in the cyclotron instability (see section 2). Essentially, the proton speed must exceed the local Alfvén speed of the medium. Stated another way, the proton energy must exceed the magnetic energy per particle, $E_M = B^2/8\pi N$, where B is the the magnetic field strength and N is the ambient plasma density. E_M exhibits considerable variation throughout the magnetosphere and one can thus readily locate the regions of instability (Thorne & Kennel 1971a). For this purpose E_M is schematically plotted along an equatorial slice through the radiation belts in Fig. 2.

Notice that high-energy particles, E > 100 keV, should be susceptible to the cyclotron instability at all locations throughout the magnetosphere. The self-generating resonant interaction therefore limits the flux levels of high-energy particles to the stably trapped levels described by Cornwall (1966) or Kennel & Petschek (1966). Storm-time injection of such high-energy particles is consequently restricted to values which are insufficient to produce the observed global main phase magnetic field depression. This provides a theoretical motive for ruling out high-energy particles as important contributors of the ring current which agrees well with direct observations (Davis & Williamson 1963, Frank 1967).

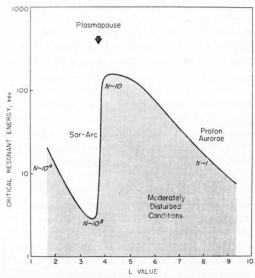

Fig. 2. The threshold energy for unstable cyclotron resonance $E_M = B^2/8\pi N$ is schematically plotted against radial distance along the equatorial plane. The curve is drawn for moderately disturbed conditions and the hatched area indicates stability.

187

On the other hand, at lower energies (say between 10 and 100 keV) Fig. 2 predicts two regions of permitted cyclotron instability separated by a broad stable zone just outside the plasmapause. This predicted zone of stability is precisely where Frank observes the ring current to develop during a storm. The means of injecting protons into this stable region during a storm and their subsequent transport into the highly unstable plasmasphere will be discussed in section 3. Cornwall et al. (1971a) have in fact associated the two unstable regions for low-energy plasma with the location of mid-latitude SAR arcs and proton precipitation emissions observed at auroral latitudes. (An alternative description of this precipitation has been given by Haerendel (1970) and Eather & Carovillano (1971).) These and other processes associated with the ion-cyclotron turbulent decay of the ring current protons will be discussed in section 4. I finally summarize in section 5 with an overall view of a geomagnetic storm.

2. TURBULENT ION-CYCLOTRON INTERACTIONS WITH RING CURRENT PROTONS

Plasma turbulence theory predicts a wide variety of possible unstable wave modes that could contribute to the rapid precipitation loss of ring current protons (Kennel & Englemann 1966, Kennel 1969). Magnetospheric turbulence theories, however, have concentrated primarily on cyclotron resonant interaction with electromagnetic waves (Andronov & Trakhtengerts 1964, Cornwall 1966, Kennel & Petschek 1966). Because our understanding of these particular wave-particle interactions is most secure, we choose to discuss the precipitation loss of ring current protons arising solely from turbulent ion-cyclotron pitch-angle scattering. The contribution of turbulence in other plasma modes (e.g. electrostatic) to proton loss rates has not yet been evaluated and could be important.

The linear instability theory of the parallel ion cyclotron wave is first reviewed. The region of maximum ion cyclotron wave growth for 10 to 100 keV ring current protons is estimated to occur along the sharp plasmapause density gradient. Wave propagation, however, is unlikely to be strictly parallel to the inhomogeneous geomagnetic field. We shall therefore consider the possibility that cold plasmaspheric electrons, which have thermal speeds comparable to typical Alfvén speeds, might Landau damp oblique ion-cyclotron waves. Furthermore, it is also necessary to evaluate the Coulomb collision rates, because they might reduce unstable wave growth rates within the high-density plasmasphere.

Parallel ion-cyclotron interactions. – To simplify the discussion we consider only the maximally unstable (Kennel & Wong 1967) parallel ion-cyclotron wave. Although the loss cone property of the geomagnetic field provides a constant source of pitch-angle anisotropy of the correct sign for instability, ion-cyclotron wave growth results only if the anisotropy exceeds a critical value given by Kennel & Petschek (1966):

$$A_c = \frac{1}{(\Omega_+/\omega) - 1}. \qquad (1)$$

Here $\Omega_+ = eB/M_+c$ is the ion-cyclotron frequency, ω is the wave frequency, e is the electronic charge, B is the magnetic field strength, M_+ is the proton mass, and c is the velocity of light. Gaussian units are used throughout. For example, if the proton pitch-angle distribution has the form $(\sin \alpha)^n$, instability occurs if the anisotropy index exceeds $n_c \equiv 2A_c$ (Cornwall 1966). (Of course, the proton distribution function need not be of this particular form. For an alternative discussion of anisotropy effects, see Haerendel (1970).) The critical anisotropy is fixed, through ω/Ω_+, by the relation between the energy of the resonant ions, E_R, and the magnetic energy per particle, $E_M = B^2/8\pi N$ (Kennel & Petschek 1966):

$$E_R/E_M = (\Omega_+/\omega)^2 [1 - (\omega/\Omega_+)]^3 \equiv \\ A_c^{-2} (1 + A_c)^{-1}. \qquad (2)$$

Equation (2) is simply the statement that the protons must have enough energy to satisfy the Doppler-shifted cyclotron resonance condition $\omega - k_{||} V_{||} = \Omega_+$, which implies that the particles feel waves at their gyrofrequency. Because $E_R \sim E_M$, the most favorable region for unstable cyclotron interactions with the low-energy ring current protons is near the equatorial plane inside the plasmapause or at a large radial distance in the auroral zone (see Fig. 2). For the moment we will concentrate on losses at the plasmapause. It is hard to estimate anisotropics near the plasmapause, because the protons rapidly diffuse in velocity space under the influence of wave turbulence. But it would be very difficult to believe that the proton anistropy could greatly exceed unity during the main phase injection (the geomagnetic loss cone anisotropy is about $\frac{1}{4}$ at L = 4). Therefore, equation (2) suggests that $E_R > \frac{1}{2} E_M$ is a necessary condition for instability. This is probably a conservative estimate. When A_c is larger, the diffusion of the protons in energy is more important (Gendrin 1968, Kennel 1969, Haerendel 1970); for small A_c, diffusion is primarily in pitch angle, as is well known. The effect of energy diffusion could be significant if ring current protons are unstable on the outer edge of the plasmapause, where their anisotropy has not yet been smoothed out by wave turbulence. This will be further discussed in section 4.

A_c is plotted against E_R in Fig. 3 for the range of densities measured across the nightside plasmapause at $L \sim 4$ (Chappell et al. 1970a). Assuming an anisotropy A^+ of order unity we find that ring current protons, $E_p \sim 10$ to 50 keV, are unstable to ion-cyclotron waves for densities between 10 and 100 cm^{-3} (i.e. inside the plasmapause). Ion-cyclotron instability for ring current protons exterior to the plasmapause is therefore unlikely. If, as first suggested by Cocke & Cornwall (1967), ring current protons penetrate the plasmapause, then unstable ion-cyclotron turbulent pitch-angle diffusion causes their precipitation loss. Note that the highly anisotropic Davis-Williamson protons with energies ~ 100 keV are unstable outside the plasmapause (Cornwall 1965, 1966), as is implied in Fig. 2.

The linear parallel ion-cyclotron growth rate is given by

$$\gamma_{CYC} = \frac{\pi}{2} \frac{\Omega_+^2}{\omega} \frac{(1 - (\omega/\Omega_+))^2}{(1 - (\omega/2\Omega_+))} \eta^+ [A^+ - A_c]. \quad (3)$$

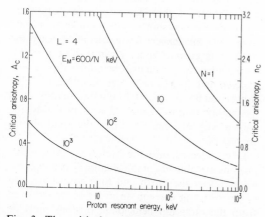

Fig. 3. The critical proton pitch-angle anisotropy required for ion-cyclotron instability is shown as a function of the proton energy for representative total electron densities across the plasmapause at $L = 4$.

Both η^+, the fractional number of protons near resonance, and A^+, the ion pitch-angle anisotropy, have been precisely defined by Kennel & Petschek (1966). Recall that in terms of the $(\sin \alpha)^n$ pitch-angle distribution, $A^+ = n/2$. Because the density of ring current protons inside the plasmapause is probably less than at the ring current maximum, we take the energetic proton density to be ~ 5 cm^{-3}; this is half the main phase value given by Frank (1967). Thus, for a total density of 10^3 cm^{-2}, we find that $\eta^+ \sim 0.005$. We further estimate $A^+ - A_c \sim \frac{1}{4}$. Substitution into equation (3) yields an ion-cyclotron growth rate at $L = 4$ of $\gamma_{CYC} \approx 1$ sec^{-1}. On the outer edge of the plasmapause, where η^+ can be larger, it is possible for growth to occur with even smaller values of $A^+ - A_c$.

Landau resonant interactions. – Although ion-cyclotron waves propagating strictly parallel to the magnetic field have no Landau interactions (Barnes 1966), the inhomogeneities of the propagation medium will force slightly oblique propagation somewhere along the ray path, even if the initial wave generation is restricted to maximally growing parallel waves (Kennel & Petschek 1966). Oblique ion-cyclotron waves, however, are subject to Landau damping (Kennel & Wong 1967). The only important Landau particles within the plasmasphere are thermal electrons (temperature $T \sim 1$ eV) because their thermal speed c_T is comparable to the Alfvén speed c_A, which is roughly the ion cyclotron wave phase velocity. By assuming an isotropic Maxwellian distribution for the cold electrons and slightly oblique wave propagation, the electron Landau damping decrement is easily estimated from the general expressions of Kennel & Wong (1967) to be

$$\frac{\gamma_{Landau}}{|\omega|} \sim -\frac{1}{\sqrt{\pi}} \left[\frac{\tan \theta}{\tan \theta_{res}} \right]^2 T \left(\frac{c_A}{c_T} \right), \quad (4)$$

where $T(x) = x^3 \exp(-x^2)$. Here θ is the angle between the propagation vector and the magnetic field and $\theta_{res} \cong \arctan \left[\frac{\Omega_+ \, \Omega_-}{\omega^2} \right]^{\frac{1}{2}}$ is the angle for wave resonance. Because the electron thermal speeds and the Alfvén speeds are comparable in the plasmasphere, $T \left(\frac{c_A}{c_T} \right) \approx 1$. The electron Landau damping interaction with oblique ion-cyclotron waves is therefore unimportant for $\theta \ll 1$ but can be significant for highly oblique waves (section 4).

189

Collisional damping of wave growth. – For low-frequency phenomena one cannot, a priori, consider the high-density, low-temperature plasma inside the plasmasphere to be collision-free. The electron-electron and electron-ion collision frequency is given by Spitzer (1962) to be approximately

$$v \sim \frac{\pi e^4 N}{M^{\frac{1}{2}} T^{3/2}} \log A, \qquad (5)$$

where A is the Coulomb or plasma multiple scattering parameter. For $T_- \sim 1$ eV and $\log A \sim 20$, we find that $v \sim 10^{-4} N$ sec^{-1}. Thus at plasmaspheric densities the electron collision frequency is $v \sim 10^{-1}$; this is an order of magnitude smaller than the maximum ion-cyclotron wave growth rate, as given in equation (3). This collision frequency provides a negative contribution to this growth rate; the most important effect is electron-ion collisions that dissipate wave currents.

Discussion. – Ring current protons that penetrate the plasmasphere destabilize ion-cyclotron

waves with growth rates $\gamma_{CYC} \sim 1$ sec^{-1}. Just outside the plasmapause the low plasma densities imply that the ring current proton anisotropy must be unreasonably large for instability. To determine the spatial variation of γ_{CYC} we must account for the precipitation loss of ring current protons as they penetrate into the plasmasphere. Therefore, η^+ is expected to decrease with distance into the plasmasphere so that at some point γ_{CYC} and v become comparable, thus prohibiting wave growth. The ion-cyclotron growth rate will consequently maximize just inside the plasmapause, falling to zero with both decreasing L (because of electron-ion collisions) and increasing L (because of the high critical anisotropy). A sketch of γ_{CYC} and v against L is given in Fig. 4.

3. PROTON SPATIAL TRANSPORT AND PRECIPITATION LOSS RATES

During a magnetic storm enhanced convection associated with an increase in the substorm electric field across the geomagnetic tail probably provides a major source for the ring current. Energetic plasma sheet particles would thus be impulsively injected into the region of trapping over a broad range of local times around midnight. They would also be subject to betatron acceleration, which is sufficient to energize them to the observed ring current energies between 10 and 100 keV (Axford 1969). However, in order to reach the stable ring current location predicted in Fig. 2 the particles must be transported across the highly unstable auroral zone where they are subject to precipitation loss. Strong diffusion electron lifetimes in this region ($\approx$ several minutes) are considerably shorter than convection time scales. We thus expect few electrons to reach the stable ring current zone. Plasma sheet protons, on the other hand, can only be removed on a time scale comparable to or longer than the substorm convection flow time and should thus readily reach the stably trapped zone. This is probably the reason why protons dominate the ring current energetics.

Once injected into the cyclotron-stable zone, protons are able to complete guiding center drifts orbits about the Earth and thus contribute to a symmetric ring current. In order to be removed from the radiation belts these protons must be transported into either of the unstable regions where they are subject to precipitation loss. In what follows I will concentrate on processes which transport protons into the plasmasphere. Although

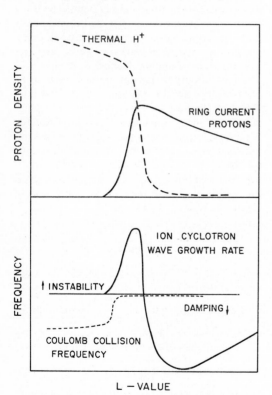

Fig. 4. A schematic plot of the distribution of thermal plasma and ring current protons is shown together with the theoretically expected ion-cyclotron growth rate.

many transport processes are possible in the magnetosphere, consideration here will be limited to convection, guiding center drifts, radial diffusion, and outward expansion of the plasmasphere. The proton loss rate is determined by the transport rate and the precipitation lifetime, which in the limit of strong pitch-angle diffusion is approximately one hour. The corresponding ion-cyclotron wave intensity is predicted to be about one gamma.

Proton transport mechanisms

a. *Magnetospheric convective.* – Convection models of the magnetosphere (Axford & Hines 1961, Axford et al. 1965) predict a hydromagnetic flow of plasma from the magnetospheric tail into the near-Earth region. Recent theories (Nishida 1966, Brice 1967) consider that the plasmapause separates regions of corotational flow (the plasmasphere) from the externally driven convective flow. Enhanced convection flow fields at storm times are important in transporting protons from the injection region to the vicinity of the plasmapause. Since the plasmapause is an equipotential, however, the flow stream lines are everywhere tangential to the boundary. Hence no transport across the plasmapause can result from convection.

b. *Guiding center drifts.* Just exterior to the plasmapause, the motion of ring current protons is governed by magnetic gradient and curvature drifts. Protons injected just exterior to the plasmapause at $L = 4$ near midnight therefore drift westward into the high-density region of the plasmaspheric bulge, located at $L \sim 5$ to 6 near dusk (Carpenter 1970, Chappell et al. 1970b). Before protons drift out of the bulge region, ion-cyclotron turbulence should precipitate at least part of the ring current flux.

c. *Radial diffusion.* Cross field line radial diffusion can also carry protons into the region of ion cyclotron instability within the plasmasphere. Although radial diffusion theories abound in the geophysical literature (Fälthammar 1966, Roederer 1968), Cornwall (1968) has argued that only Bohm diffusion can compete with precipitation losses. Bohm diffusion can be roughly interpreted as the scattering of a particle by its gyroradius in a gyroperiod and hence represents a maximum transport rate.

Bohm diffusion, however, cannot be the predominant transport mechanism throughout the entire magnetosphere, because it can only lead to a decrease of the total plasma energy, whereas observationally the plasma energy is known to increase as a result of diffusion from a source near $L \sim 7$ to the plasmapause. Nevertheless, the temperature and density gradients at the ring current inner edge and plasmapause provide a source of free energy for low-frequency drift waves. Therefore, Bohm diffusion might produce rapid spatial transport over a limited radial distance, drawing on parallel particle energy to increase the perpendicular energy as required by first invariant conservation. Since the pitch-angle anisotropy increases in this process, Cornwall (1970) has suggested that drift-wave radial diffusion and anisotropy-driven precipitation form a nonlinear feedback system, whereby the dissipation rates of both are enhanced.

Although the turbulent wave fields required for Bohm diffusion have yet to be theoretically evaluated, a reasonable assumption is that Bohm diffusion can rapidly transport protons across the plasmapause or onto drift orbits that intersect the plasmapause when the spatial plasma gradients are large, namely on the nightside during storms. Extension of this mechanism to other local times and to the ring current outer edge is uncertain. The Bohm diffusion coefficient can be roughly estimated as

$$D_B \sim \frac{1}{10} \left(\frac{T_+}{M_+} \right) \frac{1}{\Omega_+}, \tag{6}$$

where T_+ is the ion thermal energy. The numerical factor multiplying the Bohm scaling parameters has arbitrarily been taken as $1/10$. Assuming that the 50 keV protons diffuse approximately on Earth radius from the ring current maximum to the plasmapause at $L \sim 4$, equation (6) yields a Bohm diffusion time of $\tau_B \sim 4 \times 10^3$ sec. Thus radial diffusion can maintain a rapid source of protons into the plasmasphere, whereupon they are precipitated by a resonant interaction with ion-cyclotron turbulence. In this way the effective lifetime of the bulk of the protons outside the plasmasphere is governed by the speed of transport across the plasmapause. Those protons at or near the plasmapause may be expected to have lifetimes of an hour or so, as governed by wave turbulence.

d. *Plasmasphere expansion.* – During the recovery phase the region of co-rotating plasma moves outward to $L \sim 6$, and the plasmasphere reforms by ambipolar diffusion of cold plasma from the ionsphere (Carpenter 1966) or by co-rotation of the bulge region (Chappell et al. 1970b). The expanding plasmasphere envelops the outer part of the ring current, which, since it is now in a region of high density, becomes unstable to ion-cyclotron waves. Therefore, even if the spatial plasma gradients are too small to drive Bohm diffusion during the recovery phase of a geomagnetic storm, ion-cyclotron turbulent precipitation is still an effective sink for ring current protons.

Turbulent precipitation lifetimes and wave intensities

We now estimate the loss rate for ring current protons that have been transported into the plasmasphere. A wave traversing the unstable region, within $\varDelta \simeq \pm 10°$ of the equatorial plane, is amplified by a factor e^G where

$$G = \int \frac{ds}{v_G} \, \gamma_{CYC} \approx \frac{2 \, L \, R_E \, \varDelta}{C_A} \, \gamma_{CYC}. \tag{7}$$

Here ds is the arc length along the field lines, v_G is the group velocity which is essentially the Alfvén speed, $C_A = B/(4\pi \, NM_+)^{\frac{1}{2}}$, and R_E is 1 Earth radius. For $L \sim 4$ and $\gamma_{CYC} \approx 1$ sec^{-1}, equation (7) yields $G \sim 20$. Long before amplification of this order is reached, the growth rate and anisotropy are reduced by diffusion and precipitation. The large total wave growth, however, indicates that ring current protons and ion cyclotron waves should approach the strong pitch-angle diffusion limit (Kennel & Petschek 1966).

In strong diffusion the proton loss rate is given by the minimum precipitation lifetime (Kennel & Petschek 1966, Kennel 1969).

$$\tau_{min} = 2 \, \tau_B/\alpha_o^2, \tag{8}$$

where τ_B is the quarter bounce time of a proton in the geomagnetic field, and α_o is the equatorial half angle of the loss cone. For a 50 keV proton at $L \sim 4$, we find $\tau_{min} \sim 2000$ sec. This lifetime is consistent with the estimates made by Frank (1970) based on observations of the ring current midnight-noon asymmetry and it also agrees with the substorm recovery time scale during the storm main phase. Also note that turbulent precipitation lifetimes can be an order of magnitude less than those attributed to charge exchange.

We may now estimate the expected equatorial intensity of ion-cyclotron waves by equating the pitch-angle diffusion coefficient to the inverse of the minimum lifetime:

$$D_\alpha \sim \Omega_+ \left(\frac{B'}{B}\right)^2 \approx \frac{1}{\tau_{min}}. \tag{9}$$

At $L = 4$, we find $\tau_{min} = 2000$ sec, and (9) yields $B' \sim 1 \, \gamma$. It is clear that such intensities will not be seen on the ground, because of internal reflection and damping along the high-latitude regions of the line of force (see section 4) and in the ionosphere. We note, however that recently Kenney et al. (1968) and Heacock (1971) have observed Pc 1 micropulsations localized on the plasmapause and that the substorm associated IPDP emissions have a local time and latitude range (Jacobs 1970) similar to the waves predicted above.

Although a precise identification of the ion-cyclotron turbulence associated with the ring current decay will be difficult, these concepts can still be tested experimentally by measuring precipitated proton fluxes. Cornwall et al. (1971b) have recently measured the precipitation of ring current protons on a low-altitude satellite and find approximate agreement with the above theoretical model. During disturbed conditions they report precipitation proton fluxes in the range 10^7 to 10^8 cm^{-2} sec^{-1}. On passes where a correlation with the plasmapause location can be made, they observed either peaks in the precipitation flux or an inner edge of an extended precipitation

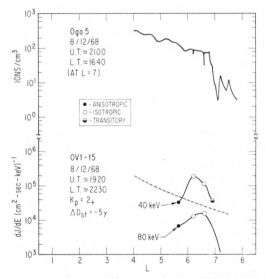

Fig. 5. Late afternoon plasmapause measurements and fitted omnidirectional 40 and 80 keV proton fluxes vs L taken at approximately the same universal time (Cornwall et al. 1971b). The L^{-4} function, shown as the dashed curve, separates the isotropic 40 keV fluxes from those with anisotropic pitch-angle distributions. These precipitating fluxes occurred during a relatively quiet time (see K_p) near midnight. $\varDelta D_{st}$ is the change in D_{st} from 1900 to 2000 UT.

192

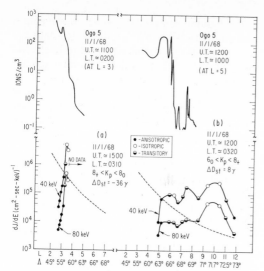

Fig. 6. Comparison of both early and late morning Ogo 5 plasma measurements and OV1–15 40 and 80 keV proton fluxes for November 1, 1968 (Cornwall et al. 1971 b). Lack of high L measurements in (a) was due to telemetry shut-off.

region near the plasmapause, as depicted in Figs. 5 and 6. Furthermore the peak precipitation fluxes are essentially isotropic, in agreement with the concept of strong pitch-angle diffusion. While the particle energies shown in Fig. 5 and 6 are a little too high to be considered as the main bulk of the ring current, the results are indicative that considerable proton energy is dissipated just within the plasmapause. Implications of the energy dissipation will be considered in the following sections.

4. PHENOMENA RELATED TO THE STORM–TIME GENERATION OF INTENSE ION–CYCLOTRON TURBULENCE AT THE PLASMAPAUSE

The turbulent dissipation of ring current energy in the vicinity of the plasmapause provides an intense source of ion-cyclotron wave energy which has the potential of severely modifying the distribution of other particles in the magnetosphere with which it can resonate. The ramifications of such parasitic interactions will be explored in the present section. We shall concentrate on two processes which have already received detailed evaluation. These are the Landau absorption of obliquely propagating wave energy by thermal plasmaspheric electrons (Cornwall et al. 1971a) and the Doppler shifted cyclotron resonance with re-

lativistic electrons (Thorne & Kennel 1971 b). Other processes such as the parasitic removal of high energy Davis-Williamson protons at the plasmapause should undoubtedly also occur and they are currently under investigation.

SAR arc formation at the plasmapause

Stable auroral red arcs are highly monochromatic 6300°A emissions resulting from the decay of the first excited state of atomic oxygen. Their basic properties have already been reviewed by Noxon in this symposium so I will not describe them in detail. Several points, however, should be reemphasized:

There is now a considerable body of experimental evidence linking SAR arcs to geomagnetic field lines passing just within the plasmapause or alternatively with the equatorial edge of the ionospheric trough (Clark et al. 1969, Norton & Findlay 1969, Glass et al. 1970, Chandra et al. 1971, Chappell et al. 1971). The spectral purity of the 6300°A red line emissions indicate excitation by thermal conduction from a magnetospheric heat source (Cole 1965, 1967) rather than by direct particle precipitation. Local electric field heating has been ruled out by recent temperature measurements (Norton & Findlay 1969, Roble et al. 1970, Chandra et al. 1971). Finally, the energy source for the SAR must be capable of maintaining a roughly constant arc intensity for periods exceeding 10 hours. During this period, which is usually associated with the recovery phase of a storm, approximately one quarter of the energy content of the ring current must be efficiently transferred to the ionosphere.

In 1965 Cole established the direct link between the dissipation of ring current energy and the SAR arc and established a model for the thermal conduction of heat to the ionosphere. One major problem with Cole's theory is the means by which ring current proton energy is used to heat plasmaspheric electrons. Cole employed the process of Coulomb dissipation. This was possible for the 1 keV protons that Cole hypothesized to be the major ring current constituent, but it is completely inadequate at the observed mean ring current energy near 30 keV (Frank 1967). Cornwall et al. (1971a) have recently considered an alternative energy exchange process which utilized the absorption of the intense ring current generated ion-cyclotron turbulence as a major heat source for SAR arcs. The salient features of this theory are described below.

13

We have already indicated that highly oblique propagating ion cyclotron waves will undergo a damping Landau resonant interaction with thermal electrons in the plasmasphere. The rate of wave damping is given by equation (4). The interaction is important since thermal (few eV) electrons have a velocity close to the wave phase velocity and oblique propagation is required to ensure sufficient wave electric fields which are needed for a net wave-particle energy exchange.

An inspection of the Landau damping rate (equation 4) shows it to be an extremely sensitive function of the wave frequency, the wave normal angle θ, and the ratio between the electron thermal speed and the local Alfvén speed. Because our ultimate goal is to determine the total path-integrated absorption of the ion-cyclotron turbulence generated by ring current protons near the geomagnetic equatorial plane, it is mandatory that wave parameters be known precisely along a ray path. Calculations were therefore performed using the Stanford ray tracing program to follow representative ion-cyclotron waves propagating through a model magnetosphere. A dipole magnetic field was adopted and the computations were performed at $L = 3$ which is the most probable location of red arcs (Roach & Roach 1963). Two density models were used: a) diffusive equilibrium, which is probably most representative of the quiet time plasmasphere; b) the gyrofrequency model, $N/B = $ constant, which is more appropriate for collisionless plasma conditions encountered during the plasmasphere repopulation when large-density gradients along the field are possible. The actual density distribution near the expanding plasmapause probably resides between these two extremes.

The selection of initial conditions for the ray tracing calculations is, of course, somewhat arbitrary. Ion-cyclotron unstable growth probably occurs for a latitude range of order $\pm 20°$ about the equator. In addition, a large range of wave normal angles are likely to be unstable (Kennel & Wong 1967, Dobes 1970). Clearly, the fate of every wavelet in the turbulent wave spectrum cannot be determined. Therefore we choose to follow test waves which start at a latitude of $-20°$ with propagation vectors parallel to the ambient field and then propagate across the equatorial plane towards the ionosphere. These waves spend a maximum time in the unstable growth region, and hence might be expected to dominate the wave spectrum. We can thus at best determine a representative electron Landau absorption rate.

The Landau damping decrement was evaluated at small latitude intervals along the ray path, and then integrated to obtain the total residual wave energy exp $[- \int 2\,|\gamma_L|\, dt]$ or the total electron absorption coefficient a $= 1 - \exp [- \int 2\,|\gamma_L|\, dt]$. As an example, in Fig. 7 the instantaneous Landau damping rate $|\gamma_L|$ for waves with $\omega/\Omega_+ = 2/3$ at the equator is plotted against latitude; recall that ion-cyclotron instability at the equator requires a proton anisotropy $A^+ \sim 2$ for $\omega/\Omega_+ = 2/3$. As will be demonstrated below, the electron temperature of 2 eV is typical of SAR-arc conditions and the equatorial electron density $N = 300$ cm^{-3} is appropriate for the expanding plasmapause. Notice that $|\gamma_L|$ remains small for the first 20° of propagation, thus ensuring a large region of uninhibited ion-cyclotron unstable growth; it then peaks strongly near 15°-20° latitude. $|\gamma_L|$ rises due to the increase in the wave normal angle θ, which reaches about 80 to 85° near the peak. The rapid decrease in $|\gamma_L|$ at high latitudes is due to the increase of the Alfvén velocity which from equation (4) exponentially reduces $|\gamma_L|$ when $c_A \gg c_T$. Both density models yield similar damping decrements although the $N/B = $ constant model has a slightly broader region of wave damping. Since the density models differ appreciably only at high latitudes, where $|\gamma_L| \to O$ anyway, the calculation is expected to be reasonably insensitive to the actual density

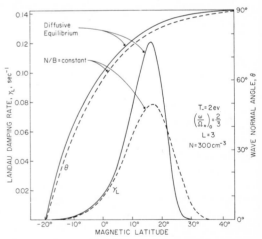

Fig. 7. The thermal electron Landau damping rate of ion-cyclotron waves is plotted against latitude along a typical magnetospheric ray path for both diffusive equilibrium and gyrofrequency (N/B = const.) density models. The wave normal angle between the magnetic field and propagation vector is also shown.

194

distribution. The path-integrated damping decrement for this case was $\int 2\,|\gamma_L|\,dt \sim 2$, so that approximately 80% of the wave energy should have been absorbed by plasmaspheric electrons.

In Fig. 8 the residual wave energy $(B'_{final})^2/(B'_{initial})^2 = \exp\,[-\int 2\,|\gamma_L|\,dt] = 1 - a(T)$ is plotted against plasmaspheric electron temperature using the wave frequency ω/Ω_+ or critical anisotropy A^+ as a parameter. Again an equatorial density $N = 300\,\mathrm{cm}^{-3}$ at $L = 3$ was used. At low temperatures little Landau damping occurs since very few electrons are in Landau resonance with ion cyclotron waves. At temperatures above a few eV Landau absorption essentially saturates. Again note the relative insensitivity of the calculations to the model of electron density distribution. From Fig. 4 we conclude that under typical storm and recovery phase conditions when $A^+ \geq 1$, a sizeable fraction of the ion cyclotron wave energy will be Landau absorbed by thermal plasmaspheric electrons.

By starting waves at $-20°$ latitude, the above ray tracing computations are weighted in favor of attaining large wave normal angles and consequently large Landau damping decrements. Calculations have shown that waves starting parallel to the magnetic field at the equator reach wave normal angles of only about 60° near the peak in $|\gamma_L|$, and hence are only weakly Landau damped.

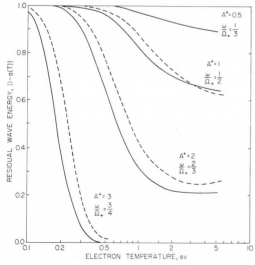

Fig. 8. Ray path integrated damping rates for both diffusive equilibrium (solid lines) and gyrofrequency (dotted lines) density models are used to plot the residual wave energy against electron temperature for various wave frequencies normalized to the equatorial proton gyrofrequency along the ray path.

On the other hand, such waves originating at the equator experience less unstable growth than waves starting at $-20°$ latitude and, due to the exponential nature of wave growth, should have considerably smaller amplitudes. However, since we have not solved for the ion-cyclotron unstable wave spectrum, our calculations are at best an approximate estimate of the overall electron Landau absorption of ion-cyclotron turbulence. Finally, since the group velocity of ion-cyclotron waves is essentially guided along the magnetic field (a result which is confirmed by all ray tracing computations performed here), the wave energy is absorbed by electrons in a small region approximately $1/2\,R_e$ wide just within the plasmapause.

The electron heating rate from Landau absorption of ion-cyclotron turbulence is approximately given by

$$F_L = a(T)\,F_{wave}, \tag{10}$$

where $a(t) = 1 - \exp\,[-\int 2\,|\gamma_L|\,dt]$ is the absorption coefficient evaluated in Fig. 8 and F_{wave} (≈ 0.15 ergs cm^{-2} sec^{-1}) is the total wave energy flux into the ionosphere which is obtained by assuming a turbulent r.m.s. wave amplitude $B' = 2$ gammas. Since some waves may never attain large wave normal angles and are consequently not Landau damped, we compensate for this inefficiency by taking $F_{wave} = 0.1$ ergs cm^{-2} sec^{-1} in what follows.

Electrons are also heated by proton Coulomb dissipation. Since ring current protons are lost before they can penetrate $1/2\,R_e$ into the plasmasphere (Cornwall et al. 1970), the Coulomb dissipation will also be confined to a narrow region just inside the plasmapause. The energy flux to the ionosphere due to Coulomb dissipation of the ring current protons is

$$F_c = W_+/\tau_c, \tag{11}$$

where W_+ is the total energy contained in a tube of flux above an area of 1 cm^2 in the ionosphere and τ_c is the Coulomb dissipation time scale. For a storm of magnitude $D_{st} = 100$ gammas, we estimate $W_+ = 3 \times 10^4$ ergs cm^{-2}. Also for the ring current energy spectrum given by Frank (1967), we find $\tau_c = 10^6$ sec when $N \approx 300$ cm^{-3}. The net Coulomb energy flux to the ionosphere is therefore 0.03 ergs cm^{-2} sec^{-1}. Walker & Rees (1968) estimate that this should produce a red arc of intensity 100 Rayleighs.

Combining (10) and (11) we obtain a total energy flux to the ionosphere

$$F_{tot} = 0.1\,a\,(T) + 0.03\,(\mathrm{ergs\,cm}^{-2}\,\mathrm{sec}^{-1}). \tag{12}$$

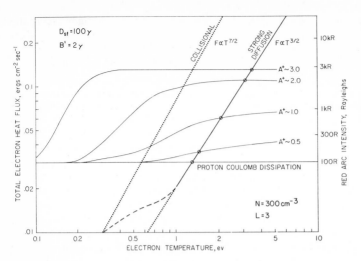

Fig. 9. The total electron heat flux to the ionosphere due to both proton Coulomb dissipation and Landau wave absorption is plotted against electron temperature. Intersection points with the collisionless 'Strong diffusion' conduction curve specify the equilibrium equatorial electron temperature and SAR-arc intensity.

In Fig. 9 the ray path calculations of a (T) are used to plot F_{tot} against electron temperature T_E for several proton anisotropies A^+ (or alternatively unstable wave frequencies $\omega/\Omega_+ = A^+/(1 + A^+)$). On the right-hand side of Fig. 9 the total electron heat flux is converted to SAR-arc intensity using the results of Walker & Rees (1968) or Roble (1969).

The equilibrium electron temperature and electron heat flux incident upon the ionosphere is obtained by equating F_{tot} to the heat conduction flux. For densities and temperatures under SAR arc conditions the plasmaspheric electrons are essentially collisionless and heat conduction is maintained by strong diffusion precipitation. The heat conduction flux appropriate for this case is shown by the heavy solid line in Fig. 9. (For comparison we have also indicated the collisional heat conduction flux used by Cole (1965)). At the intersection between the strong diffusion conduction curve and F_{tot} the electron heating rate is balanced by heat conduction losses. Thus for $A^+ = 1$, we obtain $T_E = 2.0$ eV and $F_{tot} = 0.06$ ergs cm^{-2} sec^{-1}; the corresponding SAR arc intensity is about 800 R. At larger proton anisotropies, the wave spectrum is dominated by higher frequency ion cyclotron waves which are subject to stronger electron Landau absorption. This results in a higher electron temperature, larger electron heat flux, and a more intense SAR arc. We furthermore observe that the ring current proton; ion-cyclotron wave; electron Landau absorption model when combined with proton Coulomb dissipation can provide a sufficient electron heat flux to the ionosphere to excite the observed range of SAR arc intensities.

So far only the equilibrium state has been discussed. The temporal evolution of the electron temperature from cold plasmaspheric values of perhaps as low as 0.2 eV to SAR arc values is undetermined. Although we do not explicitly solve for it, the temporal development of the electron temperature can be qualitatively obtained from. 9. Suppose initially that $T_E \ll 0.6$ eV. Then, as soon as the ring current overlaps the plasmapause, proton Coulomb dissipation starts electron heating. Landau absorption contributes negligibly unless $A^+ \sim 2$ to 3. The electron temperature rises since heat conduction losses are less than heat input. By the time $T_E \sim 0.6$ eV, electron Landau absorption of ion cyclotron turbulence has begun to contribute to the total heat flux F_{tot}. The energy flux and electron temperature continue to increase until the heating rate is balanced by strong diffusion heat conduction to the ionosphere. Thus, although capable of sustaining only about a 100 R SAR arc, proton Coulomb dissipation is important for raising the electron temperature to values at which electron Landau absorption becomes efficient. Of course, during main phase, there may be other processes acting in conjunction with Coulomb dissipation to heat the electrons to this critical temperature.

The numerical estimates in Fig. 9 are based on specific values of various magnetospheric parameters: $D_{st} = 100$ gammas, $L = 3$, $N = 300$ cm^{-3}, and $B' = 2$ gammas. Clearly, the sensitivity of the equilibrium red arc intensity to plasmapause location and structure, proton anisotropy, and the ion-cyclotron turbulent wave spectrum suggests that red arc intensities are not uniquely determined by D_{st} alone, and that for a given D_{st} value a wide

196

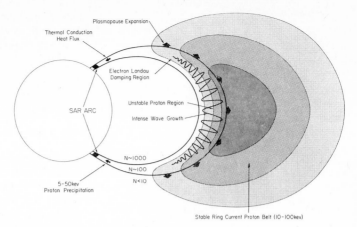

Fig. 10. A synopsis of the energy transfer processes responsible for SAR-arc formation at the plasmapause.

range of arc intensities is possible. Since our theoretical estimates are rather imprecise, simultaneous measurements of all the above variables are needed to firmly establish the interrelations between the various parameters and red arc intensity.

The major features of this unified model for SAR arc formation are summarized in Fig. 10.

a) During the rapid recovery phase of a magnetic storm, the plasmapause moves outward into the approximately symmetric ring current. When N reaches ~ 100, ring current protons destabilize ion-cyclotron waves and are precipitated; a narrow zone, $1/2$ R_e wide, of ion-cyclotron turbulence is formed just inside the expanding plasmapause.

b) Ring current protons dissipate about half their energy in ion-cyclotron waves. A small fraction of the proton energy is dissipated in Coulomb collisions with thermal electrons. The remaining proton energy is lost as precipitation.

c) Obliquely propagating ion-cyclotron waves have resonant Landau damping interactions with thermal plasmaspheric electrons. The rate of Landau absorption depends sensitively on total density, electron temperature, wave normal angle, and proton anisotropy.

d) Calculations of the total path-integrated electron Landau absorption coefficient demonstrate that a significant fraction, approaching unity for high electron temperatures and large proton anisotropies, of the ion-cyclotron turbulent wave energy is converted into electron heat.

e) For a 100 gamma D_{st} storm the total electron heat flux provided by Landau absorption and proton Coulomb dissipation is sufficient to excite SAR arcs with intensities of several hundred R's to a few kR's.

The above model predicts that:

f) SAR arcs should be localized to lines of force which lie just inside the plasmapause.

g) The north-south latitudinal extent of SAR arcs should be several hundred kilometers.

h) SAR arcs should occur at essentially all local times, with a latitude vs local time dependence similar to that of the plasmapause. Hence at a given local time SAR arcs should exhibit a general motion to higher latitudes as the rapid recovery phase progresses.

i) SAR arcs should persist throughout the rapid recovery phase, or about half to one day. Red arc intensities should greatly diminish after proton fluxes are reduced to the stably trapped limit; after this point only Coulomb dissipation remains but is weakened by the lower proton fluxes.

j) The SAR arc intensity depends sensitively on the proton anisotropy; large anisotropies produce more intense red arcs.

Relativistic electron precipitation at the plasmapause

Early geiger tube measurements of trapped relativistic electrons found pronounced flux depletions in the outer radiation belts during magnetic storms (Forbush et al. 1961, 1962, Rosser 1963). Somewhat later, this characteristic *drop* in relativistic electron flux was shown to coincide with a pronounced *injection* of lower energy particles (Frank et al. 1964, Craven 1966, Frank 1966, Owens & Frank 1968). This storm-time anticorrelation is typically most pronounced near $L = 4$, where the relativistic electrons fluxes can decrease by factors of 10 to 100 (see Fig. 11), coincident with a low energy ($E_e \ll 1$ MeV) electron flux increase by a similar factor. In the remainder of

197

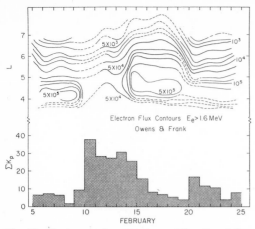

Fig. 11. Contours of constant omnidirectional flux for electrons (E > 1.6 MeV) at the magnetic equator. Notice the pronounced dropout between 3.5 < L < 5 at the onset of the geomagnetic storm.

this section I will outline a mechanism which accounts for this selective loss of high-energy electrons from a region bounded by the minimum and maximum L-shells intersected by the storm-time plasmapause. The loss involves resonant Doppler-shifted pitch-angle scattering of relativistic electrons throughout the region of intense ring current generated ion-cyclotron turbulence.

The condition for Doppler-shifted cyclotron resonance with relativistic electrons is

$$\omega - k_{\parallel}v_{\parallel} = \frac{n\Omega}{\gamma}, \tag{13}$$

where ω is the wave frequency, $k_{\parallel}$ and $v_{\parallel}$ are the wave propagation vector and the electron velocity components parallel to the ambient magnetic field respectively, n is an integer denoting the harmonic order of the resonance, Ω_- is the non-relativistic electron cyclotron frequency, $\gamma = (1 - v^2/c^2)^{-\frac{1}{2}}$ is the relativistic mass enhancement factor, and c is the velocity of light. Using the ion-cyclotron wave dispersion relation $\mu \simeq (c/c_A)(1 - \omega/\Omega_+)^{-\frac{1}{2}}$, where c_A is the Alfvén speed, (13) becomes

$$(\gamma^2 - 1)^{\frac{1}{2}} \simeq$$
$$\frac{n}{\cos \alpha} \left(\frac{2E_M}{E_0} \frac{M_+}{M_-} \right)^{\frac{1}{2}} \frac{\Omega_+}{\omega} \left(1 - \frac{\omega}{\Omega_+} \right)^{\frac{1}{2}}, \tag{14}$$

where α is the pitch angle, $E_M = B^2/8\pi N$ is the magnetic energy per particle, $E_0 = M_-c^2$ is the electron rest energy, and M_+/M_- is the ion to electron rest mass ratio. Using the relation $E_R/E_0 = \gamma - 1$, where E_R is the kinetic energy of the resonant electrons, and knowing the spatial varia-

tion of $E_M = B^2/B\pi N$, we can estimate E_R at each point in the magnetosphere. The variation of this resonant energy along the equatorial plane is plotted in Fig. 12 assuming a typical wave frequency $\omega/\Omega_+ = \frac{1}{2}$. We see that throughout the magnetosphere only electrons with energies $E_R \gtrsim$ 1 MeV can resonate with ion-cyclotron waves. Furthermore, the resonant energy is near 1 MeV only in the equatorial region just inside the plasmapause. Outside the plasmapause the resonant energy is a factor of 10 to 30 larger. Thus, even if ion-cyclotron waves existed beyond the plasmapause, they would not interact with MeV electrons. The MeV electron precipitation region should therefore be restricted to a narrow zone just within the plasmapause.

Since the resonant relativistic electrons Doppler-shift the low frequency ion cyclotron waves to their own gyrofrequency we can use an approximate estimate of the quasi-linear diffusion coefficient given by Dungey (1965) or Kennel & Petschek (1966) for weak pitch-angle scattering:

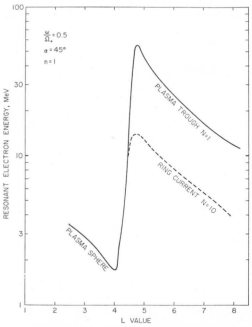

Fig. 12. The energy of electrons with 45° pitch angle resonant at the magnetic equator with $\omega/\Omega_+ = 0.5$ ion-cyclotron waves is plotted against L value. The sharp increase at L ≃ 4.5 is caused by the pronounced drop in density at the plasmapause. Beyond the plasmapause, two curves have been plotted, one assuming typical thermal plasma densities (N ≃ 1 cm^{-3}) and the other assuming ring current proton densities (N ≃ 10 cm^{-3}).

198

$$D_{\alpha} = \frac{< (\Delta\alpha)^2 >}{2\,\Delta t} \simeq \left(\frac{B'}{B}\right)^2 \frac{\Omega_-}{\gamma}\, f. \qquad (15)$$

Here B' is the ion cyclotron wave amplitude, B is the ambient magnetic field strength, and f is the fraction of the electron bounce period spent in resonance with the ion-cyclotron waves. During the main phase of a geomagnetic storm, we have estimated that ion cyclotron wave amplitudes $B' \simeq 1$ gamma are needed to remove the ring current proton within one hour. At $L = 4$ we take $f = \frac{1}{4}$, $\Omega_- = 10^5$ rads sec^{-1}, and $B = 500$ gammas to give a rough estimate for the effective $> $ MeV electron loss time as

$$\tau_{\text{loss}} \sim D_{\alpha}^{-1} \sim 30 \text{ secs.} \qquad (16)$$

This, however, is comparable to the minimum lifetime τ_{min} expected from strong pitch-angle diffusion (Kennel & Petschek 1966, Kennel 1969) of relativistic electrons at $L = 4$;

$$\tau_{\text{min}} = \frac{2\,\tau_B}{\alpha_0^2} \approx 20 \text{ secs.} \qquad (17)$$

Here τ_B is the quarter bounce time for the electrons and α_0 is the size of the atmospheric loss cone. We therefore conclude that the intense ion-cyclotron turbulence generated by ring current protons should remove relativistic electrons near the maximum rate. Such a rapid removal of relativistic electrons should produce a nearly isotropic precipitation flux J_P. The ratio of the precipitated to trapped fluxes J_P/J_T (Coroniti & Kennel 1970) is

$$\frac{J_P}{J_T} \simeq \frac{\tau_{\text{min}}}{\tau_{\text{loss}}}. \qquad (18)$$

Thus the observed omnidirectional prestorm fluxes of 10^5 to 10^6 electrons cm^{-2} sec^{-1} measured by Pfitzer et al. (1966) and Owens & Frank (1968) for $E_e > 1$ MeV indicate that precipitation fluxes the order of a few times 10^5 cm^{-2} sec^{-1} might be observable during the initial phase of a magnetic storm. This precipitation should be localized to a region just within the plasmapause, and should produce significant ionization in the D-region of the upper atmosphere.

It remains for us to consider the morphology of the region of rapid electron removal. In Fig. 13 we sketch the drift orbits and the expected spatial distribution of ring current protons during main phase. The proton lifetimes estimated by Cornwall et al. (1970) imply that protons are only able to drift the order of $\frac{1}{2}$ R$_E$ into the plasmasphere before they are precipitated. Assuming a storm-

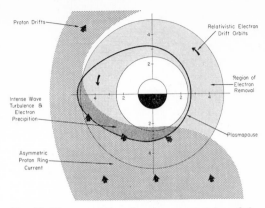

Fig. 13. The expected main-phase asymmetry of the ring current protons is shown in relation to the local time asymmetry of the plasmapause. Strong ion-cyclotron turbulence, generated in the region of overlap, causes a rapid precipitation of both low-energy protons (5–50 keV) and relativistic electrons in the region just within the plasmapause between dusk and midnight.

time injection of protons from the magnetospheric tail we thus expect intense ion-cyclotron turbulence along the outer edge of the bulge region (Carpenter 1966, Chappell et al. 1970b) of the plasmasphere. This is shown by the heavily hatched region in Fig. 13. Relativistic electrons have roughly circular drift orbits for $L < 6$. Because of the asymmetry of the plasmasphere in the bulge region, electron drift orbits between $L \sim 2.5$ and $L \sim 5$ can pass through the storm-time region of ion-cyclotron turbulence. The short electron lifetimes estimated above suggest that the relativistic electrons on these drift orbits should be completely removed after a few drifts across the turbulent region. This expected L range of electron loss compares favorably with that found experimentally (Fig. 11). It should, however, be emphasized that the region of electron precipitation is determined by the region of ion-cyclotron turbulence and is probably confined to the dusk to midnight quadrant. Shortly after this work was completed Vampola (1971) reported direct experimental evidence for the preferential strong diffusion precipitation of relativistic electrons near the plasmapause.

5. MAGNETIC STORM MODEL

I will conclude by summarizing the principal phenomena associated with the turbulent decay of the ring current in the form of a speculative model for a magnetic storm, sketched in Fig. 14

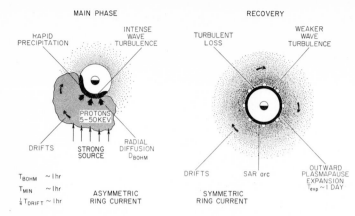

Fig. 14. A review of the magnetic storm model presented by Cornwall et al. (1970). Five to 50 keV protons injected from the magnetospheric tail during magnetic storm main phase become highly unstable and are precipitated just inside the plasmapause. During the storm recovery the slow outward expansion of the plasmasphere erodes the symmetric ring current along the inner edge.

Main phase

Our major conclusion is that low-energy ring current protons with energies between 10 to 100 keV are stable to ion-cyclotron turbulence over a broad zone just outside the plasmapause, but are subject to strongly unstable pitch-angle scattering inside the plasmasphere and at large radial distance in the proton auroral zone. During magnetospheric substorms, plasmasheet protons are rapidly convected towards the Earth across the unstable auroral zone and thereby injected into the stable ring current zone. Plasmasheet electrons are subject to more rapid precipitation throughout the region of mantle auroras and are probably removed before they reach the stable ring current belt.

Successive substorm injection during the main phase of a geomagnetic storm produces a strong asymmetric proton ring current in the dusk to midnight quadrant of the outer radiation belts (see Fig. 14). Subsequent guiding center drifts and radial diffusion carry the protons into the ion-cyclotron unstable bulge region of the plasmasphere, where they experience rapid precipitation loss within a period of a few hours. The protons between 3 to 5 Earth radii are thereby removed from the ring current before they can drift to local noon, thus establishing the highly asymmetric ring current belt observed during main phase (Frank 1970).

The ion-cyclotron turbulent amplitude required to remove protons at the strong pitch-angle diffusion rate ($\tau_{loss} \sim 1$ hr) typically exceeds 1 gamma. The loss is sufficiently rapid to prevent the energetic protons from penetrating more than $\frac{1}{2}$ R_e into the plasmasphere. This accounts for the striking coincidence between the plasmapause and the inner edge of the ring current shown in Fig. 1.

The intense ion-cyclotron turbulence generated by the decay of the ring current will also interact with other particles in the radiation belts. During the main phase we expect relativistic electrons with energies above 1 MeV and high-energy protons to be parasitically removed throughout the zone of intense ion-cyclotron turbulence.

Recovery

With the cessation of substorm associated injection events the protons located in the regions of trapping exterior to the plasmapause but interior to the auroral zone complete drift orbits around the earth to produce a symmetric ring current belt (see Fig. 14). The reduction of the average convection electric field across the geomagnetic tail allows the region of co-rotation to move to larger radial distances. The plasmasphere thus expands outwards into the enlarged co-rotation region due to the combined processes of bulge co-rotation or by upward ambipolar diffusion. When the plasma density exceeds the threshold value required for ion-cyclotron instability protons are removed by precipitation. The symmetric ring current belt is thus eroded away along its inner edge which keeps pace with the expanding plasmapause (Fig. 1).

Low-energy protons injected deep into the stable ring current zone probably have highly anisotropic pitch-angle distributions. Rothwell et al. (1970) have already reported large proton anisotropies at energies above 100 keV and the lower-energy protons may be expected to exhibit even large anisotropy since they are not subject to any known form of resonant scattering. Be-

200

cause of this we expect the ensuing ion-cyclotron turbulence to be dominated by high frequencies, $\omega \approx \Omega_+/2$. This is important on two accounts. Resonance at high frequencies implies a considerable energy loss from the particles in the process of scattering towards the loss cone (Gendrin 1968) and in addition high-frequency waves are subject to severe Landau damping when they propagate obliquely to the magnetic field. Ray tracing calculations show that waves generated along the magnetic field direction near the equator rapidly rotate the direction of their propagation vector as as they travel towards the ionosphere. A considerable portion of the wave energy can thus be absorbed by resonant thermal plasmaspheric electrons. Approximately one quarter of the total ring current energy can be efficiently transferred to heating the plasmaspheric electrons in this two-step process. The dissipation of ring current energy into ion-cyclotron turbulence is therefore an important energy source for SAR arcs.

Because the 'proton ring current; ion-cyclotron wave; thermal electron' energy exchange process is confined to a narrow region just inside the plasmapause, SAR arcs should be located in a narrow region along the expanding plasmapause. Associated with the SAR arc emissions one expects to see precipitating relativistic electrons, ring current protons and higher energy Davis-Williamson protons. All of these have recently been observed in association with SAR arcs and it now remains for us to detect the ion-cyclotron waves which are thought to be the cause of such phenomena.

Acknowledgements: The work presented here has resulted from an extended collaboration with J. M. Cornwall, F. V. Coroniti, and C. F. Kennel. It has been supported in part by NASA grant NGR 05-007-190, Air Force contracts F04701-68-C-0200 and F 19628-71-C-0075, and NSF Grant GA-28045.

REFERENCES

Akasofu, S. I. 1968. *Polar and Magnetospheric Substorms*, Reidel Pub. Co., Dordrecht, Holland.
Andronov, A. A. & Trakhtengerts, V. Y. 1964. *Geomagn. Res. 4*, 181.
Axford, W. I. 1969. *Rev. Geophys. 7*, 421.
Axford, W. I. & Hines, C. O. 1961. *Can. J. Phys. 39*, 1433.
Axford, W. I., Petschek, H. E. & Siscoe, G. L. 1965. *J. Geophys. Res. 70*, 1231.
Barnes, A. 1966. *Phys. Fluids 9*, 1483.
Brice, N. 1967. *J. Geophys. Res. 73*, 5193.

Carpenter, D. L. 1966. *J. Geophys. Res. 71*, 693.
Carpenter, D. L. 1970. *J. Geophys. Res. 75*, 3837.
Chandra, S., Maier, E. J. R., Troy, B. E., Jr. & Narasinga Rao, B. C. 1971. *J. Geophys. Res. 76*, 920.
Chappell, C. R., Harris, K. K. & Sharp, G. W. 1970 a. *J. Geophys. Res. 75*, 50.
Chappell, C. R., Harris, K. K. & Sharp, G. W. 1970 b. *J. Geophys. Res. 75*, 3848.
Chappell, C. R., Harris, K. K. & Sharp, G. W. 1971. *J. Geophys. Res. 76*, 2357.
Clark, W. L., McAfee, J. R., Norton, R. B. & Warnock, W. M. 1969. *Proc. I. E. E. E. 57*, 493.
Cocke, W. J. & Cornwall, J. M. 1967. *J. Geophys. Res. 72*, 2843.
Cole, K. D. 1965. *J. Geophys. Res. 70*, 1689.
Cole, K. D. 1967. In Matsushita, S. & Campbell, W. M. (eds.). *Physics of Geomagnetic Phenomenon*, Academic Press, New York.
Cornwall, J. M. 1965. *J. Geophys. Res. 70*, 61.
Cornwall, J. M. 1966. *J. Geophys. Res. 71*, 2185.
Cornwall, J. M. 1968. *Radio Sci. 3*, 740.
Cornwall, J. M. 1970. In McCormac, B. M. (ed.). *Particles and Fields in the Magnetosphere*, Reidel Pub. Co., Dordrecht, Holland.
Cornwall, J. M., Coroniti, F. V. & Thorne, R. M. 1970. *J. Geophys. Res.* 4699.
Cornwall, J. M., Coriniti, F. V. & Thorne, R. M. 1971 a. *J. Geophys. Res. 76*, 4428.
Cornwall, J. M., Hilton, H. H. & Mizera, P. F. 1971 b. *J. Geophys. Res. 76*, 5220.
Coroniti, F. V. & Kennel, C. F. 1970. *J. Geophys. Res. 75*, 1279.
Craven, J. D. 1966. *J. Geophys. Res. 71*, 5643.
Davis, L. R. & Williamson, J. M. 1963. *Space Res. 3*, 365.
Dessler, A. J. & Parker, E. N. 1959. *J. Geophys. Res. 64*, 2239.
Dessler, A. J., Hanson, W. B. & Parker, E. N. 1961. *J. Geophys. Res. 66*, 3631.
Dobes, K. 1970. *Planet. Space Sci. 18*, 395.
Dungey, J. W. 1965. *Space Sci. Rev. 4*, 199.
Eather, R. M. & Carovillano, R. L. 1971. *Cosmic Electrodynamics 11*, 142.
Fälthammer, C. G. 1966. *J. Geophys. Res. 71*, 1487.
Forbush, S. E., Pizzella, G. & Venkatesen, D. 1962. *J. Geophys. Res. 67*, 3651.
Forbush, S. E., Venkatesan, D. & McIlwain, C. E. 1961. *J. Geophys. Res. 66*, 2275.
Frank, L. A. 1966. *J. Geophys. Res. 71*, 4631.
Frank, L. A. 1967. *J. Geophys. Res. 72*, 3753.
Frank, L. A. 1970. *J. Geophys. Res. 75*, 1263.
Frank, L. A., Van Allen, J. A. & Hills, H. K. 1964. *J. Geophys. Res. 69*, 2174.
Gendrin, R. 1968. *J. Atmos. Terr. Phys. 31*, 1313.
Glass, N. W., Wolcott, J. M., Miller, L. W. & Robertson, N. M. 1970. *J. Geophys. Res. 75*, 2579.
Haerendel, G. 1970. In McCormac, B. M. (ed.). *Particles and Fields in the Magnetosphere*, Reidel Pub. Co., Dordrecht, Holland.
Heacock, R. R. 1971. *J. Geophys. Res. 76*, 100.
Jacobs, J. A. 1970. *Geomagnetic Micropulsations*, Springer Verlag, New York.
Kennel, C. F. 1969. *Rev. Geophys. 7*, 379.
Kennel, C. F. & Englemann, R. 1966. *Phys. Fluids 9*, 2377.
Kennel, C. F. & Petschek, M. E. 1966. *J. Geophys. Res. 71*, 1.

Kennel, C. F. & Wong, M. V. 1967. *J. Plasma Phys.* *1*, 81.

Kenney, J. F., Knaflich, M. B. & Liemohn, H. B. 1968. *J. Geophys. Res. 73*, 6739.

Nishida, A. 1966. *J. Geophys. Res. 71*, 5609.

Norton, R. B. & Findlay, J. A. 1969. *Planet. Space Sci. 17*, 1867.

Owens, H. D. & Frank, L. A. 1968. *J. Geophys. Res. 72*, 199.

Pfitzer, K. A., Kane, A. S. & Winckler, J. R. 1966. *Space Res. 6*, 702.

Roach, F. E. & Roach, J. R. 1963. *Planet. Space Sci. 11*, 523.

Roble, R. G. 1969. Ph.D. thesis, University of Michigan.

Roble, R. G., Hays, P. B. & Nagy, A. F. 1970. *Planet. Space Sci. 18*, 431.

Roederer, J. G. 1968. In McCormac, B. M. (ed.). *Earth's Particles and Fields*, Reinhold, New York.

Rosser, W. G. 1963. *J. Geophys. Res. 68*, 3131.

Rothwell, P. L., Webb, V. M. & Katz, L. 1970. In McCormac, B. M. (ed.). *Particles and Fields in the Magnetosphere*, Reidel Pub. Co., Dordrecht, Holland.

Russell, C. T. & Thorne, R. M. 1970. *Cosmic Electrodynamics 1*, 67.

Sckopke, N. 1966. *J. Geophys. Res. 71*, 3125.

Spitzer, L., Jr. 1962. *Physics of Fully Ionized Gases*, Interscience, John Wiley, New York.

Swisher, R. L. & Frank, L. A. 1968. *J. Geophys. Res. 73*, 5665.

Taylor, H. A., Brinton, M. C. & Pharo, M. V. 1968. *J. Geophys. Res. 73*, 961.

Thorne, R. M. & Kennel, C. F. 1971a. *Comments on Astrophys. and Space Phys. 3*, 115.

Thorne, R. M. & Kennel, C. F. 1971b. *J. Geophys. Res.* In press.

Vampola, A. L. 1971. *J. Geophys. Res. 76*, 4685.

Walker, J. C. G. & Rees, M. M. 1968. *Planet. Space Sci. 16*, 915.

Magnetospheric Flows and Substorms

G. ATKINSON

Communications Research Center, Department of Communications, Ottawa

Abstract: The magnetospheric shape and the internal magnetospheric flow are discussed in view of recent measurements. It is likely that the flow is asymmetric with respect to the noon-midnight meridian plane and affected by ionospheric conductivity and plasma diamagnetism. The driving force for the flow is determined by the merging rate on the dayside and is independent of neutral sheet processes, except possibly during substorms.

The plasma sheet is discussed and the following conclusions are reached. There is a normal component of magnetic field in the neutral sheet. The plasma sheet is formed by flux tubes convecting in through the sides of the magnetotail. The flux tubes either reconnect immediately (merging model) or remain closed (viscous-drag model). The plasma in the plasma sheet provides the brake which a) creates the magnetotail by trapping field lines between it and the solar wind, and b) inhibits the collapse of field lines from a tail-like configuration to a dipole-like configuration between substorms, without restricting the large-scale flow. Substorms observations are summarized, and current theoretical models are discussed. A specific model of the substorm development is presented which fits the observations of substorm associated events in some detail, including the three-dimensional development.

1. INTRODUCTION

The aim in this paper is to review and clarify current understanding of the large-scale flow within the magnetosphere, with emphasis on the magnetospheric substorm. The discussion of the large-scale flow, which occupies the first half of the paper, is therefore limited to those areas which are relevant to an understanding of substorms. Several important topics such as the plasmasphere formation and the polar wind are omitted. Topics covered include the static configuration of the magnetosphere, current models of the large-scale flow and their weaknesses, stresses acting on and within the magnetosphere and the magnetospheric response to these, and the inferences that can be drawn about the large-scale flow from the existence of the plasma sheet.

The substorm is the subject of the second half of the paper. First the observations are reviewed, with emphasis on processes involving the most energy, then theoretical substorm models are discussed in the light of the earlier coverage of the response of the magnetosphere to stresses, and finally some of my previously published ideas are reorganized into a model that explains the three-dimensional development of the substorm.

Papers on the above topics are numerous. The review by Axford (1969) contains an extensive list of references, and the referencing herein is confined to more recent publications and to a few highly relevant older papers. Magnetohydrodynamic terminology will be used throughout, and we shall speak of the flow and convection of magnetic flux tubes in accord with the frozen field line concept, i.e. magnetic field lines and plasma move with the same velocity in the directions perpendicular to the magnetic field.

2. THE MAGNETOSPHERE – CONFIGURATION

Fig. 1a shows the generally-accepted magnetic field-line configuration in the noon-midnight meridian plane of the magnetosphere. The topology is important for the study of magnetospheric dynamics because the presence of plasma and the consequent freezing of field lines restricts the motions of field lines and plasma within the topology. There are two topologically diffferent forms of field lines: 'dipole-like' and 'tail-like'. The latter are field lines that are severely distorted from the dipole form, and are stretched on the nightside in a direction parallel to the solar wind velocity. Many of the interesting problems of magnetospheric dynamics are concerned with the changing of field lines from one topology to the other.

The neutral sheet divides the tail in half. It is

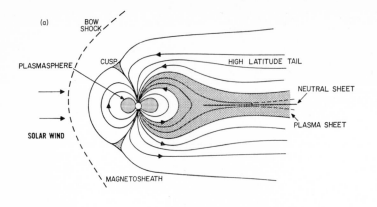

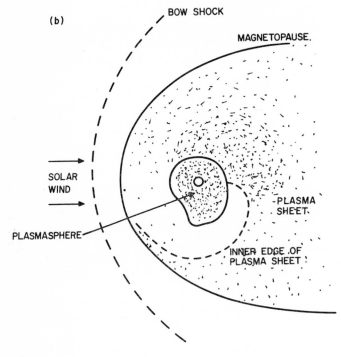

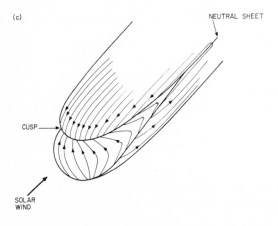

Fig. 1. The magnetosphere. a) Noon-midnight meridian section showing field lines and low energy (< 10 kev) plasma distribution. b) Equatorial section, composite of diagrams from Vasyliunas (1968b) and Frank (1971a). c) Pictorial view (similar to Walters 1966).

probable that most of the time there is a north-ward component of magnetic field through the neutral sheet (Mihalov et al. 1968, Behannon 1970), although Dessler & Hill (1970) argue otherwise. The latter configuration is shown by dashed lines in Fig. 1a. Arguments favouring a northward component through the neutral sheet will be presented later in the paper.

Adjacent to the neutral sheet, and extending into the region of dipole-like field lines is the plasma sheet, with two horns extending down to the auroral ovals (Vasyliunas 1968a). The plasma sheet reaches around the dusk equatorial plane of the dipole-like region toward noon and on the morningside probably extends into the plasma-pause (Frank 1971a). Fig. 1b is an equatorial section showing the plasma sheet location. It is obtained by combining the diagrams of Frank (1971a) and Vasyliunas (1968b). This may be an oversimplification and should be regarded as a schematic drawing of a time-averaged configuration.

The three-dimensional appearance of the magnetosphere is shown in Fig. 1c. It is similar to the model described by Piddington (1965). The surface field lines between the cusps are shown as being severely distorted in the antisolar direction, since even a weak viscous drag at the surface requires a small radius of curvature of the field lines to balance this force. The surface Chapman-Ferraro currents also add to the bending of field lines in the antisolar direction. One should add to a picture such as Fig. 1c a number of field lines coming out of the surface and connecting to the interplanetary field. The distribution of these depends on the interplanetary field and flow conditions.

Many features of the gross dynamics of the magnetosphere can be understood from a static magnetospheric model in which it is assumed:

1. The Chapman-Ferraro approximation holds on the boundary,
2. The neutral sheet is perfect (no normal magnetic component, and only normal plasma pressure).

In this model there are two dimensionless parameters and there exists a functional relationship between them:

$$\frac{F}{y_0^2 B_0} = f\left(\frac{M}{y_0^3 B_0}\right), \tag{1}$$

where F is the magnetic flux in the half-tail, B_0 is the magnetic field strength at the subsolar point (nose) of the magnetosphere (determined by the

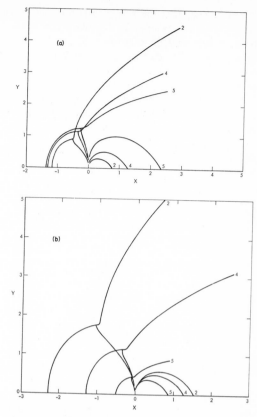

Fig. 2. Solutions to Chapman-Ferraro flow around a two-dimensional dipole, showing boundary, cusp, and last closed field lines. a) Three solutions with the same nose field strength, different tail fluxes. b) Three solutions with the same tail flux, different nose field strengths. Distances along the axes are in dimensionless units.

solar wind stagnation pressure), y_0 is a scale distance of the system (e.g. distance from the equatorial plane to the dayside cusp), and M is the dipole moment. The two independent variables are the tail flux and the solar wind stagnation pressure, and these two vary with time, giving different magnetospheric shapes. Unfortunately, we do not know the function f, although the equivalent problem has been solved for solar wind flow about a two-dimensional dipole (Unti & Atkinson 1968, Atkinson & Unti 1969a,b). Figs. 2a and 2b each show three solutions (upper half plane). Fig. 2a shows the behaviour of the boundary field line, field line to the cusp, and last closed field line on the nightside as F is varied with constant B_0 (case 2 has the largest F). Fig. 2b shows the same field lines for B_0 varying, F being held constant (case 5 has the largest B_0).

It can be seen that the major response to an increase in tail flux is an inward displacement of the neutral sheet and an expansion of the tail. The major response to increase in stagnation pressure is an inward motion of the nose of the magnetosphere.

Equation 1 describes equilibrium solutions for a static magnetosphere. In a dynamic magnetosphere, at any given time, the magnetic flux tubes are convecting toward the static solution for the existing F and B_0. Conversely, the existence of a flow indicates that the magnetosphere is distorted from the static configuration, and that the resulting unbalanced magnetic stress is the means by which the solar wind drives the internal convection of the magnetosphere.

3. THE MAGNETOSPHERE – DYNAMICAL FEATURES

The usual picture of the magnetospheric flow is the one shown in Fig. 3, which originated in the work of Dungey (1963). In this picture, a southward-directed interplanetary field line is convected by the solar wind to the dayside of the magnetosphere and merges with the outermost field line of the magnetospheric nose. The solar wind flow then drags the merged field lines over the polar cap and adds them to the outside of the magnetic tail. The field lines and plasma are subsequently convected to the neutral sheet where the field lines reconnect and collapse to a dipole-like form. They are then convected azimuthally around the earth to the dayside where they are ready to merge with the interplanetary field again. Axford (1969) gives a comprehensive review of the development of this model.

The above model is schematic, and is intended to be only a gross description of the flow. The complications are numerous, and I wish to discuss three of them here:

A three-dimensional dependence
B forces acting within the magnetosphere,
C temporal dependence.

Three-dimensional dependence

The stream lines of and the magnetic field lines in the interplanetary plasma are not confined to planes parallel to the noon-midnight meridian plane of the earth, as shown in the model of Fig. 3. The interplanetary magnetic field near the earth generally has a large component parallel to the plane of the ecliptic. Field line merging on the dayside of the magnetosphere would be expected to occur for any direction of the interplanetary field. For the case where the merging rate is limited by Alfvén wave velocities (Petschek 1964, Petschek & Thorne 1967), the rate is proportional to sin ($\theta/2$) where θ is the angle between the field lines in the two merging regions. Thus merging is still quite fast for $\theta = 90°$. The resulting magnetic stresses on the dayside of the magnetosphere should have east-west components. An 'away sector' in the solar wind would tend to drag north polar cap field lines around the morning side, and south polar cap field lines around the evening side. Another three-dimensional effect is introduced by the flow, which is axially symmetric about the sun-earth line.

The effects can be summarized as follows:

a. Merging is most rapid for the interplanetary field pointing southward, encouraging a flow that is symmetric about the noon-midnight meridian plane. Field lines are added to the top and bottom of the tail.

b. The interplanetary field is most frequently parallel to the ecliptic plane, encouraging a

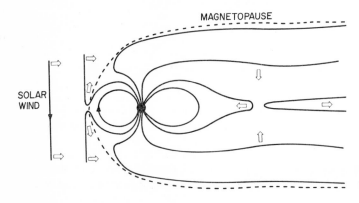

Fig. 3. Idealized picture of the magnetosphere flow. The arrows indicate the flow of plasma and field lines.

flow which is assymetric and most rapid just poleward of the cusps. The merged field lines are added at the sides of the tail.

c. The hydrodynamic flow is axially symmetric about the sun-earth line, tending to convect field lines away from the subsolar point.

The result must be a highly variable flow, as indicated by the diversity in the observations (Maynard 1971). The addition of field lines to the tail should be highly variable with time, and would occur frequently at the sides. In fact, if the merging is limited by Alfvén velocities, the sin $(\theta/2)$ term changes by only a factor of two in the range $60° < \theta < 180°$, and hence it is likely that b and c above dominate, with *most* of the field lines being added to the sides of the tail. Since the plasma sheet occupies one fifth of the tail surface, and is favourably located for this flow, one might expect that a reasonable fraction of the flow would be into the plasma sheet. This topic will be pursued further in a later section.

Magnetohydrodynamic forces acting within the magnetosphere

Neglecting anisotropies and considering time scales longer than proton gyro periods, the forces acting within the magnetosphere can be divided into three types:

Ionospheric forces: the ionosphere creates a stress at the feet of flux tubes due to their motion, or due to neutral winds. This stress is proportional to and antiparallel to the convective velocity relative to the E-region neutrals, and proportional to the Pedersen conductivity. It is usually called 'line-tying', or sometimes 'foot-dragging'. One result is that non-uniformities in the Pedersen conductivity should greatly modify the flow. In particular, day-night asymmetries (Axford 1969), and high conductivities in the auroral oval would be expected to be important in determining the flow.

Inertial forces: these are associated with waves and flows in the magnetosphere and, together with pressure gradients, provide the means by which flux tubes interact.

Diamagnetic force: this force is represented by the pressure gradient term in the magnetohydrodynamic equation. A blob of plasma in a magnetic field produces currents which

a. reduce the magnetic field strength within the blob,

b. provide a net $J \times B$ force in the direction of negative gradients of the local magnetic field.

In terms of the large-scale (dipole) field of the earth, the plasma in the magnetosphere is pushing outwards, away from the earth.

In summary the flux tubes in the magnetosphere may be visualized as having their feet 'tied down' in the ionosphere (only slow motions are permitted), whereas their outer portions are free to 'flop around' as dictated by external, inertial, and diamagnetic forces.

Now let us look at some of the calculations of steady-state magnetosphereric flows with these forces in mind. Most models assume that the solar wind produces a shear stress which acts to build up an excess of flux tubes on the nightside, which in turn drives a flow within the magnetosphere towards the dayside. This is customarily included in models by arbitrarily specifying a dawn-dusk electric field (Axford & Hines 1961, Nishida 1966, Brice 1967). The ionospheric conductivity is usually included only to the extent that a corotation electric field is introduced, representing the tendency of the rotating ionosphere to drag magnetic flux tubes with it. Progress is being made by the Swedish Group (Karlson 1971) towards including the effects of plasma diamagnetism. In Karlson's approach the trajectories of representative particles are calculated in a system of externally imposed and self-created electric fields.

A route to a self-consistent solution to the magnetospheric flow problem was pointed out by Vasyliunas (1970) and it is apparent that all the above-mentioned forces are important, particularly in the prediction of such quantities as the depth of penetration of the flow (plasmapause location). The overall form of the flow cannot be expected to vary much if the flow is smooth and well behaved, because the boundary conditions corresponding to current beliefs are quite restrictive. These are a source of dipole-like flux tubes on the nightside, a sink on the dayside, corotation near the earth, and an elongated channel (the magnetosphere) in which to flow.

Temporal dependence

From equation (1) it can be seen that the external parameters that govern the magnetospheric topology are the magnetic flux in the tail and the stagnation pressure of the solar wind. A change in either of these will cause a convective flow as the magnetosphere adjusts towards its new equilibrium configuration. From the two-dimensional model, Atkinson & Unti (1969b) concluded that

207

pressure changes produce a significant convective flow only at times of sudden impulse or sudden storm commencement. Hence the transfer of field lines to and from the tail is the usual cause of convective flow. In fact the instantaneous rate of convection, except possibly during substorms, is determined by the rate at which field-line merging is occurring on the dayside of the magnetosphere and hence on the rate of transfer of field lines to the tail. It is not inhibited by neutral sheet processes, i.e. the magnetospheric shape can change, allowing flow without neutral sheet reconnection. Evidence that this is the case comes from the whistler measurements (Carpenter & Stone 1967) that the inward velocity of flux tubes did not change when an impulsive event occurred in the tail. Later in the paper, we note that viscous drag forces may also play an important part in the flow.

Non-steady flow results when flux-tube flow into the tail does not equal the outflow. Observations show that potential energy is stored in the magnetic-field configuration and is released in bursts (magnetospheric substorms). Thus a 'brake' or 'gate' must exist which restricts the collapse of flux tubes from the tail-like configuration to the dipole-like configuration. This brake is removed on time scales of ~ 10 minutes at the beginning of the expansive phase of a substorm. I emphasize that the brake acts mainly to prevent the collapse of field lines from a tail-like configuration to a dipole-like configuration but does not significantly impede the large-scale flow. Much of the current argument and discussion of substorms is about the nature of this brake and the mechanism of its removal. This will be the subject of later sections of this paper. It is apparent that if we understand the brake, we understand the basic reason for the existence of the magnetotail, because the tail field lines are trapped, on the outer boundary by the solar wind and at the neutral sheet by the action of the brake.

4. THE PLASMA SHEET – ORIGIN AND IMPLICATIONS

Vasyliunas (1971) has shown recently that the plasma-sheet particles could originate either in the ionosphere, in which case an acceleration mechanism must be invoked, or in the solar wind, in which case heating by the bow shock is sufficient acceleration. Recent proton spectra published by Frank (1971b) provide strong support for the second theory. Frank shows first that the spectra in the magnetosheath are identical to those just inside the dayside cusp, and second that the lower energy particles are no longer present deeper in the cusp. The energy spectra in the cusp have adjusted towards the same shape and maximum as those in the plasma sheet. Thus it is probable that the bulk of plasma-sheet particles originate in the magnetosheath with preferential entry into the magnetosphere of particles at the higher end of the energy spectrum.

There is a problem in maintaining the high plasma density of the plasma sheet (0.1 to 1 cm^{-3}). If the field lines were open, the particles would be lost at somewhat less than the thermal velocity down the tail. This represents an unacceptably large flux of particles and would require almost free entry of the solar wind into the region to maintain the densities. Moreover, flow velocities of this size have not been reported. The most obvious way to contain the particles is with a normal component of magnetic field across the neutral sheet, i.e. all the magnetic field lines in the plasma sheet are closed.

Consider now the restrictions placed on the flow by the existence of the plasma sheet, and hence the mechanism by which the particles enter the sheet. The ratio of electron density in the plasma sheet to that in the high-latitude tail is ~ 10–100. If the flow were that of the simplified model of Fig. 3, the field lines would have to contract by a factor of 10–100 in length after reconnection to create the observed densities. Since the plasma sheet is observed to extend beyond the lunar radius (Behanon 1970) the neutral line would be 600–6000 earth radii down the tail. The tail appears to be segmented at these distances (Ness 1969) and it is unlikely that plasma can flow all the way into the earth. Therefore there must be significant cross-tail components to the flow with stream lines approximately along constant-density contours (Hruska 1971). Thus flux tubes and plasma presumably flow in from the sides of the tail. Fig. 4 shows a cross section of the tail, and the proposed flow. Flux tubes that enter at the top and bottom of the tail lose their plasma rapidly, and become part of the high-latitude tail. Flux tubes that enter from the sides reconnect immediately before they can be drained of plasma. Fig. 4 is schematic, and as pointed out earlier, considerable asymmetry and time variation would be expected.

Another model for the origin of the plasma sheet consistent with the above flow is one in which the field lines that form the plasma sheet

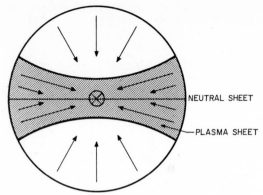

Fig. 4. Cross section of the magnetotail showing flows.

are *never opened*, but are dragged by viscous and frictional forces (Parker 1958, Axford & Hines 1961, Axford 1964) from the sides of the dipole-like region and flow into the sides of the tail. Axford (1969) dismissed this possibility because of the improbability of two competing processes (viscous drag and merging) being of similar size. However, it is likely that a back pressure can exist such that conditions on the nightside control the viscous-drag-induced flow. Flux tubes on the nightside at L = 5 to 15 oppose radial motions. Inward motion is opposed by the diamagnetic plasma and outward motion by the magnetic forces. Thus flux tubes flow more readily in the azimuthal directions, and can exert a back pressure to restrict the flow around the sides of the dipole-like regions. High-latitude field lines would still be the result of dayside merging, which, being a non-reversible process, would steadily increase the tail flux until a burst of inflow and merging occurred. This model would explain the similarity of Fig. 1b to the Axford & Hines (1961) diagrams.

In summary, we conclude that the plasma sheet is composed of flux tubes which have either flowed into the sides of the magnetotail and reconnected immediately, or which have flowed from the sides of the magnetosphere and into the sides of the tail without connecting to the interplanetary field. Conversely, high-latitude tail field lines are those which are open long enough to lose their plasma.

5. MAGNETOSPHERIC SUBSTORM – OBSERVATIONS

With this picture of the magnetosphere and its internal large-scale flow we turn our attention to the magnetospheric substorm and the nightside part of the flow. The review and discussion of the observations is confined to those processes which must be part of the basic substorm since they involve large energy changes.

Auroral breakup

A model of the morphological behaviour of the visible aurora during substorms was presented by Akasofu (1964). Fig. 5 (Montbriand & Vallance Jones 1971) shows the basic features of this model for a strong substorm, plus the morphology of the proton precipitation. It is a north polar view and includes geomagnetic latitudes 60 to 90 degrees and 1500–0600 Corrected Geomagnetic Time (Montbriand 1970). The various lines represent electron aurora, with thickness indicative of brightness. The arrows show the direction of motion of the structures. The dotted lines show the boundaries of the accompanying unstructured proton precipitation. Times are given in minutes from the start of the substorm.

The electron precipitation is essentially that

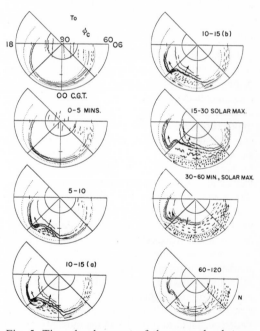

Fig. 5. Time development of the auroral substorm (Montbriand & Vallance Jones 1971). The lines are electron auroras, the arrows directions of motion, and the dotted lines the boundaries of the structure-less proton precipitation. Additional Figures in the original showed the development of north-south structures inside the bulge at T = 15–30 minutes (subsidiary breakups).

described by Akasofu – first a southern arc brightens (T = 0–5 minutes), then the arcs move poleward forming a bulge (T = 5–30 minutes), which expands westward by the westward travelling surge and spreads eastward, and finally in the recovery phase (T = 30–120 minutes) the bulge subsides, though still spreading eastward and propagating westward. Throughout the substorm patchy and segmented and pulsating forms develop to the south of the continuous arcs, and drift generally away from midnight.

The boundaries of hydrogen precipitation are shown by the dotted lines in the Figures. The widening of the hydrogen precipitation region lags behind the electron oval expansion by several minutes. The hydrogen precipitation is generally structureless, although a few patches of hydrogenic aurora do separate from the southern boundary in the expansive phase. The hydrogen emission intensity increases by a factor of 1–4 from T = 0 to T = 30 minutes inside the bulge. In the recovery phase, the intensity slowly decreases to the pre-substorm values. The total energy in the hydrogen precipitation is comparable to that in the electron precipitation.

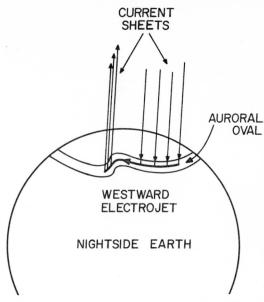

Fig. 6. Three-dimensional sketch of the nightside of the earth and the westward electrojet current system.

Polar magnetic substorm (geomagnetic bay)

The substorm-associated magnetic fluctuations observed at the surface of the earth are determined principally by ionospheric Pedersen and Hall currents, field-aligned currents, and to a lesser extent by the closure of these currents in the outer magnetosphere. At auroral latitudes on the nightside, the dominant features can be satisfactorily explained by an intense U-shaped current system (Atkinson 1967, Meng & Akasofu 1969, Bonnevier et al. 1970). Fig. 6 is a sketch of the three-dimensional current system and the auroral oval. The current flows downward along magnetic field lines to the east of the bulge, along the oval as the westward electrojet, and upwards at the westward travelling surge. There seems to be a weaker eastward electrojet west of the surge. At other locations, the magnetic disturbance is probably the result of this intense U-shaped current system and its closure, and of local weaker Pedersen, Hall, and field-aligned currents, which are determined by the local convective flow and conductivity.

Plasma injection and ring current formation

The occurrence of plasma injection into the nightside dipole-like region during substorms is well established. See review articles by Gringauz (1969) and Van Allen (1969). A recent paper by DeForest & McIlwain (1971) shows this effect convincingly for plasma clouds seen at the A.T.S.-5 satellite. Very clear energy dispersion of particle fluxes is seen corresponding to the injection of protons and electrons near midnight and their subsequent drift (higher energy particles drift faster) around to the satellite. Further clouds are recorded corresponding to particles that are passing the satellite for the second and third time after drifting completely around the earth. Another plasma cloud is created on the dayside. This is probably the result of a spatial redistribution of particles by the enhanced convection that occurs prior to and throughout breakup.

Magnetic signature in the nightside magnetosphere

Magnetic measurements near the midnight meridian at distances beyond 6 earth radii show that in the half- to three-hour period before breakup, the field lines gradually become distorted to a more tail-like form. At breakup, there is a collapse in a few minutes to a more dipolar form even out to 30 earth radii. (Cummings et al. 1968, Camidge & Rostoker 1970, Fairfield & Ness 1970, Lezniak & Winckler 1970, Russell et al. 1971). Horning et al. (1971) from a study of ground and satellite measurements, suggest that

210

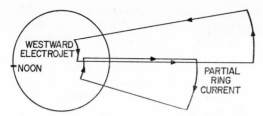

Fig. 7. Polar cap view of the current system proposed by Horning et al. (1971) to explain the magnetic perturbations. The radial currents are along magnetic field lines.

the magnetic perturbations during the auroral breakup are best explained as the result of the two current systems shown in Fig. 7. In addition to the westward electrojet current system, there is a second sytem to the west of the midnight meridian, with an eastward ionospheric current, field-aligned currents, and closure in the outer magnetosphere as shown.

Convective motions and electric fields

This topic is reviewed by Maynard (1971). Here only the major substorm effects are noted. The westward electric field is enhanced with the appearance of a southward component of interplanetary magnetic field. This field builds up in the hour or two before breakup. At breakup, a strong southward component of electric field occurs in the nightside auroral zone.

Plasma sheet thinning

The thinning of the plasma sheet is not yet as well documented as most of the other data discussed here. It does involve major energy changes and has to be included as a large energy process. Hones et al. (1971) report that the plasma sheet thickness in the north-south direction decreases by as much as a factor of 3 in the period before breakup at the Vela satellite orbit (18R_E). It regains its usual thickness ~ 30 minutes after the onset of breakup, although the plasma tends to be hotter than before it thinned and has about the same energy density.

6. MAGNETOSPHERIC SUBSTORM THEORY

The requirements of a successful substorm theory are as follows:

a. The theory must explain all the data listed in parts 1 to 6 of the previous section, preferably including the three-dimensional development.

b. The theory must specify the brake which prevents the collapse of tail-like field lines to the dipole-like form. It must indicate how the brake is applied, and the mechanism of its sudden removal.

c. The theory must predict flows which average to the general flow pattern of the magnetosphere.

The substorm can be divided into three phases:

i the growth phase (pre-substorm development),
ii the expansive phase
iii the recovery phase.

The first of these is the period in which the magnetic flux in the tail is increasing, and a stressed condition is being set up – the brake is applied. The second is the removal of the brake and consequent rapid energy release. Flux tubes collapse from a tail-like to a dipole-like configuration. The third is a period of slower energy release in which the magnetosphere is flowing back to the equilibrium configuration. We shall discuss each of these in turn.

The growth phase (pre-substorm development)

This phase is associated with the appearance of a southward component in the near-earth interplanetary magnetic field. Merging is enhanced on the dayside. Magnetic forces drag field lines around to the nightside and add them to the top and bottom of the tail, where they presumably become part of the low-plasma density high-latitude tail. The increase of tail flux drives the large scale magnetospheric convection, as discussed in earlier sections, resulting in inward motion toward the earth on the nightside. The neutral sheet and plasma sheet are displaced inwards (Atkinson & Unti 1969b, Siscoe & Cummings 1969). The resulting increase in the plasma and neutral sheet current produces significant distortion of the magnetic field lines as far in as 6 earth radii, creating a more tail-like configuration. This accounts for the magnetic signature of this phase of the substorm in the nightside magnetosphere.

The thinning of the plasma sheet in the growth phase is presumably the result of the increased addition rate of low-plasma density field lines. The model, involving both viscous forces and field-line merging, is particularly attractive here, since the incoming flow of closed (high-plasma density) field lines can be slowed down and possibly even reversed as the tail field strength increases.

It is appropriate to discuss the nature of the brake in this section since the growth phase is the period in which the brake is being applied. A few years ago, it was generally believed that a perfect neutral sheet was the brake, and that the onset of field line reconnection started the expansive phase of the substorm. This idea has fallen into disrepute, primarily because events in the expansive phase are observed to start at lower latitudes ($L \approx 6$) on closed field lines. Furthermore, observations do favour a normal component of magnetic field at the neutral sheet most of the time.

Our earlier discussion of forces within the magnetosphere produced two possibilities for the brake: the stress produced by the ionosphere opposing convective flow (ionospheric line-tying), and diamagnetic forces. I reject the first possibility since line-tying can only tie down the feet of field lines, leaving the outer parts relatively free to flop around, i.e. line-tying cannot maintain a severe distortion of field lines in the outer magnetosphere. The ATS observations that the expansive phase is simultaneous with the collapse of field lines from a distorted tail-like configuration to a dipole-like form suggests that the forces must be acting in the outer magnetosphere. The diamagnetic force satisfies the requirements of the brake.

The picture then is that the increase of magnetic flux in the tail throws the magnetosphere out of equilibrium, and causes the inward flow in the growth phase. The plasma in the neutral and plasma sheets prevents the collapse of tail-like field lines, though not significantly affecting the magnetosphere-wide flow, i.e. the shape changes.

The expansive phase

The expansive phase occurs when the plasma providing the braking action is removed, allowing the collapse of $\sim 10^8$ webers of magnetic flux from the tail-like to the dipole-like configuration. Where do the particles go? Comparison of ground and satellite data shows that the collapse is simultaneous with electron and proton precipitation into the ionosphere, and ring current injection into the nightside magnetosphere. The total number of particles observed to be precipitated and injected ($\sim 10^{28}$) corresponds to the plasma in a volume of the plasma sheet of 10^{22} to 10^{23} m^3 (assuming a number density of 0.3 cm^{-3}) or a linear dimension of several earth radii. This is a large loss of plasma sheet particles and

it is unnecessary to invoke other sinks. The above numbers are consistent with the energy requirements of a substorm (Axford 1964, Atkinson 1966).

The remainder of the discussion of the expansive phase will deal with the mechanisms of particle removal from the plasma sheet.

Pitch-angle scattering of particles into the loss cone seems to be a necessary part of substorm theory in order to account for the intense particle precipitation. I am not going to discuss this area, but refer the reader to Kennel (1969). Here the assumption is made that scattering occurs on nightside magnetic flux tubes as they collapse towards the dipole form. The general picture of the collapse is as follows: as particles are removed from the inner edge of the plasma sheet, their diamagnetic effects disappear, allowing further

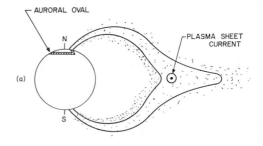

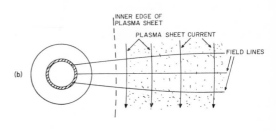

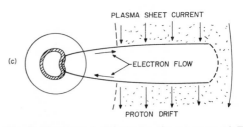

Fig. 8. The neutral and plasma sheet current. a) The midnight meridian section showing the distortion of field lines and current. b) The same – polar cap view. c) The introduction of a sector of dipole-like lines. The current closure via the ionosphere is shown as electron and proton flows.

inward collapse of tail-like magnetic field lines to the dipole-like form. The inward collapse occurs much faster than the large-scale convection, resulting in a buildup of dipole-like field lines on the nightside, i.e. the magnetospheric shape has changed and the region of dipole-like field lines now extends further out on the nightside. This shape change is seen at the feet of field lines as the northward expansion of the auroras.

We turn now to a model that explains the three-dimensional development of the expansive and recovery phases. We assume that the current in the westward electrojet is the deflection of part of the plasma sheet and neutral sheet currents (the current that causes the tail-like distortion of field lines). Fig. 8a shows the westward current, and distorted field lines as seen in the noon-midnight meridian plane in the growth phase. Fig. 8b shows the polar view of the same current and field lines. The current flows all the way across the tail. If the plasma is removed from a sector near midnight, corresponding to the expansive phase, this sector contains dipole-like (curl-free) magnetic field. The plasma sheet current is diverted along field lines at the eastern boundary of the sector, through the ionosphere, and back up the western edge as in Fig. 8c. The plasma sheet current is carried mainly by protons because of their higher energy density. The current along field lines is carried by electrons because of their greater mobility. This results in a reduction of plasma density and therefore pressure at the west edge of the sector, and an increase at the east edge. The reduction at the west edge means that the diamagnetic force has been removed, and flux tubes collapse to the dipole-like form. This leads to a westward propagation of the sector edge. Presumably this motion maps along field lines to the earth as the westward travelling surge.

There are two numerical checks one can make on the model:

a. The west edge of the sector should propagate at approximately the drift velocity of the protons. Protons with energies of a few tens of kev at 6 to 10 earth radii do drift around the earth with an angular velocity similar to that of the westward travelling surge ($\sim .01$ deg sec^{-1}).

b. The electrojet current must represent the deflection of a substantial amount of the tail current. The electrojet current is 10^5 to 10^6 amps. The sheet current in the tail is $\sim 10^{-2}$ amps m^{-1} to account for the observed perturbation fields. From these numbers we see that the current in the electrojet is sufficient to be the deflection of the inner several earth radii of the tail current sheet. This is consistent with the dimensions given earlier in this section for the dimension of tail involved in the substorm, and with the extent of northward advance of the auroral breakup bulge (field lines 500 km apart at the earth are several earth radii apart in the outer magnetosphere).

Thus the model is consistent with observation.

Consider now the mechanism of the formation of the ring current. The slowest drifting (lowest energy) protons are caught up in the inflowing flux tubes and compressed until they have sufficient energy to drift westward ahead of the west edge of the sector. This leads to the formation of the asymmetric ring current just west of the westward travelling surge. This is consistent with Fig. 7. Note that the addition of a cross-tail current makes the resultant current the same as in Fig. 8c.

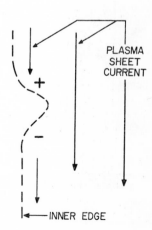

Fig. 9. Same as 8b, showing a perturbation in the inner edge of the plasma sheet, and the resulting space charge.

This model describes the development once the process has started. In fact, the system would be expected to grow from a perturbation of the inner edge of the neutral sheet once the ionospheric electric fields were strong enough to produce a significant electrojet. Fig. 9 shows such a perturbation. The resulting space charge produces the necessary electric fields for collapse inflow and growth. (It should be noticed that the outward pressure gradient at the inner edge of the plasma sheet produces an eastward current. This current can be thought of as composed of the motion of guiding centres westwards, and the gyration about these. The current due to gyration is *divergence-free*, and hence only the guiding-centre motion which is a westward current can produce space charge and electric fields).

The model presented above explains the three-dimensional development of the substorm expansive phase in some detail. Once the electrojet is sufficiently strong, it can control plasma densities and leads to the westward surge. Observations show that the electrojet current results from the appearance of a strong southward electric field in the ionosphere, and an explanation of the origin of this field is needed to understand what triggers the expansive phase. I shall briefly discuss two models for the production of this field.

A recent model of Coroniti & Kennel (1971) explains the southward electric field as the polarization field due to convective flow across conductivity variations in the ionosphere. In this model, the auroral oval is regarded as an east-west strip of high conductivity imbedded in a background ionosphere of lower conductivity. The westward electric field causes a southward component of electric current. If there were no ionosphere-magnetosphere electric coupling, a southward polarization electric field would appear. This is assumed to be discharged in the growth phase by field-aligned currents which close in the outer magnetosphere. The expansive phase starts when instabilities (Kindel & Kennel 1971) reduce these field-aligned currents and the southward polarization electric field develops. The major unexplained feature of this model is the closure of the field-aligned currents in the outer magnetosphere.

I would like to suggest an alternative or complementary model in which the southward electric field is produced by the precipitating electrons. The assumption is made that the upward flow of ionospheric electrons is restricted and that consequently electric fields parallel to the magnetic field are produced which increase the upward flow of cold electrons and inhibit precipitation.

The situation is depicted in Fig. 10a, which shows a vertical north-south section through the ionosphere and lower magnetosphere. The shaded flux tube is assumed to contain plasma sheet electrons in the loss cone. The long dashed lines represent precipitating electrons, the short dashed lines the upward cold electron flux, and the solid arrows the electric field that equalizes the flow of the two. However, the magnetosphere-ionosphere system can allow a faster precipitation of the hot electrons if a perpendicular electric field (Alfvén wave) propagates upward as shown in Fig. 10b. This allows the return current to the outer magnetosphere to occur over an area greater than the

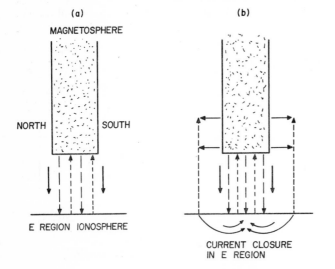

Fig. 10. Particle precipitation into a conducting ionosphere when return currents are limited. Dotted lines show upward cold electron flow. Dashed lines show hot electron precipitation. Solid vectors are electric fields. a) Without perpendicular electric fields. b) With Alfvén wave electric fields propagating upward.

area of precipitation. The complete current system has the following parts, precipitating electrons, ionospheric current, upward cold electron flow, and polarization current across magnetic field lines in the outer magnetosphere ($\propto dE/dt$). The picture is still not quite complete because the horizontal electric field that is shown in Fig. 10b is in the wrong sense to carry the ionospheric part of the current. This difficulty is resolved if the precipitation undergoes temporal variations or, in the case of convecting flux tubes, has spatial structure, and is suggestive of the auroral arc theory of Atkinson (1970).

In summary, the expansive phase begins when the southward electric field becomes strong. In terms of the two models discussed this means either field-aligned currents have gone unstable and the electric field appears due to polarization effects of the convection, or pitch-angle scattering has become strong and the electric field arises because of the large numbers of electrons in the loss cone. The resulting westward electrojet current and its closure in the outer magnetosphere decreases the plasma density on flux tubes at the west end of the auroral breakup bulge, allowing inward collapse of these flux tubes, and thereby causing the westward propagation of the breakup bulge and the region of plasma drainage and collapse of flux tubes. The collapse from the tail-like form to the dipole-like form occurs much faster than the large-scale convection, with the result that an excess of dipole-like flux tubes exists on the nightside of the magnetosphere.

The recovery phase

In the recovery phase two processes are occurring:

a. The westward travelling surge is still propagating westward, implying that the collapse of tail-like field lines is still occurring on flux tubes that are successively further west.

b. The magnetosphere, which was thrown out of equilibrium in the expansive and growth phases, is flowing toward the new equilibrium configuration defined by equation (1). Since this flow involves the motion of magnetic flux-tube feet through the ionosphere, the time scale of the recovery (~ 1 hour) is determined by the ionospheric conductivity.

7. SUMMARY

The static-equilibrium shape of the magneto-sphere is determined by the magnetic flux in the tail, the solar-wind stagnation pressure, and the dipole moment of the earth. A change in either of the first two upsets the existing equilibrium, and causes a convective flow within the magnetosphere towards the new equilibrium configuration. In fact, a study of the magnetospheric shapes given by the Chapman-Ferraro flow about a two-dimensional dipole with a perfect neutral sheet has led to the conclusion that the large-scale flow of the magnetosphere is determined principally by the merging rate on the dayside. It is not usually the result of stagnation-pressure changes, or of neutral-sheet processes. Modifications of the flow are caused by variations in the ionospheric conductivity, plasma diamagnetism, and asymmetries in the surface stresses on the magnetosphere. It is concluded that the plasma sheet is formed by flux tubes that convect into the tail through the sides and either reconnect immediately or never become opened. The high-latitude tail is formed by flux tubes which are open long enough to lose their plasma.

The forces resulting from the diamagnetism of the plasma in the plasma sheet act as a brake which restrains the collapse of tail-like magnetic flux tubes to the dipole-like shape, but does not significantly impede the large-scale flow. The magnetotail consists of magnetic flux tubes trapped between the solar wind and the braking effect of the plasma sheet.

In the growth phase of the magnetospheric substorm, enhanced dayside merging and the resulting increase of magnetic flux in the tail drives a magnetosphere-wide flow. The brake inhibits the collapse of field lines from the tail-like to the dipole-like form, resulting in an inward motion of the plasma and neutral sheets and a change in the shape of the magnetosphere.

In the expansive phase of the substorm, the appearance of a strong southward electric field in the ionosphere enhances the westward electrojet. Since the electrojet-magnetotail current system is carried by proton motion in the plasma sheet, and by electron motion along field lines, plasma is removed from flux tubes at the west edge of the auroral bulge. This removal of plasma forming the brake allows the rapid collapse of flux tubes from the tail-like to the dipole-like form on successively further west flux tubes.

The recovery phase of the substorm is the period in which the above effects are dying out, and the magnetosphere is flowing towards equilibrium.

REFERENCES

Akasofu, S.-I. 1964. *Planet. Space Sci. 12*, 273.
Atkinson, G. 1966. *J. Geophys. Res. 71*, 5157.
Atkinson, G. 1967. *J. Geophys. Res. 72*, 6063.
Atkinson, G. 1970. *J. Geophys. Res. 75*, 4746.
Atkinson, G. & Unti, T. 1969a. *J. Geophys. Res. 74*, 3713.
Atkinson, G. & Unti, T. 1969b. *J. Geophys. Res. 74*, 6275.
Axford, W. I. 1964. *Planet. Space Sci. 12*, 45.
Axford, W. I. 1965. *J. Geophys. Res. 70*, 1231.
Axford, W. I. 1969. *Rev. Geophys. 7*, 421.
Axford, W. I. & Hines, C. O. 1961. *Can. J. Phys. 39*, 1433.
Behannon, K. W. 1970. *J. Geophys. Res. 75, 743*.
Bonnevier, B., Bostrom, R. & Rostocker, G. 1970. *J. Geophys. Res. 75*, 107.
Brice, N. M. 1967. *J. Geophys. Res. 72*, 5193.
Camidge, F. P. & Rostoker, G. 1970. *Can. J. Phys. 48*, 2002.
Carpenter, D. L. & Stone, K. 1967. *Planet. Space Sci. 15*, 395.
Coroniti, F. V. & Kennel, C. F. 1971. Paper SM 77, *Trans. Am. Geophys. Un. 52.*
Cummings, W. D., Barfield, J. N. & Coleman, P. J., Jr. 1968. *J. Geophys. Res. 73*, 6687.
DeForest, S. E. & McIlwain, C. E. 1971. *J. Geophys. Res. 76*, 3587.
Dessler, A. J. Hill, T. W. 1970. *J. Geophys. Res. 75*, 7323.
Dungey, J. W. 1963. In DeWitt, C., Hiebbt, J. & Lebeau, A. (eds.). *Geophysics: The Earth's Environment*, p. 526, Gorden & Breach Science Publishers, New York.
Fairfield, D. H. & Ness, N. F. 1970. *J. Geophys. Res. 75*, 7032.
Frank, L. A. 1971a. *J. Geophys. Res. 76*, 2265.
Frank, L. A. 1971b. *J. Geophys. Res. 76*, 5202.
Gringauz, K. I. 1969. *Rev. Geophys. 7*, 339.
Herring, B. L., McPherron, R. L. & Coleman, P. J., Jr. 1971. Paper SM 45, *Trans. Am. Geophys. Un. 52.*
Hones, E. W., Jr., Asbridge, J. R. & Bame, S. J. 1971. Preprint LA-DC-12176, Los Alamos Scientific Laboratory, Los Alamos.
Horning, B. L., McPherron, R. L. & Coleman, P. J., Jr. 1971. Paper SM 45, *Trans. Am. Geophys. Un. 52.*

Hruska, A. 1971. Preprint, Killam Earth Sciences, University of Alberta, Edmonton.
Karlson, E. T. 1971. *Cosmic Electrodynamics, 1*, 474.
Karlson, E. T. 1972. In Folkestad, Kr. (ed.). *Magnetosphere-Ionosphere Interactions*, Universitetsforlaget, Oslo.
Kennel, C. F. 1969. *Rev. Geophys. 7*, 379.
Kindel, J. M. & Kennel, C. F. 1971. *J. Geophys. Res. 76*, 3055.
Lezniak, T. W. & Winckler, J. R. 1970. *J. Geophys. Res. 75*, 7075.
Maynard, N. C. 1972. In Folkestad, Kr. (ed.). *Magnetosphere-Ionosphere Interactions*, Universitetsforlaget, Oslo.
Meng, C.-I. & Akasofu, S.-I. 1969. *J. Geophys. Res. 74*, 4035.
Mihalov, J. D., Colburn, D. S., Currie, R. G. & Sonett, C. P. 1968. *J. Geophys. Res. 73*, 943.
Montbriand, L. E. 1970. *J. Geophys. Res. 75*, 5634.
Montbriand, L. E. & Vallance Jones, A. 1971. In McCormac, B. M. (ed.). *The Radiating Atmosphere*, Reidel, Dordrecht.
Ness, N. F. 1969. *Rev. Geophys. 7*, 97.
Nishida, A. 1966. *J. Geophys. Res. 71*, 5669.
Parker, E. N. 1958. *Phys. Fluids 1*, 171.
Petschek, H. E. 1964. In Hess, W. N. (ed.). Proc. AAS-NASA Symp. Phys. Solar Flares, NASA SP–50, p. 425, Washington, D. C.
Petschek, H. E. & Thorne, R. M. 1967. *Astrophys. J. 147*, 1157.
Piddington, J. H. 1965. *Planet. Space Sci. 13*, 363.
Russel, C. T., McPherron, R. L. & Coleman, P. J., Jr. 1971. *J. Geophys. Res. 76*, 1823.
Siscoe, G. L. & Cummings, W. D. 1969. *Planet. Space Sci. 17*, 1795.
Van Allen, J. A. 1969. *Rev. Geophys. 7*, 233.
Unti, T. & Atkinson, G. 1968. *J. Geophys. Res. 73*, 7319.
Vasyliunas, V. M. 1968a. *J. Geophys. Res. 73*, 2839.
Vasyliunas, V. M. 1968b. *J. Geophys. Res. 23*, 7519.
Vasyliunas, V. M. 1970. In McCormac, B. M. (ed.). *Particles and Fields in the Magnetosphere*, Reidel, Dordrecht.
Vssyliunas, V. M. 1971. Paper SM 84, *Trans. Am. Geophys. Un. 52.*
Walters, G. K. 1966. *J. Geophys. Res. 71*, 1341.

Stationary Adiabatic Plasma Flow in the Magnetosphere

E. T. KARLSON

Division of Plasma Physics, Royal Institute of Technology,
100 44 Stockholm 70, Sweden

Abstract: The possibility of understanding main features of the magnetosphere in terms of stationary adiabatic plasma flow is investigated. It is pointed out that as a result of the existence of forbidden regions, and of inertia effects, the MHD equations are not adequate for the description of the flow. Therefore, the energy distribution of the particles is simulated by two groups of particles with different energy.

In the first part of this work, the flow in the magnetosphere is 'self-consistent' in the sense that there is no exchange of charge between the magnetosphere and the ionosphere. It is shown that if the two groups are taken to represent a Maxwellian distribution of particle energies in the plasma sheet, a sharp inner edge of the plasma sheet will result. However, in this case there will be no flow inside this, and the interpretation of the plasmapause as the outermost closed streamline cannot be upheld. If we take into account the fact that the plasma in the plasma sheet is mixed with the low energy plasma of the polar wind, it becomes possible to identify the forbidden region for the high energy plasma with the inner edge of the plasma sheet, and the forbidden region of the low energy plasma with the plasmapause.

In the second part, the interaction of magnetospheric flow with the ionosphere is taken into account. It is pointed out that the 'self-consistent' solution above solves this problem also, for one extreme case, namely when there are longitudinal electric fields, and no field-aligned currents. In the other extreme, when the field lines are equipotentials, field-aligned currents must flow, and the solution must be found by an iterative process. It is shown that a modified form of the previous solution is a convenient starting point for such a process.

1. INTRODUCTION

The aim of the present work is to investigate the possibility of interpreting main features of the magnetosphere in terms of a self-consistent stationary adiabatic flow. It is obvious that non-stationary, and probably also non-adiabatic, effects are of importance for many phenomena in the magnetosphere. However, I believe that the main features could be found in terms of stationary adiabatic flow. Furthermore, it seems necessary to find the consequences of such flow in order to decide which are the effects that must be caused by more complicated phenomena.

The features of the magnetosphere that I would like to understand in terms of this flow are:

1. The plasma sheet, terminating at a sharp inner edge, where the electron energy changes drastically whereas the density stays nearly constant.
2. The sharp change in plasma density at the plasmapause.
3. The shape of the plasmapause, with the well-known bulge in the evening sector.

4. The electric field distribution, to the extent that it is known for the magnetosphere.

My starting point is thus that I assume that there is a flow of plasma on the nightside of the earth, in the sunward direction, or, equivalently, a constant dawn-to-dusk electric field across the tail. Whether this flow of plasma and the associated field are caused by some kind of viscous force at the magnetopause, as suggested by Axford & Hines (1961) or by field-line merging, as suggested by Dungey (1961), or by some other mechanism, will not influence the discussion here. Furthermore, it seems reasonable that the detailed shape of the magnetic field in the magnetosphere should not have a decisive influence on the main features of the flow, and thus a rather crude model of the magnetosphere should be sufficient in order to understand these features.

Plasma flow in the magnetosphere was first treated by Alfvén more than 30 years ago (Alfvén 1939, 1940, 1950). He assumed the existence of a homogeneous electric field in the equatorial plane, i.e. he neglected the influence of the space charges. As is well known, he found forbidden regions, which are different for ions and electrons. This gives space charges which were assumed to be discharged along the field lines to the ionosphere through field-aligned (Birkeland) currents, this discharge causing the aurora. Though it was argued early that the neglect of space charges might be disastrous to the theory, a self-consistent treatment of the flow, taking the space charges into account, was not made until much later (Karlson 1962, 1963). In this work it was assumed that all space charges stay in the equatorial plane. This is at the opposite extreme from the case treated by Alfvén, where all space charges are supposed to leave the equatorial plane, so that their influence on the motion can be neglected. The result of this work is that though the electric field is changed drastically, the main features of the flow are changed much less. Thus, for this case as well there are forbidden regions, though these are different in size and shape from the regions found by Alfvén. My reasons for mentioning these old papers here are that so much of Alfvén's original idea seems to be fundamentally correct, and that much later work on plasma flow in the magnetosphere is based on a simpler (in fact, oversimplified) model than the one used by Karlson.

The model used in most work on magnetospheric flow is as follows. The 'frozen-in' condition $E + V \times B = 0$ means (with $E = - \nabla \emptyset$) that the flow is given by the equipotentials. The idea is now that one can 'add' flows just by adding the corresponding potentials. For the magnetosphere the flows to add are:

1. convection, caused by viscous force, or by field-line merging,
2. corotation of the inner part of the magnetosphere with the earth.

Such a procedure was first carried out by Nishida (1966) for the case of a viscous force. He found that the flow has an outermost closed streamline. On the open streamlines outside this plasma is transported to the tail, where it is easily lost. The density on these streamlines should thus be much lower than on the closed streamlines. This gives an explanation for the sharp decrease in density at the plasmapause, identified as the outermost streamline. The same type of computation was carried out by Brice (1967) for the Dungey case. His flow pattern also gives observed features of the plasmapause, such as the bulge in

the evening sector. In the work of Kavanagh et al. (1968) a third potential, the effect of the conducting plasmasphere, is added.

If the magnetic and electric fields are given, it is possible to find the particle trajectories. The plasma in the plasma sheet consists mainly of particles with such high energy (keV), that the gradient drift must be taken into account. The motion of these particles was studied by Schield et al. (1969) for an electric field found as above. In the same way as Alfvén they find forbidden regions, causing charge separation, electric fields, and Birkeland currents. The forbidden region is identified with the inner edge of the plasma sheet, which is therefore named the *Alfvén layer*. This is mapped (on the nightside) along the field lines on the auroral zone.

As is well known, there is also another interpretation of the inner edge of the plasma sheet. Kennel & Petschek (1966, see also Kennel 1969) suggested that strong pitch-angle diffusion leads to a loss of particles from the field tubes. These particles must of course be replaced by low energy particles from the ionosphere. The loss mechanism becomes more effective with decreasing distance from the earth, and at the same time the flow velocity becomes lower. This would give a rather sharp boundary for the plasma sheet electrons, an inner edge. The consequences of such a mechanism will be discussed only very briefly in this paper, in accordance with our general aim of studying the consequences of adiabatic flow only.

Let us now analyse the meaning of the flow-adding method described above. Take an arbitrary flow of this kind (e.g. as found by Brice), with the corresponding potential distribution. The motion of ions and of electrons will be different, generally giving rise to space charges, large enough to change the electric field completely. This must mean that one of the following two things happens:

1. The space charges produced are discharged along the field lines to the ionosphere so effectively that the electric field is not changed.
2. The electric field is changed into a self-consistent field.

However, the first possibility seems to be inconsistent with the idea of a (weakly damped) flow in the magnetosphere. Indeed, if all the space charges produced by the motion are assumed to be discharged along the field lines to the iono-

218

sphere, one should assume also that the primary electric field is discharged, so that the motion would be strongly damped. The flow-adding method thus means that the arbitrarily given electric field is not discharged at all, whereas the much stronger electric field, resulting from the motion of the particles, is completely discharged.

In the work of Schield et al. this is even more of a dilemma. At the Alfvén layer there are forbidden regions for the particles in the plasma sheet, and thus there is no flow of these particles inside this. Only if the large space charges produced here are completely discharged (by longitudinal electric fields), and the particles (ions or electrons) replaced by low energy particles from the ionosphere, can the flow continue inside the Alfvén layer. Thus, at this boundary we should have *longitudinal* electric fields, strong enough to provide the necessary charge transport, and at the same time the *transverse* electric field should be fairly constant across the layer. It is obvious that a similar difficulty is present also for the Petschek-Kennel explanation of the inner edge.

We have seen that the existence of a flow means that space charges are not effectively discharged. This leads us to the study of a case where *no* space charges are discharged. The electric field must then be self-consistent, i.e. the electric field given by the space charges should be the electric field causing the motion. This means that we assume that the field-aligned currents can be neglected and we will see later under what conditions this assumption is self-consistent for the whole magnetosphere-ionosphere system. For the moment I use the term 'self-consistent electric field' to mean the electric field we get in the magnetosphere if there is no exchange of charges between the ionosphere and the magnetosphere.

My main reasons for a treatment of self-consistent stationary adiabatic plasma flow in the magnetosphere are the following:

1. We want to know if we can explain observations at the inner edge of the plasma sheet through the existence of forbidden regions for the plasma sheet particles (as suggested by Schield et al.)
2. We want to know if it is possible to reconcile this interpretation of the inner edge with the Nishida interpretation of the plasmapause.
3. We will see later that we need this kind of treatment as a starting point for the 'complete' problem of the magnetosphere-ionosphere.

2. TWO–DIMENSIONAL FLOW

The existence of forbidden regions means that ions and electrons move along very different trajectories. Thus, we must at least use the two-fluid theory for our treatment. However, the forbidden regions are also different for particles of different energies, and thus we should work with a distribution of particle energies; consequently the Vlasov equation should be appropriate for the treatment. As we will understand later, this would lead to a problem too complicated to be solved, and thus simplifications must be made. First, I shall make the seemingly drastic simplification of two-dimensionality, studying only the motion perpendicular to the magnetic field. I shall comment on this later. Furthermore, I shall simulate the energy distribution using two groups of particles of different energy (two groups of ions, two groups of electrons, a four-fluid model). The details of this calculation have been published elsewhere (Karlson 1971).

My method of solution is to find an expression for the density variation along a streamline, and then introduce this into the Poisson equation. From the equation of motion for the ions

$$Mn_i \frac{dV_i}{dt} = en_i [E + V_i \times B] - \text{div} / P_i, \quad (1)$$

we get for the two-dimensional, stationary case ($E = - \nabla \emptyset$), if to the lowest order we neglect the inertia term

$$V_i^{(0)} = \frac{B}{B^2} \times \left[\nabla \emptyset + \frac{1}{en_i} \nabla P_i \right] = \frac{B}{B^2} \times \nabla \psi_i, \quad (2)$$

where we have assumed that the pressure is a function of the density $p_i = p_i (n_i)$. Introducing $V_i^{(0)}$ in the continuity equation, we get

$$n_i^{(0)} = n_{i0} \frac{B}{B_0}, \quad (3)$$

where n_{i0} and B_0 are the density and the magnetic field at infinity. Using the constancy of the magnetic moment, we find that the pressure is proportional to B^2 on a streamline. Introducing this, and using the lowest order expression for the velocity in the inertia term, we find an expression for the velocity to the next order

$$V_i^{(1)} \left[1 + \frac{M}{eB^2} \left(\nabla^2 \emptyset - \frac{1}{B} \frac{dB}{dr} \frac{\partial \emptyset}{\partial r} \right) \right] =$$

$$\frac{B}{B^2} \times \nabla \left[\varnothing + \frac{\mu_i}{e} B + \frac{M}{2e} \left(\frac{\nabla \varnothing}{B} \right)^2 \right], \qquad (4)$$

where we have taken B to be a function of r only, $B = B(r)$. Again using the continuity equation, we find

$$n_i = n_{i0} \frac{B}{B_0} \left[1 + \frac{M}{eB^2} \left(\nabla^2 \varnothing - \right. \right.$$
$$\left. \left. \frac{1}{B} \frac{dB}{dr} \frac{\partial \varnothing}{\partial r} \right) \right] \qquad (5a)$$

for ions, and

$$n_e = n_{e0} \frac{B}{B_0} \qquad (5b)$$

for electrons. With several groups of particles we get one expression of the type (5) for each group of particles. The existence of forbidden regions means that we get different expressions for the charge density in different regions of space. With two groups of particles of each kind, we get four regions (Fig. 1). The charge densities in the different regions are

I : $\varrho_e = e(n_{i1} + n_{i2} - n_{e1} - n_{e2})$
II : $\varrho_e = e(n_{i1} - n_{e1} - n_{e2})$
III : $\varrho_e = e(n_{i1} + n_{i2} - n_{e1})$
IV : $\varrho_e = e(n_{i1} - n_{e1})$

where the n : s are given by (5). It should be remarked that using these expressions for the charge density means that we assume that there are no particles on closed trajectories, i.e. no trapped particles.

If the densities are introduced in the Poisson equation (or rather the charge neutrality condition $\varrho_e = 0$), we get an equation of the form

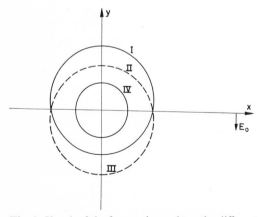

Fig. 1. Sketch of the four regions where the different density expressions are valid.

$$\nabla^2 \varnothing - \frac{1}{B} \frac{dB}{dr} \frac{\delta \varnothing}{\partial r} = \lambda (r, \theta), \qquad (6)$$

where $\lambda (r, \theta)$ is a function which changes discontinuously at the borders between the regions.

The problem is thus that we have four different regions with different equations in each. We do not know the boundaries between these regions until we have found the solution, and of course we cannot find the solution, unless the boundaries are known. The problem cannot be solved by an iterative procedure, where we guess the boundaries, find a solution that gives new boundaries, etc. It is easily seen that this procedure will not converge, unless the original guess was already extremely good.

Instead, we proceed as follows. We assume that the forbidden regions are of the form

$$r = \sum_n a_n \cos n \left(\frac{\pi}{2} - \theta \right), \qquad (7)$$

where the a_n : s are coefficients that should be determined. We can solve equation (6) and get a solution that is a function of the a_n : s. Now, such a solution will also give forbidden regions which in size and shape are functions of the a_n : s. These forbidden regions are now identified with the forbidden regions given by (7). This gives a system of algebraic equations for the a_n : s, and this system can be solved numerically. Obviously, it is possible to extend this method to more groups of particles. However, it should be clear that the complexity of the problem increases rapidly with the number of groups.

First, let us assume a (two-dimensional) Maxwellian distribution for the plasma in the plasma sheet. We make two groups through a partition at a certain energy, so that all particles below this energy belong to one group (1), all above this energy to the other group (2). The mean energy of the particles in each group is taken as the energy for this group. The size of the forbidden regions then depends on at what energy the cut is made. This is plotted in Fig. 2. The upper curve shows the size of the forbidden region for the high energy group of ions, the lower for the low energy group as a function of the density ratios. It can be seen that the regions come quite close to each other as soon as the density ratio rises to around one per cent. From this we draw the conclusion that the forbidden regions for all particles in a Maxwellian distribution lie quite close to each other, except for a few particles with very high energy. It can be seen from Fig. 2 that with

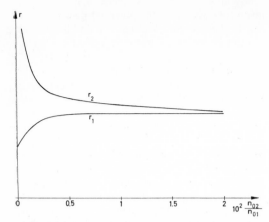

Fig. 2. The sizes of the forbidden regions for the low energy group (r_1), and the high energy group (r_2) of a Maxwellian plasma, as a function of the number of particles in the groups.

the forbidden regions at the inner edge of the plasma sheet, i.e. at 8–10 R_e, the width of the layer where the forbidden regions for most of the particles are is of the order of 1 R_e. This agrees very well with observations (Schield & Frank 1970). Also, the particles with highest energy have their forbidden regions furthest out, which would give a decrease in energy as we move inwards through the layer. This is also in agreement with the observations. Unfortunately, our model is too crude to give the details of the temperature and density distribution in the layer. This can only be found if we use a distribution of particle energies.

Now, with a Maxwellian distribution, or any other smooth distribution, the innermost forbidden region will also be out at about 10 earth radii. No particles will move inside this boundary, and thus there is no flow and no electric field. Thus, we *cannot* explain the plasmapause as the outermost closed streamline for a stationary adiabatic flow of a Maxwellian plasma. One might suggest several ways to get around this difficulty:

1. The interaction with the ionosphere is such that the missing kind of particles is immediately replaced so effectively that the electric field is not changed. We have already dismissed that possibility as inconsistent.
2. The inner edge of the plasma sheet is caused not by forbidden regions but by the Petschek-Kennel mechanism. This is no way out of the difficulty, unless it is connected with replacement as in 1.
3. The plasma in the plasma sheet might be far from Maxwellian. Indeed, we know that the

plasma in the plasma sheet consists mainly of high energy (keV) particles. On the other hand, the polar wind (Banks & Holzer 1968, 1969 a, b, c, Axford 1968, Lemaire & Scherer 1970) implies a transport of low energy plasma from the ionosphere to the tail. We suggest, therefore, that the plasma in the plasma sheet might be a mixture of two components, a high energy plasma of solar wind origin, a low energy plasma of terrestrial origin. This is, of course, liable to be unstable, but on the other hand the polar wind provides cold plasma to the field tube during the whole of inward motion.

We have analysed the motion of such a plasma, and the results are shown in Figs. 3 and 4. In Fig. 3 we have plotted the dawn-to-dusk electric field at midnight for about equal densities of the components, and starting energies 1 eV and 1 keV respectively. We see that the field is growing steadily for decreasing L-values, until it decreases sharply at the inner edge of the plasma sheet (identified as the forbidden region for high energy particles). In agreement with this, observations indicate that the region of strong convection does not reach all the way into the plasmapause (Maynard 1971). In our model, the plasmapause is identified as the forbidden region for the low energy particles.

In Fig. 4 we have plotted the equipotentials, i.e. the streamlines for zero energy particles. In the outer part of the magnetosphere, the streamlines are nearly straight. Near the inner edge of the plasma sheet the streamlines are deflected, corresponding to the weaker field inside. We also see that there is a strong radial electric field at the inner edge of the plasma sheet.

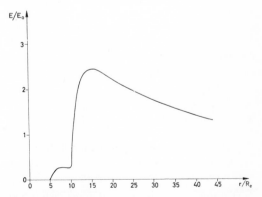

Fig. 3. The electric field on the x axis (at midnight) when the plasmapause is at $5R_e$, and the inner edge of the plasma sheet at $10R_e$.

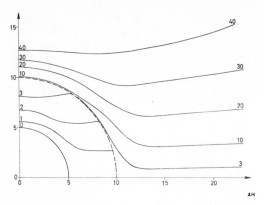

Fig. 4. Equipotential curves for plasma flow in the magnetosphere, when the plasmapause is at $5R_e$, and the inner edge of the plasma sheet at $10R_e$.

Let us make a few remarks on the results:

1. Corotation has not been introduced. In fact, it should be regarded as a result of the interaction with the ionosphere, which we have neglected so far.
2. We have assumed that the plasmapause is a circle. This is natural from our present assumptions (no trapped particles, no interaction with the ionosphere). We will see later how the interaction with the ionosphere might change this.
3. The flow as given in Fig. 4 is completely symmetric with respect both to the x axis, and the y axis (ion and electron energies are assumed to be equal). This means that there are stagnation points for the flow at midnight and at noon.

3. INTERACTION WITH THE IONOSPHERE

Obviously, one important thing is missing from my treatment so far. As already said, I have neglected the interaction with the ionosphere completely. There are several reasons for expecting that this interaction should be important, such as

1. The plasma in the plasma sheet reaches the ionosphere.
2. The conductivity along the field lines is very high.
3. Auroral phenomena seem to have close connections with the flow.
4. Birkeland currents are observed.

The interaction between the magnetosphere and the ionosphere can be described as follows: assume that the flow in the magnetosphere is given (and thus also the potential distribution in the magnetosphere). We can then find the particle motion in the given magnetic and electric fields, and from this we get transverse currents. There is no reason why these currents should be divergence-free, and thus field-aligned currents must exist. Another way to express this is to say that forbidden regions and inertia effects cause space charges that must be discharged. On the other hand, if it is assumed that the field lines are equipotentials, the potential distribution in the magnetosphere can be mapped along the field lines in the ionosphere. When the potential distribution in the ionosphere is known, the current distribution can be found from the generalized Ohm's Law. Again, the current is not divergence-free, and field-aligned currents must exist. Now, obviously, if the whole system is to be self-consistent, it is necessary for the potential distribution to be such that the field-aligned currents found in these two different ways are identical. This leads to the closed self-consistent chain of equations, first introduced by Fejer (1964). Let us make two remarks concerning this scheme here:

1. We have seen above that it is necessary to use something better than the MHD equations for the description of the flow in the magnetosphere, i.e. the Vlasov equation, or many-group equations as above.
2. Though it is often assumed that the field lines are equipotentials, this is not necessarily a good approximation. We will return to this question later.

The problem posed here is too complicated to be solved as it stands. The only way suggested so far to find a solution is to separate it into one ionospheric part and one magnetospheric part. The potential distribution is found for one of these, assuming that there are no Birkeland currents, and then mapped along the field lines on the other system (if the field lines are equipotentials). Here, this potential distribution gives rise to Birkeland currents as described above, and these currents are then used to find the second approximation for the potential distribution in the first system, and so on.

Obviously, this is a useful method only if the resulting Birkeland currents are small, in the sense that the potential distributions found as lowest order solutions should not be changed appreciably by the resulting currents. Otherwise there is no reason why the procedure should converge towards a unique solution.

From what we have said, it is clear that there are two conceivable starting points, i.e. zero-order distributions:

1. We have just analyzed the magnetosphere 'self-consistently', i.e. with $j_{||} = 0$, and this gives one possible starting point.
2. The other possibility is to start with the ionosphere, again putting $j_{||} = 0$ (Vasyliunas 1969, Wolf 1970). The equation to solve in this case is div $I = 0$, where I is the height-integrated horizontal current density, given by

$$I = - \Sigma \cdot \nabla \emptyset,$$

where Σ is the height-integrated conductivity tensor.

Both the above computations are thus based on the assumption $j_{||} = 0$. If there are no longitudinal electric fields, $E_{||} = 0$, we can, for example, map the potential distribution of the magnetoshpere on the ionosphere. There is no reason why the resulting distribution should be equal to the distribution found for the ionosphere, and thus the assumptions $j_{||} = 0$ *and* $E_{||} = 0$ lead to a discrepancy. Therefore, we must have either E different from zero, or j different from zero, or both. Thus, there are two different situations to study:

1. The assumption $E_{||} = 0$ is then made. There must then exist field-aligned currents, $J_{||} \neq 0$, and the only way to find a solution is by means of an iterative procedure.
2. On the other hand, there are theoretical reasons (e.g. Alfvén & Fälthammar 1963, Persson 1963, 1966) why $E_{||}$ should not always be zero, and also some observational evidence for $E_{||} \neq 0$ (Hultqvist et al. 1971). This gives us a reason to study the case $E_{||} \neq 0$, $j_{||} = 0$.

It is obvious that $j_{||} = 0$ does not follow from the assumption $E_{||} \neq 0$. As a rule both quantities are probably different from zero. However, as we know very little about the role of $E_{||}$ and its dependence on known quantities, the best we can do is to analyse the two extreme cases, and if the results are not too different we should be able to say something about the intermediate situation found in nature.

The case $E_{||} \neq 0$, $j_{||} = 0$ is easily taken care of. In fact, this means that the assumptions made in the analysis of the magnetosphere (Karlson 1971), *and* of the ionosphere (Vasyliunas 1970, Wolf 1970) are both correct, and thus we have found the potential distribution both in the magnetosphere and in the ionosphere.

The other extreme, $E_{||} = 0$, $j_{||} \neq 0$, is much more difficult. We must use an iteration procedure, and as said before, this will converge only if we have a zero-order solution, for which the resulting Birkeland currents are small. For an arbitrary potential distribution, there are three sources for Birkeland currents:

1. The different forbidden regions for ions and electrons in the magnetosphere cause space charges that must be discharged, producing the Birkeland current J_I.
2. The difference in motion caused by inertia effects in the magnetosphere causes space charges that produce the Birkeland current J_{II}.
3. The horizontal currents in the ionosphere are not divergence-free. This produces the Birkeland current J_{III}.

If we take an arbitrary potential distribution, i.e. a potential distribution which is not chosen so as to minimize any of these currents, it is easy to estimate the relative importance of the currents from the different sources. The 'ionospheric' current J_{III} is of course larger on the dayside than on the nightside due to the higher conductivity on the dayside. Our estimate gives

	Day	Night
J_I	200	200
J_{II}	8	8
J_{III}	50	1

We have taken the 'ionospheric' current J_{III} on the nightside as the unity.

If we now compare the different possible starting points from the point of view that the resulting Birkeland currents should be small, we find

a. Starting from the *magnetosphere*, we minimize the currents on the nightside in the best possible way, putting the two largest contributions, J_I and J_{II}, equal to zero. On the dayside, we have been somewhat less successful, as here J_{III} is more important than J_{II}.
b. Starting from the *ionosphere*, we minimize only J_{III}, and this means that we neglect the most important contribution, J_I.

Thus we see that although the first alternative is much better than the second, it is quite possible that an iterative procedure, based on our magnetospheric flow as the lowest-order approximation, will not converge. In fact, the 'ionospheric' current

J_{III} is quite large on the dayside, and might change the potential distribution considerably.

To be sure that the iterative procedure converges, we must make a better choice of a zero order solution. What we should do is to minimize the currents by asking that the two most important contributions should be equal to zero, both on the nightside and on the dayside (it is obvious that not all three currents can be put equal to zero). From the discussion above, it is seen that on the nightside the same conditions as above should be used, i.e. we take a 'self-consistent' flow (no exchange of charge with the ionosphere). On the dayside, the zero-order solution should fulfill:

1. The forbidden regions for ions and electrons should be (almost) equal, in order to minimize J_I.
2. div I = 0 should be equal to zero, in order to minimize J_{III}.

The solution on the nightside and the solution on the dayside should then be joined by a boundary condition that again minimizes the resulting current. The same method of solution as before is used, and again we get a system of algebraic equations, that must be solved numerically. The main features of the flow for this case are:

1. The width of the Alfvén layer, and the conclusions about density and temperature variations in the layer are not changed.
2. To explain both the inner edge of the plasma sheet and the plasmapause, two populations with quite different energies are needed.
3. On the night side the flow is not changed much, on the day side the interaction with the ionosphere means that the flow become partly corotating.
4. Connected with this, the stagnation point which for the symmetric flow of the previous section occurred at noon, now moves to the afternoon. The region between this stagnation point, and the mid-night stagnation point, might be associated with the bulge region of the plasmasphere.
5. The electric field inside the Alfvén layer is much weaker than the field outside.

From the potential distribution found in this way, we can compute the resulting Birkeland currents. These can then be used to find the potential distribution to next order. This has not been done so far, but it is expected that with the optimal zero order approximation used here, the next order approximation should not differ too much from it.

As said in the introduction, this is only a crude model of the magnetospheric flow, and it cannot be expected to give all the details of the flow. Thus, the model used involves the following features that should be improved in order to get a realistic model of stationary adiabatic flow in the magnetosphere.

1. The model is two-dimensional, treating only the motion in the equatorial plane.
2. A very simple model is used for the magnetic field.
3. It is assumed that the currents resulting from the motion do not change the magnetic field appreciably.
4. It is assumed that there are no trapped particles.

Obviously, the magnetospheric flow is a three-dimensional phenomenon, and to understand all features of it it is certainly not sufficient to use a two-dimensional model. This is certainly true for features like the driving mechanism for the flow, field-line merging in the neutral sheet and on the sunward side of the magnetosphere, flow across the polar cap, and so on. On the other hand, we do not expect the three-dimensionality to have a great effect on the characteristics of the sunward flow in the magnetosphere. In fact, the drift equation as used above describes the motion perpendicular to the magnetic field. Superimposed on this, there is of course an oscillating motion of the particles along the lines of force, but it is obvious that for example the existence and shape of the forbidden regions are determined by the drift equation.

In the same way, it should be clear that the detailed shape of the magnetic field, or, specifically, the change of the magnetic field due to the induced currents, should have a fairly small influence on the results listed above.

The observation of high energy ions inside the inner edge of the plasma sheet suggests that trapped particles should be included. This might give important changes in the quantitative results, though again we do not expect the qualitative features to change.

REFERENCES

Alfvén, H. 1939. *Kungl. Sv. Vetenskapsak. Handl.* *18*, 3.
Alfvén, H. 1940. *Kungl. Sv. Vetenskapsak. Handl.* *18*, 9.

Alfvén, H. 1950. *Cosmical Electrodynamics*, Clarendon Press, Oxford.

Alfvén, H. & Fälthammar, G. G. 1963. *Cosmical Electrodynamics*, Clarendon Press, Oxford.

Axford, W. I. 1968. *J. Geophys. Res. 73*, 6855.

Axford, W. I. & Hines, C. O. 1961. *Can. J. Phys. 39*, 1433.

Banks, P. M. & Holzer, T. E. 1968. *J. Geophys. Res. 73*, 6846.

Banks, P. M. & Holzer, R. E. 1969 a. *J. Geophys. Res. 74*, 3734.

Banks, P. M. & Holzer, T. E. 1969 b. *J. Geophys. Res. 74*, 6304.

Banks, P. M. & Holzer, T. E. 1969 c. *J. Geophys. Res. 74*, 6317.

Brice, N. M. 1967. *J. Geophys. Res. 72*, 5193.

Dungey, J. W. 1961. *Phys. Rev. Letters 6*, 723.

Fejer, J. A. 1964. *J. Geophys. Res. 69*, 123.

Hultquist, B., Borg, H., Riedler, W. & Christophersen, P. 1971. *Planet. Space Sci. 19*, 279.

Karlson, E. T. 1962. *Phys. Fluids 5*, 476.

Karlson, E. T. 1963. *Phys. Fluids 6*, 708.

Karlson, E. T. 1971. *Cosmic Electrodynamics 1*, 474.

Kavanagh, L. D., Jr. Freeman, J. W., Jr. & Chen, A. J. 1968. *J. Geophys. Res. 73*, 5511.

Kennel, C. F. 1969. *Rev. Geophys. 7*, 379.

Kennel, C. F. & Petschek, H. E. 1966. *J. Geophys. Res. 71*, 1.

Lemaire, J. & Scherer, M. 1970. *Planet. Space Sci. 18*, 103.

Maynard, N. C. 1972. In Folkestad, Kr. (ed.). *Magnetosphere-Ionosphere Interactions*, Universitetsforlaget, Oslo.

Nishida, A. 1966. *J. Geophys. Res. 71*, 5669.

Persson, H. 1963. *Phys. Fluids 6*, 1756.

Persson, H. 1966. *Phys. Fluids 9*, 1090.

Schield, M. A. & Frank, L. A. 1970. *J. Geophys. Res. 75*, 5401.

Schield, M. A., Freeman, J. W. & Dessler, A. J. 1969. *J. Geophys. Res. 74*, 247.

Vasyliunas, V. M. 1970. In McCormac, B. M. (ed.). *Particles and Fields in the Magnetosphere*, Reidel, Dordrecht.

Wolf, R. A. 1970. *J. Geophys. Res. 75*, 4677.

Some Properties of Magnetic Neutral Sheet Systems

S. W. H. COWLEY

Physics Department, Imperial College, London

Abstract: The basic properties of a neutral sheet configuration are investigated via self-consistency between the current and the magnetic field, conservation of energy and momentum, and charge neutrality in the field reversal region. Conservation of momentum implies a varying sheet thickness across the width of the system, as does the condition for charge neutrality. Using a model magnetic field, the thickness of the sheet is calculated, and good agreement between the two calculations is obtained. The sheet thicknesses are then interpreted in terms of the electric field structure.

1. INTRODUCTION

In this paper we shall attempt to discuss some of the basic physics of magnetic neutral sheet processes in an effort to extend considerably the model first proposed by Alfvén (1968).

We shall be concerned specifically with the structure and flow in the geomagnetic tail. This consists, basically, of two cylindrical bundles of oppositely directed magnetic flux, each bundle being semi-circular in cross-section (Fig. 1). These are drawn out from the Earth in the antisolar direction by an interaction of the magnetosphere with the solar wind and are connected to the north and south polar cap. The tail field magnitude decreases with increasing distance from the Earth, being on average about 20 γ at 25 R_E, and about 8 γ at, and beyond, 60 R_E (the lunar distance). (1 gamma (γ) $= 10^{-5}$ gauss). This decrease in the field strength can be understood when both the flaring out of the tail and a small amount of field connection between the lobes is taken into account. The diameter of the tail varies from 40 R_E at a distance of 25 R_E to about 50 R_E at 60 R_E, making 'flaring' the more important of the two effects (Behannon 1970).

A cross-section of the tail has a nearly circular shape, the two bundles of oppositely directed flux being separated by a thin 'field reversal region', giving the well-known 'θ' configuration as shown in Fig. 1. The thickness of the field reversal region has been estimated to be several hundreds to several thousands of kilometres at a distance of ~ 25 R_E (Speiser & Ness 1967), decreasing to perhaps several tens to several hundreds of kilometres at a distance of about 60 R_E (Mihalov et al. 1970). This, then, is truly 'thin' when compared with a tail diameter of some 300,000 km.

A small magnetic field is observed to connect the flux bundles across the field reversal region. Its magnitude is a few gamma at 25 R_E, decreasing often to below detector threshold (~ 0.2 γ, Mihalov et al. 1970) at 60 R_E. This is usually northward pointing within the cislunar distance (the region of extensive satellite mapping), but is highly variable at a fixed distance from the Earth. During the slow growth phase of a polar substorm the field connection appears very small and variable, being generally less than 1γ at 25 R_E. It is during this period of time that the tail field magnitude increases by perhaps a factor of 2 over one or two hours (at 25 R_E). When the magnitude of the tail field starts to decline again, together with the ground activity as measured by the AE index, the field connection across the lobes increases to $5 \rightarrow 10\gamma$ at 25 R_E, as the system relaxes to a more dipole-like configuration. This field decrease takes place on a time scale only a little smaller than that of the increase, outside of the expanding plasma sheet (Camidge & Rostoker 1970, Fairfield & Ness 1970).

In the neutral sheet model to be discussed here, the field connection across the reversal layer is neglected in the interests of simplicity. The validity of this assumption will be discussed in the next section; however, we note here that this magnetic field component is very small most of the time ($\lesssim 0.1$ γ) at distances of, and exceeding, 60 R_E. It is also probably of this order during the substorm slow growth phase over a region much nearer the Earth (25 R_E or closer).

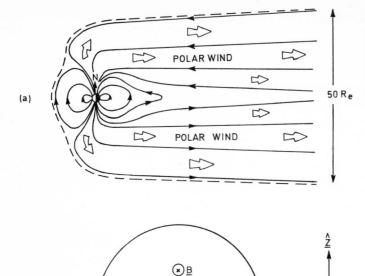

Fig. 1. a) The magnetosphere viewed in the noon-midnight meridian plane, showing the tail field lines connected to the north and south polar cap.
b) A cross-section of the tail looking towards the Earth, with the solar magnetospheric coordinate system used in this paper.

Solar magnetospheric coordinates are used throughout this paper; the z axis is perpendicular to the plane of the neutral sheet (pointing north), the y axis parallel to the sheet and perpendicular to the magnetic field (pointing from dawn to dusk across the tail), and the x-axis parallel to the magnetic field (pointing toward the Earth).

Throughout this paper the distance across the tail will be referred to as the 'sheet width' while the z distance across the field reversal region at a given y will be called the 'sheet thickness'.

2. PARTICLE ORBITS IN NEUTRAL SHEET FIELD GEOMETRIES

We will now consider the motion of particles in simple magnetic neutral sheet configurations, neglecting field line connection across the field reversal region as discussed above.

If no electric field is considered, two types of motion are possible, depending on whether the particle crosses over the neutral sheet. Above and below the neutral sheet the motion is the well-known ∇B-drift, protons moving towards dawn and electrons towards dusk. Particles crossing the

neutral sheet oscillate symmetrically about it and can drift in either direction (Fig. 2). (Seymour (1959) has given exact solutions of the equations of motion for particles moving in a field of constant gradient containing a neutral sheet.)

If we also consider an electric field parallel to the neutral sheet and perpendicular to the magnetic field, directed from dawn to dusk across the the tail ($\hat{y}$ direction), particles outside the sheet will move towards it from both sides with the usual 'electric field drift', given by

$$V_{\mathrm{E}} = \frac{c\,E \times B}{B^2}. \tag{1}$$

Particles oscillating about the neutral sheet are accelerated along it by the electric field, protons towards dusk and electrons towards dawn. We thus join up the two types of orbit discussed above when an electric field is included; protons and electrons drift towards the neutral sheet from both sides, become trapped about the neutral sheet and are accelerated along it (Fig. 3). Such trapping and acceleration are very general processes. Computed particle trajectories have shown that no special input conditions into the sheet

228

Fig. 2. Typical proton drift orbits in a magnetic field gradient containing a neutral sheet (after Seymour 1959). Electron orbits are the same as the above, the direction of the arrows need only be reversed.

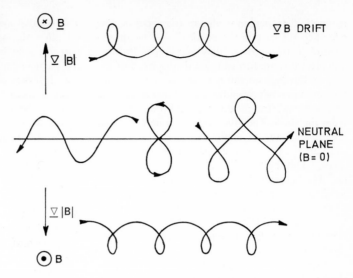

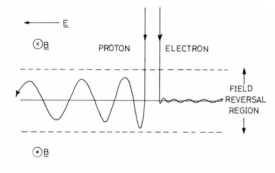

Fig. 3. Under the action of the electric field, protons and electrons drift into the field reversal region (from both sides), become trapped about the neutral plane and accelerated along it. (The z scale has been multiplied by 10 compared with the y scale.)

need be satisfied; all particles moving into the field reversal region will become trapped and accelerated.

Speiser (1965) first analysed in detail the motion of particles in a set of simple fields of this type (constant magnetic field gradient, uniform electric field). While exact solutions were not obtained, a WKB approximation for the oscillations about the sheet gives a very good account of the motion after the first oscillation. As the particles accelerate along the sheet the amplitude of the oscillations slowly decreases while the 'wavelength' slowly increases (Fig. 3). The acceleration along the sheet is almost linear in the electric field after trapping, that is, almost as if the particle

was accelerating directly along the neutral sheet, and not oscillating (Fig. 4).

We can now discuss the validity of neglecting the small magnetic field component connecting the regions of oppositely directed flux in relation to the geomagnetic tail. With no magnetic field perpendicular to the plane of the neutral sheet, we have seen that the protons and electrons are accelerate indefinitely along it, eventually being lost at the dusk and dawn boundaries respectively, of the tail (into the magnetosheath). If a uniform

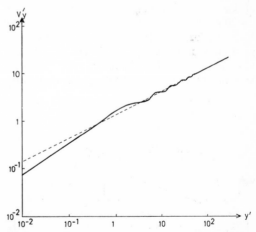

Fig. 4. Logarithmic plot of the velocity parallel to the sheet (v_y', normalized to the incoming particle velocity cE_0/B_0) against position along the sheet (y', normalized to the sheet thickness) for the proton whose trajectory is shown in Fig. 3. The dotted line represents the motion of a proton uniformly accelerating in the electric field E_0.

magnetic field perpendicular to the sheet is now added to the picture the particles will be turned around in the sheet as they accelerate. Protons and electrons are turned towards the Earth if the field is directed northward, and they turn until they are moving perpendicular to the electric field and 'looking' straight down a field line emerging from the sheet. They then leave the field reversal region, moving out along the field line towards the Earth with very small pitch angle (a few degrees). This motion has also been analysed in detail by Speiser (1965, 1968). For our model to be valid, therefore, the perpendicular magnetic field must be small enough so that particles do not turn around and leave the sheet before they have travelled across the tail and have been lost from the sides.

For a given value of the perpendicular field, B_z, the distance travelled across the tail before leaving the sheet can be easily calculated, using Speiser's results, by transforming into a frame moving towards the Earth with velocity $V_T = cE_0/B_z$, where E_0 is the uniform electric field across the tail in the rest-frame of the Earth. In this frame the electric field is zero, and the particle motion is especially simple to describe. Particles simply move down the magnetic field lines, the velocity parallel to the sheet being approximately the transformation velocity V_T. (The drift velocities of cold particles along the tail field lines from the polar wind are likely to be somewhat less than the transformation velocities of some hundreds of km/sec. For instance, if $E_0 \sim 0.05$ mV/m (~ 20 kV across the tail) and $B_z \sim 0.2\ \gamma$, we find $V_T \sim 250$ km/sec.) The velocity of the particle perpendicular to the plane of the current sheet as it moved down the field line into the sheet goes into the oscillations about the field minimum.

The parallel velocity is simply turned round in direction during the oscillatory motion by the perpendicular field, this turning continuing until the particle leaves the sheet, again along a field line. In other words, in the plane of the current sheet the particle describes half a circle from entry to exit, the radius corresponding to the gyro-radius of a particle with perpendicular velocity $\sim V_T$ in a magnetic field B_z (Fig. 5). Thus the distance moved across the tail from entry to exit is simply

$$Y = \frac{2\ V_T}{\Omega_z} = 2\ \frac{mc^2\ E_0}{e\ B_z}. \tag{2}$$

As can be seen, this distance will be much less for electrons than protons, by the mass ratio factor.

In the next section an expression for the total electrostatic potential drop across the neutral sheet system will be considered for the case where there is no field connection across the sheet (no particle ejection from the sheet). If we make the assumption that this formula applies in the present case (approximately) and further, that the electric field giving this potential drop is uniform, we find that

$$E_0 = \frac{B_x^2}{4\pi\ N_0\ ed}, \tag{3}$$

where B_x is the value of the magnetic field parallel to the plane of the sheet, N_0 is the cold particle number density in the region outside the sheet, and d is the diameter of the tail (width of the sheet). Thus

$$Y = \frac{mc^2}{2\pi\ N_0\ e^2\ d} \left(\frac{B_x}{B_z}\right)^2$$

and for $Y > d$ we require

$$B_z < \left(\frac{mc^2}{2\pi\ N_0\ e^2\ d^2}\right)^{\frac{1}{2}} B_x. \tag{4}$$

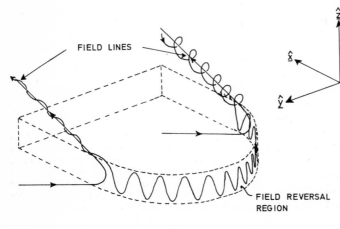

FIELD LINES

FIELD REVERSAL REGION

Fig. 5. Proton motion in a field reversal region with a weak normal component of the magnetic field threading through the sheet, seen in the transformed frame where the large scale (dawn to dusk) electric field is zero.

Table 1. Value of B_z for which $Y = d$, $B_x = 10\gamma$ in equation (4)

	$N_0 = 0.1$ cm^{-3}	$N_0 = 0.01$ cm^{-3}
Electron	$0.001\ \gamma$	$0.003\ \gamma$
Proton	$0.04\ \gamma$	$0.12\ \gamma$

The maximum values of B_z for values of N typical of those expected for polar wind plasma in the tail (Holzer, personal communication) are given in Table I. B_x has been given the nominal value of 10γ. Note that at 25 R_E, B_x varies from 20 γ at quiet times up to $\sim 40\ \gamma$ during storm times.

We see that the model will only be valid in the vicinity of the neutral line of any x-neutral field configuration in the tail (so that $B_z \lesssim 0.001\ \gamma$). However, it appears possible, in view of the measured values of B_z discussed briefly in the introduction, that protons may be accelerated across the whole sheet width without turning out of the sheet as close in as 25 R_E during storm times.

Clearly, future work should include generalizing the model to describe the situation in which protons are accelerated the whole way across the tail, while electrons are turned out of the sheet at a distance less than the tail diameter.

3. THE CURRENT IN THE NEUTRAL SHEET, CONSERVATION OF ENERGY AND MOMENTUM

Between the two bundles of oppositely directed flux a current must flow from dawn to dusk. In the steady state this current satisfies

$$\frac{\partial B_x}{\partial z} = \frac{4\pi}{c} j_y$$

or, integrating across the field reversal region

$$I_y = \frac{c B_0}{2\pi}. \tag{5}$$

B_0 is the value of the uniform magnetic field outside the field reversal region, and I_y is the total current per unit length along the tail flowing in this region.

In the absence of an electric field allowing particles within the tail lobes to drift into the sheet, this current must be provided by magnetosheath particles drifting across the tail width after gaining access at the magnetopause. From the discussion of proton orbits in the previous section we see that those gaining access near the neutral sheet on the dawn side can move along the sheet

to the dusk side (in the same direction as the current). Protons can also gain access near the neutral sheet on the dusk boundary and drift in the opposite direction. They may also $\triangledown$B-drift across the tail, but in this case only from dusk to dawn. An exactly similar paragraph applies to electrons on interchanging 'dawn' and 'dusk'.

Particle access into a magnetic field region having field gradients and a neutral sheet has been considered by Stevenson & Comstock (1968). They took only a simple plane boundary for the magnetic field; however, the detailed structure of the magnetopause should be taken into account. The details of the particle access across the boundary (i.e. the fluxes expected, etc.) will determine the currents set up within the tail and hence the magnetic structure. As this analysis has not yet been considered, it is still an open question as to whether such a source can provide the currents required.

The other source of current is cold plasma (from the polar wind) which exists on the field lines within the tail. If an electric field exists from dawn to dusk across the tail, this cold plasma drifts towards the field reversal region from both sides. Particles moving into the region become trapped about the neutral line, protons being accelerated towards dusk and electrons towards dawn, both species contributing directly to the current flowing in the field reversal layer. Alfvén (1968) first showed that self-consistency between the current provided by these trapped particles and that required by the change in the magnetic field leads to a value of the total potential drop across the tail. The dusk boundary is taken as the arbitrary zero of potential in the following, the dawn boundary is then at a potential $\Phi_A > O$ for a dawn-to-dusk electric field.

The electric field drift of particles into the sheet (equation (1)) is perpendicular to the electric field, that is, it is along equipotentials, and is independent of the particle mass or charge. Thus at each point above the sheet we have equal fluxes of protons and electrons (for equal densities) flowing along equipotentials into the field reversal region, and these fluxes are conserved as the particles accelerate along the neutral sheet, protons towards dusk and electrons towards dawn (Fig. 6). Thus each (elemental) incoming stream of plasma provides a constant current across the entire sheet. No matter how the equipotentials are distributed across the tail (non-uniform electric fields are possible), the current flowing in the reversal layer is constant across the tail width. At the dusk

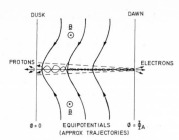

Fig. 6. Showing adiabatic flow of protons and electrons along equipotentials towards the neutral sheet.

boundary all the current is carried by protons, while at the dawn boundary an equal current is carried by electrons. At a potential φ ($0 \leq \varphi \leq \Phi_A$) the ratio of current carried by electrons to that carried by protons is

$$\frac{I_e}{I_p} = \frac{\varphi}{(\Phi_A - \varphi)}. \tag{6}$$

The flux of protons leaving the neutral sheet at dusk must be equal, in the steady state, to the flux of protons entering the sheet from both sides, and this gives us the total current in the neutral sheet at this boundary. For particle flow along equipotentials in a plane, where the magnetic field lines are perpendicular to the flow, conservation of particle flux shows that B/N is a constant (see for example Chandrasekhar 1960, p. 75). If we take B to be uniform in the region above the sheet (appropriate surface currents flow on the boundary equipotentials) then the particle density N is uniform in the region above the sheet. Thus the total flux of protons flowing into the neutral sheet from both sides is

$$F_T = 2\,N_0 \int_c \left| \left(\frac{c\,E \times B_0}{B_0{}^2} \right) \times dL \right|,$$

where dL is an element vector of contour C crossing the tail from dusk to dawn above or below the field reversal region in the plane of the flow. Expanding the cross product gives

$$F_T = \frac{2\,N_0\,c}{B_0} \int_c E \cdot dL = \frac{2\,N_0\,c\,\Phi_A}{B_0},$$

where Φ_A is the potential drop across the tail. The total current per unit tail length is then eF_T, so that from (5) we have, for self-consistency,

$$\frac{c\,B_0}{2\pi} = \frac{2\,e\,N_0\,c\,\Phi_A}{B_0} \text{ or } \Phi_A = \frac{B_0{}^2}{4\pi\,N_0\,e}. \tag{7}$$

For $B_0 \sim 10\,\gamma$ we find that $\Phi_A \sim 5\,kV$ if $N_0 \sim 0.1\ cm^{-3}$ while $\Phi_A \sim 50\,kV$ if $N_0 \sim 0.01\ cm^{-3}$.

Note that all that has been assumed in this derivation is that all inflowing protons and electrons contribute to the current, and we have seen how this occurs from the discussion of particle trajectories. The details of flow near the reversal region and the latter's structure do not enter into the derivation, nor can we learn anything about them from the result.

Alfvén's formula (equation (7)) for the total potential across the tail also satisfies conservation of energy. We have a Poynting flux S of electromagnetic energy into the sheet from above and below, while energized particles flow out from the dusk and dawn boundaries. The Poynting flux integrated across the tail is

$$E_s = 2 \int_c | S \times dL | =$$

$$\frac{2c}{4\pi}\,B_0 \int_c E \cdot dL = \frac{2c\,B_0\,\Phi_A}{4\pi}.$$

As above the flux of protons or electrons towards the sheet across element dL of contour C is

$$dF = N_0 \left| \left(\frac{c\,E \times B_0}{B_0{}^2} \right) \times dL \right|$$

and by conservation of flux dF is the flux of particles from dL emerging from the tail boundary. If dL is at potential φ, the protons will be accelerated and gain an energy $e\varphi$, while electrons gain an energy $e\,(\Phi_A - \varphi)$ by the time they emerge from the boundary. Adding proton and electron contributions, the particle energy flux from the sides of the sheet from dL is $dE_p = e\,\Phi_A\,dF$. Integrating dL across the width of the tail gives E_p the particle energy per unit time per unit length of tail flowing out of the boundaries. We multiply by two for flow in from both sides to obtain

$$E_p = \frac{2\,N_0\,ce\,\Phi_A{}^2}{B_0}.$$

Equating E_s and E_p for the steady state gives

$$\Phi_A = \frac{B_0{}^2}{4\pi\,N_0\,e},$$

regaining Alfvén's formula, equation (7).

We take this result to be in agreement with Yeh & Axford's (1970) suggestion that the rate of annihilation of field lines is not determined by local conditions near the neutral sheet (as in earlier MHD theories), but by the boundary conditions of the system, here expressed in terms of the external magnetic field B_0 and particle density N_0. (Field annihilation at a neutral sheet, which we

232

are discussing here, is a special case of reconnection at an x-type neutral line, as discussed by Yeh & Axford.)

Conservation of momentum must now be considered in the direction parallel to the sheet (and perpendicular to B), since we have protons emerging from one boundary with the same energy spectrum as electrons from the other, but carrying a factor of $(m_p/m_e)^{\frac{1}{2}}$ times more momentum.

First of all, we expect particles to emerge from the sheet travelling almost parallel to it. There will be little energy in the perpendicular motion (oscillations) compared with the parallel motion. In the WKB solution obtained by Speiser (1965) for a simple sheet field structure we find that the parallel velocity is given by

$$V_y = \frac{e}{m} E_0 t$$

(linear acceleration from $t = O$, the time of entry into the sheet), while the velocity amplitude of the oscillations V_z is approximated by (for $t > \left(\frac{a B_0}{c E_0}\right)$)

$$V_z(t) \simeq \frac{c E_0}{B_0} \left(\frac{t}{\left(\frac{a B_0}{c E_0}\right)}\right)^{\frac{1}{4}},$$

where 'a' is the sheet thickness. Thus we find

$$\frac{V_y}{V_z} \simeq R \left(\frac{t}{\left(\frac{a B_0}{c E_0}\right)}\right)^{\frac{3}{4}},$$

where R is the ratio of the sheet half-thickness to the incoming particle gyroradii

$$R = \frac{a}{\left(\frac{V_\perp}{\Omega}\right)} = \frac{ae B_0^2}{mc^2 E_0}$$

For protons we might expect $R_p \sim \vartheta(1)$ since the sheet thickness is determined by the amplitude of the particle oscillations, and these initially will be of the order of the incoming gyroradii. From the above formula $V_y \gg V_z$ for $t \gg t_1$ where $t_1 = \frac{a B_0}{c E_0}$. Now t_1 is the time for a particle to cross the sheet thickness at the incoming velocity $c E_0/B_0$. Thus initially we expect the period of the oscillations to be (very roughly) $\tau \sim 4t$, so that after one oscillation $V_y \sim 3 V_z$, and the proton will perform many oscillations before emerging from the sheet boundary. For Speiser's simple model the time taken for a proton to travel the whole width d of the sheet, from dawn to dusk, is given by

$$t/t_1 \simeq \left(\frac{2 R_p d}{a}\right)^{\frac{1}{2}}.$$

For the geomagnetic tail, taking $a \approx 20$ km (corresponding to $R_p \sim 1$, the electric field given by Alfvén's formula with $N_0 = 0.01$ and $B_0 = 10 \gamma$), gives $d/a \simeq 1.5 \times 10^4$. Then we find $t/t_1 \simeq 200$ and hence $V_y/V_z \simeq 50$. Thus we expect protons to emerge almost parallel to the sheet. Since for electrons $R_e \sim \vartheta \left(\frac{m_e}{m_p}\right)$ we expect the above conclusions to hold true for these as well (more so than protons).

These results for Speiser's simple fields are also expected to hold for more complex field geometries. This has been demonstrated by many particle trajectory computations involving non-uniform electric fields. Particles, in general, are 'directly' accelerated along the sheet by the electric field, and the energy in the oscillations grows slowly by comparison.

We can now estimate the momentum carried across an equipotential of potential φ by protons entering with initial potential energies φ_i, ($\varphi \leqslant \varphi_i \leqslant \Phi_A$), and moving towards dawn in the field reversal region. The flux of protons entering along potentials φ_i to $\varphi_i + d \varphi_i$ is (as before)

$$dF = \frac{2c N_0 d \varphi_i}{B_0} \quad \text{(no./unit length of tail/sec)}$$

and this flux is preserved as the particles are accelerated in the field reversal region across equipotential φ. Assuming, as above, that these particles are moving very nearly parallel to the sheet, by conservation of energy (and neglecting the small kinetic energy of the inflow far away from the sheet)

$$V_y \simeq \left\{\frac{2e}{m_p} (\varphi_i - \varphi)\right\}^{\frac{1}{2}}.$$

Thus the momentum per unit length of tail per sec carried across potential φ by these particles is

$$dM_p = \frac{2c N_0}{B_0} (2e m_p)^{\frac{1}{2}} (\varphi_i - \varphi)^{\frac{1}{2}} d \varphi_i$$

and integrating φ_i from φ to Φ_A to account for all incoming protons crossing equipotential φ we have

$$M_p = \frac{2c N_0}{B_0} (2e m_p)^{\frac{1}{2}} \int_\varphi^{\Phi_A} d\varphi_i (\varphi_i - \varphi)^{\frac{1}{2}} =$$

$$\frac{4}{3} (2e m_p)^{\frac{1}{2}} \frac{c N_0}{B_0} (\Phi_A - \varphi)^{\frac{3}{2}}. \quad (8)$$

233

Similarly for electrons (travelling in the opposite direction)

$$\mathrm{Me} = \tfrac{4}{3}(2em_e)^{\frac{1}{2}}\frac{c\,N_0}{B_0}\,\varphi^{\frac{3}{2}}. \tag{9}$$

We note that any motion of the particles perpendicular to the sheet on crossing equipotential φ will reduce the above values, but, as discussed above, we expect this to be a small effect for particles accelerating in the field reversal region. It is clear from the above expressions that over most of the region we have a net particle momentum flux towards dusk carried by the protons (due to the mass factor). This must be balanced by electromagnetic momentum, as expressed by the second (momentum) moment of the steady-state collisionless Boltzmann equation

$$\mathrm{div}\left(\sum_j m_j \int_{-\infty}^{\infty} d^3v\, f_j\, vv - \mathbf{T}\right) = O, \tag{10}$$

where f_j is the particle distribution function in (v, x) space of particle species j, and $\mathbf{T}$ is the Maxwell stress tensor, given by

$$\mathbf{T} = \frac{1}{4\pi}(EE + BB - \tfrac{1}{2}(E^2 + B^2)\,\mathbf{1}).$$

Quadratic terms in E will be of order $(v/c)^2$ compared to those in B, where v is the particle flow velocity. They are thus neglected, and since $B = B_x(y, z)\,\hat{x}$ we have $\mathbf{T}$ diagonal with

$$T_{zz} = T_{yy} = -T_{xx} = -B_x^2/8\pi.$$

Performing a volume integral on (10) and using the divergence theorem we have

$$\oint_S dS\cdot\left(\sum_j m_j \int_{-\infty}^{\infty} d^3v\, f_j\, vv - \mathbf{T}\right) = O, \tag{11}$$

which is just a statement that the net momentum in any direction flowing through the boundaries of a closed surface is zero in the steady state. The volume is generated by taking a closed contour on a cross-section of the tail and displacing it by a unit distance along the tail length. The contour on the cross-section has been chosen to consist of the dawn boundary equipotential, equipotential φ, and is closed at large distance from the sheet where the flow is uniform and directed towards the sheet (Fig. 7). There is no momentum flow in the x direction, and that in the z direction cancels to zero because of the symmetry of the incoming streams. We are left with the momentum flux in the y direction across the dawn equipotential (Φ_A) and equipotential φ. These equipotentials are approximate trajectories of particles if the flow is adiabatic outside the sheet, so we need only consider the momentum associated with the accelerating particles in the field reversal region moving almost parallel to the sheet. Equation (11) is then simply

$$\int_\varphi dz\left(M_{yy} + \frac{B_x^2}{8\pi}\right) = \int_{\Phi_A} dz\left(M_{yy} + \frac{B_x^2}{8\pi}\right),$$

where M_{yy} is the particle momentum flux. The integrals of these latter quantities along the equipotentials have already been found in equations (8) and (9):

$$\int_\varphi dz\, M_{yy} \simeq \tfrac{4}{3}(2e\,m_p)^{\frac{1}{2}}\frac{c\,N_0}{B_0}$$

$$\left\{(\Phi_A - \varphi)^{\frac{3}{2}} + \left(\frac{m_e}{m_p}\right)^{\frac{1}{2}}\varphi^{\frac{3}{2}}\right\}$$

$$\int_{\Phi_A} dz\, M_{yy} \simeq \tfrac{4}{3}(2e\,m_p)^{\frac{1}{2}}\frac{c\,N_0}{B_0}\left(\frac{m_e}{m_p}\right)^{\frac{1}{2}}\Phi_A^{\frac{3}{2}}.$$

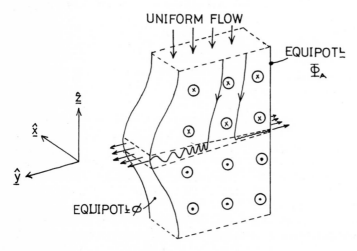

UNIFORM FLOW

EQUIPOT$^{\mathtt{L}}$ Φ_A

EQUIPOT$^{\mathtt{L}}$ ϕ

Fig. 7. Showing the volume through which the momentum flux of particles and field is calculated.

Hence

$$\int_{\Phi_A} dz \frac{B_x{}^2}{8\pi} - \int_\varphi dz \frac{B_x{}^2}{8\pi} = \frac{4}{3} (2e\, m_p)^{\frac{1}{2}} \frac{c\, N_0}{B_0}$$

$$\{(\Phi_A - \varphi)^{\frac{3}{2}} - \left(\frac{m_e}{m_p}\right)^{\frac{1}{2}} (\Phi_A{}^{\frac{3}{2}} - \varphi^{\frac{3}{2}})\} \qquad (12)$$

Thus, neglecting the small electron contribution to the r.h.s., the integral of $B_x{}^2/8\pi$ along an equipotential is monotonically decreasing with decreasing potential in the sheet. We interpret this as simply a change in thickness of the field reversal region, it being thicker on the dusk side than on the dawn. This is expected (in a qualitative way) from the model we are considering, since at the dawn boundary the current is carried by the electrons in a very thin layer near the reversal surface (as we can see from the particle trajectories), while the current layer at the dusk boundary will be much thicker, consistent with the large proton gyroradius.

We will now propose an idealized model for the current distribution in the reversal region in order to use equation (12) to obtain some idea of the consistent sheet thickness. At a potential φ in the sheet a proportion $(1 - \varphi/\Phi_A)$ of the current is carried by protons, the remainder by electrons. We postulate that (in agreement with the trajectories) the electron current is carried in a very thin layer near the neutral sheet, while the proton current is uniform over a region of half-thickness a. The magnetic field structure at potential φ in the field reversal region is then given by

$$B_x(z) \simeq B_0 \left\{ \frac{\varphi}{\Phi_A} \operatorname{sgn}(z) + \left(1 - \frac{\varphi}{\Phi_A}\right) \frac{z}{a} \right\} \qquad (13)$$

for $|Z| \leqslant a$ and outside of the thin electron current layer. It is then easily shown that

$$\int_{\Phi_A} dz \frac{B_x{}^2}{8\pi} - \int_\varphi dz \frac{B_x{}^2}{8\pi} =$$

$$\frac{2}{3}\left(1 - \frac{\varphi}{\Phi_A}\right)\left(2 + \frac{\varphi}{\Phi_A}\right) \frac{B_0{}^2\, a}{8\pi}.$$

Thus from equation (12) we have

$$a \simeq \frac{2c}{e}\left(\frac{2\, m_p}{\pi\, N_0}\right)^{\frac{1}{2}}$$

$$\left\{ \frac{(1 - \varphi/\Phi_A)^{\frac{3}{2}} - \left(\frac{m_e}{m_p}\right)^{\frac{1}{2}}(1 - (\varphi/\Phi_A)^{\frac{3}{2}})}{\left(1 - \frac{\varphi}{\Phi_A}\right)(2 + \varphi/\Phi_A)} \right\}. \qquad (14)$$

'a' as a function of φ/Φ_A is plotted for $N_0 = 0.1, 0.01$ cm^{-3} in Fig. 8, and we find that a typical half-thickness of order $\sim 10^3$ km is indicated. However, as has been pointed out before, we expect at a first examination that the sheet thickness should be of the order of the incoming proton gyroradii, so that the initial oscillations of the protons about the sheet should be consistent with the thickness of the reversal region. However, if the electric field is uniform across the tail this predicts a sheet thickness given by

$$a \simeq \frac{V_\perp}{\Omega} = \frac{m_p\, c^2\, E_0}{e\, B_0{}^2} = \frac{m_p\, c^2}{4\pi\, N_0 e^2\, d}.$$

Thus $a \sim 2$ km for $N_0 \simeq 0.1$ cm^{-3} and $a \sim 20$ km for $N_0 = 0.01$ cm^{-3} much smaller than the values indicated above.

We can reconcile these two calculations in either of two ways (or both):

a. The electric fields are much higher than those predicted by a uniform drop of the Alfvén potential, leading to much larger amplitudes of oscillation for the Speiser particles (i.e. a non-uniform potential gradient).

b. The sheet *is* much wider than the incoming proton gyroradii, but a localized potential in the field reversal region distributes the trapped protons over a larger thickness than expected.

In either case we require electric fields whose scale lengths will approach that of the proton gyroradii. Electrons, however, have a gyroradius a factor of (m_e/m_p) smaller, and these will continue to behave adiabatically (move along equipotentials) and produce a thin current layer near the neutral sheet. A choice between the above two alternatives cannot be made here, the electric field structure (and hence the flow) being dependent on the distribution of particle charge density, which will now be discussed.

4. PARTICLE CHARGE IN THE FIELD REVERSAL REGION

We have seen that neutral plasma flowing towards the current sheet charge-separates at the sheet, protons flowing away towards dusk and electrons towards dawn. Clearly, the charge content of the reversal region needs to be considered, as pointed out by Cowley (1971). If the field reversal region has any net charge as a function of the potential across the sheet, then the electrostatic field produced will modify the overall flow in the system, and a self-consistent flow-charge-field system needs to be set up (leading to alternative 'a' above).

235

However, the charge densities required to produce significant perturbations of Alfvén's uniform electric field are very small compared with the individual charge densities of protons or electrons (as we shall show) so that the plasma approximation is expected to hold in the sheet. Thus we expect

$$\frac{\sigma_p - \sigma_e}{\sigma_p} \ll 1,$$

where the σ are the particle content of the sheet at a given (y) position, integrated through its thickness, i.e. particles per unit sheet (x–y) area. In addition, even if $\sigma_p = \sigma_e$ at a given position along the neutral sheet (i.e. no large-scale electric fields), the distribution of positive and negative charge through the thickness of the sheet may be expected to differ, leading to localized potentials in the field reversal region(and alternative b).

The contributions to σ_p and σ_e from the oscillating and accelerating particles is fairly readily calculated from conservation of flux. The calculation is especially simple if the incoming particle energies associated with the flow velocity are small compared with the electrostatic energy of the Alfvén potential. For a uniform electric field across the tail, the kinetic energy of the particles associated with the flow is

$$\varepsilon = \frac{mv^2}{2} = \frac{mc^2 E_0^2}{2 B_0^2} \text{ or } \frac{\varepsilon}{e \, \Phi_A} = \frac{mc^2}{4\pi \, N_0 e^2 \, d}$$

For tail parameters ($d \simeq 3 \times 10^{10}$ cm) we find for protons that $\varepsilon/e \, \Phi_A \sim 10^{-5}$ with $N_0 = 0.1$ ($\Phi_A = 5$ kV), and $\varepsilon/e \, \Phi_A \sim 10^{-4}$ with $N_0 = 0.01$ ($\Phi_A = 50$ kV). If, however, the electric field is enhanced over a small region by, say, factors of 10 to 100 by the effect of charge in the sheet, then significant proton energization can occur in the adiabatic flow outside the sheet. Protons drift across equipotentials gaining energy as they move into the strong electric field region. In such circumstances the incoming flow kinetic energy of protons need not be negligible compared with energies gained by direct acceleration along the neutral sheet. However, electrons with a much smaller mass have much smaller kinetic energies (for the same velocity) as protons. Thus electric field enhancements of order $10 \rightarrow 100$, which significantly perturb protons, leave electrons flowing very nearly on the same equipotential, their flow energies being much less than the potential energy.

We shall now calculate the surface charge density (charge per unit area of sheet) of trapped electrons on the assumption of negligible initial energies (a similar calculation may be performed for protons (Cowley 1971)). In the light of the above discussion, however, we shall here calculate the trapped proton surface charge taking into account initial flow energies.

Only those electrons moving along equipotentials φ_i between the limits $0 \leqslant \varphi_i \leqslant \varphi$ will contribute to the surface charge density of trapped electrons at potential φ, since they are all accelerated towards dawn in the field reversal region. We again consider element dL of a contour C crossing the equipotential system from potential $\varphi = 0$ (dusk boundary) to potential φ. If $d\varphi_i$ is the potential drop across dL then, as before, the flux across dL is

$$dF = \frac{c \, N \, d\varphi_i}{B}.$$

Since protons may move across equipotentials significantly, if the magnitude of the electric field becomes large as we approach the sheet (non-uniform drop of the Alfvén potential), currents can be present in the flow and hence B can be non-uniform. Since electrons are moving down equipotentials, however, their flux is preserved across a given potential drop $d\varphi_i$. Thus from the above we must have $N/B = N_0/B_0$ where N_0 and B_0 are the values in the uniform flow well away from the reversal region. (This is, of course, the well-known result for planar, two-dimensional equipotential flow, with B perpendicular to the plane, as was mentioned before.) These electrons then enter the field reversal region and are accelerated along the neutral sheet, preserving flux. Thus considering electrons from potentials φ_i to $\varphi_i + d\varphi_i$ moving into the sheet, we have, in the field reversal region at potential φ,

$$d \, \sigma_e \, (\varphi) \mid V_y \, (\varphi, \varphi_i) \mid = \frac{2e \, N_0 c \, d\varphi_i}{B_0}$$

by conservation of flux; $V_y \, (\varphi, \varphi_i)$ is the velocity parallel to the sheet of these electrons at potential φ. (We have multiplied by two for flow from both sides.) Neglecting the initial energies, we then have, for nearly direct acceleration

$$V_y \, (\varphi, \varphi_i) = - \left\{ \frac{2e}{m_e} \, (\varphi - \varphi_i) \right\}^{\frac{1}{2}}.$$

So $\sigma_e \, (\varphi)$ is given by integration over φ_i from $\varphi_i \, (0)$ to $\varphi_i = \varphi$

$$\sigma_e \, (\varphi) = \frac{2c \, N_0}{B_0} \left(\frac{m_e \, e}{2} \right)^{\frac{1}{2}} \int_{\Phi_i = 0}^{\Phi} \frac{d\varphi_i}{(\varphi - \varphi_i)^{\frac{1}{2}}} =$$

$$\frac{2c\,N_0}{B_0}\,(2m_e e)^{\frac{1}{2}}\,\varphi^{\frac{1}{2}}. \tag{15}$$

The calculation for protons is similar in principle, except we now include higher order terms in the drift equation, to account for motion across equipotentials as the particles move towards the field reversal region. The velocity of a proton at a point in the flow may still be expressed as a function of the local electric and magnetic fields (e.g. $v = c\,E \times B/B^2$ as a first approximation) as long as the scale length L for changes in the E and B fields is larger than the particle gyroradii. For cold particles (no magnetic moment) the gyroradius is zero, and is replaced in the theory by the distance a particle travels at the local 'frozen-in' velocity (c E/B) during $\frac{1}{2}\pi$ of a gyro-period. This length we call the gyrolength g_L

$$g_L = \frac{(c\,E/B)}{\Omega_p}.$$

Previously in this paper we have used the expression 'gyroradius', where, in fact 'gyrolength' should have been used for cold particles. In the drift theory, therefore, we obtain a series expansion for the drift velocity, the smallness parameter being g_L/L, and the zeroth order term $V^{(0)} = V_E$ (equation (1)). In the steady state the velocity vector is unique at every point, and so is the particle energy. Thus the orbits of particles of different total energies never cross. A trajectory is defined by a curve of constant total energy, so that in general, for planar two-dimensional drift-flow we may write

$$V = \frac{c\lambda}{q}\,\frac{B}{B^2} \times \nabla\left(q\varphi + \frac{mv^2}{2}\right) \tag{16}$$

for some $\lambda = \lambda\,(E, B)$. In fact, λ can be computed as a series in g_L/L from the drift velocity expansion; clearly $\lambda^{(0)} = 1$ to give $V^{(0)} = V_E = c\,E \times B/B^2$. All these details are not required here, however, since in order to calculate the charge in the sheet we only require the flux into the sheet as a function of the potential. To obtain the flux we need to calculate the particle density in the flow. Using the continuity equation and equation (16) gives

$$\mathrm{div}\left(\frac{c\,N\lambda}{qB}\,\frac{B}{B} \times \nabla\left(q\varphi + \frac{mv^2}{2}\right)\right) = 0.$$

Expanding this, and using the fact that B/B is a constant vector for a two-dimensional system, we find that

$$\nabla\left(\frac{N\lambda}{B}\right) \times \nabla\left(q\varphi + \frac{mv^2}{2}\right) = 0.$$

Since a trajectory is given by $q\varphi + mv^2/2 = $ constant, we see that $N\lambda/B$ is constant along a trajectory. Thus

$$N = \frac{N_0 B}{\lambda B_0},$$

since $\lambda_0 \equiv 1$ for the uniform flow well away from the neutral sheet. The general expression for the particle flux in the drift-flow is thus

$$F = Nv = \left(\frac{c\,N_0}{q\,B_0}\right)\frac{B}{B} \times \nabla\left(q\varphi + \frac{mv^2}{2}\right).$$

In view of the fact that particle orbits do not cross each other, the total energy (kinetic plus potential) of protons must still be a monotonically increasing function of the potential across the tail width. Thus if the velocity of incoming protons at a potential φ in the sheet is $V_p\,(\varphi)$, then only particles with initial potentials (far away from the sheet) in the range $\varphi + \frac{m_p V_p^2}{2e} \leqslant \varphi_i \leqslant \Phi_A$ contribute to the surface charge density of trapped particles at φ, as they move towards dusk in the sheet. (We have neglected the small kinetic energy in the uniform flow well away from the field reversal region). Considering again the flux across element dL of a contour C crossing the system from equipotential $\varphi + \frac{m_p V_p^2}{2e}$ to Φ_A we have

$$dF = \frac{c\,N_0}{e\,B_0}\left|\left(\frac{B}{B} \times \nabla\left(e\varphi' + \frac{mv'^2}{2}\right)\right) \wedge dL\right| =$$
$$= \frac{c\,N_0}{e\,B_0}\,d\left(e\varphi' + \frac{m_p V_p'^2}{2}\right)$$

and this flux is preserved as the particles move in the field reversal region, giving

$$d\,\sigma_p\,(\varphi)\,V_y = \frac{2c\,N_0}{e\,B_0}\,d\left(e\varphi' + \frac{m_p V_p'^2}{2}\right)$$

(again multiplying by two for flow from both sides). A particle with energy $e\varphi' + \frac{m_p V_p'^2}{2}$ in the flow will have a velocity at potential φ in the sheet given by

$$\frac{m_p V_p^2}{2} + e\varphi = \frac{m_p V_p'^2}{2} + e\varphi'$$

and again neglecting the energy in the oscillations we have

$$V_y \simeq \left\{\frac{2e}{m_p}\,(\varphi' - \varphi) + v'^2\right\}^{\frac{1}{2}}.$$

Thus the proton surface charge density is given by

237

$$\sigma_p(\varphi) = \frac{c\,N_0}{B_0}(2\,m_p e)^{\frac{1}{2}} \int\limits_{\varphi + \frac{m_p v_p^2(\varphi)}{2e}}^{\Phi_A} \frac{d\left(\varphi' + \frac{mv'^2}{2}\right)}{\left\{(\varphi' - \varphi) + \frac{m_p V_p'^2}{2e}\right\}^{\frac{1}{2}}}$$

$$= \frac{2c\,N_0}{B_0}(2\,m_p e)^{\frac{1}{2}}\left\{(\Phi_A - \varphi)^{\frac{1}{2}} - \left(\frac{m_p V_p^2(\varphi)}{2e}\right)^{\frac{1}{2}}\right\}. \quad (17)$$

If we neglect the incoming flow energy at potential φ then this reduces to the equation given by Cowley (1971). A similar calculation could be performed for electrons but, as we have seen, even if $m_p V_p^2/2 \sim e\Phi_A$ then $m_e V_e^2/2 \ll e\Phi_A$ and equipotential flow remains a good approximation.

Note that we have assumed that when the protons enter the sheet they immediately start to move towards the dusk boundary. This will only be so if $V_y(\varphi) > O$ on entry, or $E_z(z > o) > O$ at potential φ. We will have $E_z(z > o) > O$, in general, if the sheet is positively charged in this region. Equation (17) then shows that the enhanced electric field produced by the proton charge tends to reduce the proton charge-density below the uniform electric field value. If $V_y(\varphi) < O$, however, in the region near potential φ, protons entering the sheet at a smaller value of potential may contribute to the density at φ. These initially move in the sheet towards the dawn boundary, being slowed down, and then they are reflected by the electric field, finally accelerating towards the dusk boundary as usual. Adding the effect of these particles (which contribute twice to the density at φ) simply changes the sign of the $V_p(\varphi)$ term in (17). In general therefore

$$\sigma_p(\varphi) = \frac{2c\,N_0}{B_0}(2\,m_p e)^{\frac{1}{2}}$$
$$\left\{(\Phi_A - \varphi)^{\frac{1}{2}} - \mathrm{sgn}\,(V_y(\varphi))\right.$$
$$\left.\left(\frac{m_p V_p^2(\varphi)}{2e}\right)^{\frac{1}{2}}\right\}. \quad (18)$$

Again, $V_y(\varphi) < O$ gives $E_z(\varphi) < O$, which implies that the sheet is negatively charged in this region. The proton charge is then enhanced over the uniform electric-field value at this potential.

Comparing proton and electron trapped flux surface charge densities (equations (15) and (18)) we can see that, in general, the proton density will be larger by a factor $(m_p/m_e)^{\frac{1}{4}}$ over that of the electrons. This is expected since the accelerat-

ing electrons leave the system much more quickly than the heavier protons; so we might expect an overall positive charge in the sheet on this count. However, as has already been discussed in relation to the magnetic structure of the field reversal region, we expect the accelerating protons to be distributed over a fairly wide area about the neutral sheet, through which electrons flow along equipotentials towards the sheet. Only very near the neutral plane will adiabatic motion break down, the electrons then starting to accelerate and oscillate about the sheet, producing a thin current layer. Thus, throughout the region where the protons oscillate there will exist electrons still drifting towards the sheet. As we have seen, for equipotential flow in this field configuration B/N is a constant. Thus the adiabatic electron surface charge density is given by

$$\sigma_{ae}(\varphi) = 2e \int_0^a N_e(z, \varphi)\,dz = \frac{2e\,N_0}{B_0}\int_0^a B(z, \varphi)\,dz,$$

where a is the reversal region thickness. If the magnetic field structure were now known we could calculate $\sigma_{ae}(\varphi)$ and using the plasma approximation equate proton and electron surface charge densities. From equations (15) and (18) we see that this determines $V_p(\varphi)$, or since $V_p \simeq c\,E/B$ for the drift-flow region, the electromagnetic field just outside the sheet. The system would then be essentially solved. We might make an informed guess as to the structure of the magnetic field (eg. $a(\varphi) \simeq V_p(\varphi)/\Omega(\varphi)$) and use the model equation (13), suitably modified to account for currents flowing in the drift-flow region above the sheet. However the details of $V_p(\varphi)$ depend (by using the plasma approximation) on the details of σ_{ae} and these details essentially determine the overall flow in the system. An informed guess is not good enough.

We may still, however, obtain information from this discussion. For instance, we may ask, what is the sheet thickness required (using model field (13) and neglecting drift-flow currents) to produce charge neutrality. We will neglect proton flow energies, this and the neglect of drift-currents being consistent. Using the model field we have

$$\sigma_{ae} = e\,N_0\,a\left(1 + \frac{\varphi}{\Phi_A}\right)$$

and from the plasma approximation $\sigma_p \simeq \sigma_e + \sigma_{ae}$ we find

238

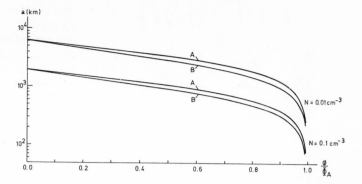

Fig. 8. Values of the half-thickness 'a' of the field reversal region, using the field model given in equation (13), calculated for A) conservation of momentum and B) charge neutrality (both assuming that the incoming proton kinetic energies are small compared with the electrostatic potential energy).

$$a \simeq \frac{2c}{e} \left(\frac{2\,m_p}{\pi\,N_0} \right)^{\frac{1}{2}}$$
$$\left\{ \frac{(1 - \varphi/\Phi_A)^{\frac{1}{2}} - (m_e/m_p)^{\frac{1}{2}}\,(\varphi/\Phi_A)^{\frac{1}{2}}}{2\,(1+\varphi/\Phi_A)} \right\}. \qquad (19)$$

The similarity to equation (14) (derived from momentum conservation) is remarkable; 'a' versus φ/Φ_A is plotted in Fig. 8 for various values of N_0, together with 'a' derived from momentum conservation. The agreement we have found here gives us confidence that the model we have been discussing (in relation to the structure of the field reversal region) bears a fairly close relation to the truth.

As regards the validity of the plasma approximation, we note that an infinite slab of surface charge density indicated by equation (17) would produce electric fields

$$E_z \sim 2\pi\,\sigma_p \simeq \frac{4c\,N_0}{B_0} (2\,m_p e)^{\frac{1}{2}}\,\Phi_A^{\frac{1}{2}}$$

or $\dfrac{E_z}{E_0} \sim \dfrac{8\,ce\,N_0 d}{B_0^2} (2\pi\,m_p\,N_0)^{\frac{1}{2}} \sim 10^9\,N_0^{\frac{3}{2}}.$

Thus, for $N_0 = 0.1$ cm^{-3} we have $E_z/E_0 \sim 10^7$ and for $N_0 = 0.01$, $E_z/E_0 \sim 10^6$ i.e. for all reasonable values of the density the electric field produced by one component of the plasma is very much larger than the uniform Alfvén electric field. Clearly, if the electric fields required to produce charge neutrality are much smaller than this (we saw that $E/E_0 \sim 100$ significantly perturb protons for these densities), then the plasma approximation is a good one.

We now proceed to discuss the structure of the electric field, in terms of the two alternatives mentioned above, to account for the sheet thickness required for charge neutrality (equation (19)).

If we first assume that the thickness is consistent with the gyroradius of protons oscillating about

the neutral sheet, then we may write, approximately

$$a\,(\varphi) \simeq V_p\,(\varphi)/\Omega\,(\varphi).$$

The sheet thickness was derived in equation (19) on the assumption that the initial flow energies were unimportant compared to the electrostatic potential. The above equation implies that this is not so. However, the results of the self-consistent theory based on the above assumption are in agreement with what follows. From equation (19) we take (near $\varphi \sim o$)

$$a \simeq \frac{c}{e} \left(\frac{2\,m_p}{\pi\,N_0} \right)^{\frac{1}{2}},$$

so that the flow velocity into the sheet near $\varphi \sim o$ is

$$V_p \simeq B \left(\frac{2}{\pi\,m_p\,N_0} \right)^{\frac{1}{2}}$$

and hence

$$E \sim \frac{B^2}{c} \left(\frac{2}{\pi\,m_p\,N_0} \right)^{\frac{1}{2}}.$$

The result of the self-consistent analysis is

$$E \simeq \frac{5}{27} \frac{B_0^2}{c} \left(\frac{2}{\pi\,m_p\,N_0} \right)^{\frac{1}{2}},$$

which is smaller than the above. Inclusion of the velocity term in the proton surface density equation reduces the latter's value, reduces the sheet thickness required, and hence reduces v_p and E. Using the latter expression, we have, near $\varphi \sim o$,

$$E/E_0 \simeq \frac{20}{27} \frac{ed}{c} \left(\frac{2\pi\,N_0}{m_p} \right)^{\frac{1}{2}}.$$

For $N_0 = 0.01$ we have $E/E_0 \sim 10^2$, while for $N_0 \sim 0.1$ we have $E/E_0 \sim 400$. The plasma approximation can be seen to be well satisfied.

Under the above assumption, therefore, the

239

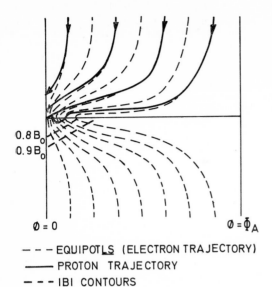

$\varnothing = 0$ $\varnothing = \tilde{\varphi}_A$

– – – EQUIPOTLS (ELECTRON TRAJECTORY)

—— PROTON TRAJECTORY

– – – IBI CONTOURS

Fig. 9. Schematic diagram of equipotential structure and particle flow when most of the potential Φ_A falls near dusk ($\Phi = 0$) boundary. Proton cross-equipotential drift and resultant magnetic field gradients in the drift-flow region are shown.

Alfvén potential falls across a narrow region near the dusk boundary where most of the particle flux enters the sheet. Protons quickly leave the system from this boundary and most electrons travel the entire width of the tail in a now almost E_y-free neutral sheet. A schematic diagram of a system of this kind is given in Fig. 9, showing proton cross-equipotential drift (some leaving the system before encountering the neutral sheet) and the associated magnetic field gradients.

If we consider a closed volume, into and out of which equal fluxes of protons and electrons flow, in the steady state the charge content of the volume is proportional to the difference in time a proton and an electron remain in the volume. Considering the field reversal region as the closed volume, on the above assumption an electron and a proton take approximately the same time to reach the neutral sheet after entering from the drift-flow region above, since the proton continues to move towards the sheet with the external drift-velocity ($\sim cE/B$) while the electron remains adiabatic. However, due to its much larger mass, the proton would spend much longer in the region than the electron during the acceleration along the sheet, if the electric field were uniform, giving a net positive charge. This charge will produce the potential drop near the dusk boundary in a

self-consistent manner (see Cowley 1971), allowing protons to move out of the system quickly and preventing the large build-up of positive charge that would otherwise occur over a wide region of the sheet.

We now turn to the second possibility, that the sheet *is* much wider than the gyrolength of incoming protons (i.e. $a \gg V_p/\Omega$), the particles being distributed over the region by the existence of a localized (positive) potential in the field reversal region. We shall be interested in electric fields for which the proton motion is non-adiabatic, so that they do not move along equipotentials, with the electrons, into the neutral plane (Such a situation would give zero current.) The non-adiabatic motion is quite simple, the protons just oscillate about the line given by

$$E_z = \frac{V_y B_x}{c}, \qquad (20)$$

where v_y is given by the potential drop the particle has undergone. This occurs only for E_z ($z > o$) > O, since B_x ($z > o$) > O and $v_y > O$ for accelerating protons, i.e. for a positive potential in the sheet. A negative potential in the sheet (E_z ($z > o$) < O) simply has the effect of accelerating the particles towards the neutral plane, then decelerating them as they move away on the other side of the sheet. It does not lead to a large redistribution of the protons about the neutral plane. For a positive potential, however, incoming protons are reflected out of the sheet by the positive electric field; they are then turned round by the magnetic field, gaining energy, and then penetrate further into the sheet only to be reflected again. Protons thus oscillate about the line where the electric force (E_z) and magnetic force ($v_y B_x/c$) balance. The velocity parallel to the sheet increases linearly in the electric field, the velocity in the oscillations remaining roughly constant at the incoming (perpendicular) particle velocity. When v_y has increased so much that the electric field can no longer balance the Lorentz force, the particle crosses the neutral sheet and oscillates symmetrically about it, continuing to accelerate in the electric field.

Thus a positive potential in the sheet can have the effect of distributing the proton current over a wide region; electrons continue to move along equipotentials into the neutral sheet.

As a simple example of the redistribution of protons by a positive potential we have computed a proton trajectory in model fields given by

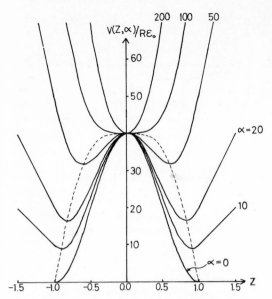

Fig. 10. The effective potential in the field reversal region for various values of α, as given by equation (21). We here plot $V(z, \alpha) / R\varepsilon_0$ for $(A/E_0) = 20$; showing the minimum ($E_z = V_y B_{x/c}$) about which protons oscillate. The dotted line is the locus of the minima.

$$B_x(z) = \begin{cases} B_0 \left(\dfrac{z}{a}\right) & |z| < a \\ B_0 \, \text{sgn}(z) \, |z| \geq a \end{cases}$$

$$\varphi(y, z) = \begin{cases} -E_0 y + \dfrac{Aa}{2}\left(1 + \cos\left(\dfrac{\pi z}{a}\right)\right) \\ -E_0 y \end{cases}$$

such that

$$E_y = E_0 \qquad E_z = \begin{cases} \dfrac{A\pi}{2} \sin\left(\dfrac{\pi z}{a}\right) & |z| < a \\ O & |z| \geq a \end{cases}.$$

The equipotential passing through the point $z = a$ and $y = O$ is chosen as the arbitrary zero.

It crosses the neutral plane ($z = O$) at $Y/a = (A/E_0)$, as shown in Fig. 11. All other equipotentials have the same shape as the zero equipotential since the electric field parallel to the sheet is assumed uniform.

The equation of motion perpendicular to the sheet is given by

$$m \frac{dv_z}{dt} = e \left(E_z - \frac{v_y B_x}{c}\right)$$

so that we have an equivalent potential $V(z, t)$ in the sheet, given by

$$\frac{\partial V}{\partial z} = -e\left(E_z - \frac{v_y B_x}{c}\right) \text{ or}$$

$$V(z, t) - V(o, t) = e\left\{\varphi(z, y(t)) - \varphi(o, y(t)) + \frac{v_y}{c}\int_0^z B_x(z)\, dz\right\}.$$

We choose to start the particle at $y = O$ on the sheet boundary ($z = a$) with the adiabatic velocity at this point, i.e. $V_z = -c\, E_0/B_0$. We thus let the point ($y = o, z = a$) define the zero of $V(z, t)$ for all time, which gives

$$V(z, t) = e\left\{\varphi(z, y(t)) - \varphi(o, y(t)) + \varphi(o, o) + \frac{v_y}{c}\int_0^z B_x(z)\, dz\right\}.$$

Using the given fields this becomes

$$V(z, t) = \frac{ea}{2}\left\{A\left(1 + \cos\left(\frac{\pi z}{a}\right)\right) + \frac{v_y}{c} B_0 \left(\frac{z}{a}\right)^2\right\}.$$

The first term is simply the electrostatic potential which repels protons from the sheet, while the second term, produced by the magnetic force, turns the particles back into the sheet. If we write $v_y = \alpha(t)\, c\, E_0/B_0$ for some value of α, and

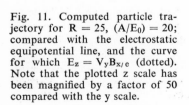

Fig. 11. Computed particle trajectory for $R = 25$, $(A/E_0) = 20$; compared with the electrostatic equipotential line, and the curve for which $E_z = V_y B_{x/c}$ (dotted). Note that the plotted z scale has been magnified by a factor of 50 compared with the y scale.

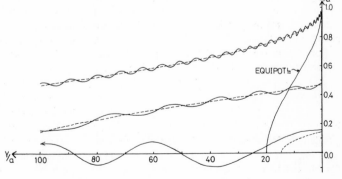

241

normalize $V(z,t)$ to the initial kinetic energy of the proton ($\varepsilon_0 = m_p c^2 E_0^2/2 B_0^2$), we find

$$\frac{V(z,t)}{\varepsilon_0} = R \left\{ \frac{A}{E_0} \left(1 + \cos\left(\frac{\pi z}{a}\right)\right) + \alpha \left(\frac{z}{a}\right)^2 \right\}. \quad (21)$$

R is again the ratio of the sheet half-thickness (a) to the incoming proton gyrolength (v_{p0}/Ω_{p0}). A graph of (21) is plotted in Fig. 10 for various values of α (v_y). It shows the minimum in the effective potential about which the proton oscillates. As the particle accelerates along the sheet (α increases) the minimum moves closer to the neutral sheet ($z = O$). When the two minima on either side of the sheet meet at $z = O$ the particle begins to move symmetrically about the neutral plane. The line about which the particle oscillates is given by equation (20). By conservation of energy, and neglecting the energy fed into the oscillations ($V_x \sim c\, E_0/B_0$) we have

$$v_y = \left\{ -\frac{2e}{m_p} \left\{ -E_0 y + \frac{Aa}{2}\left(1 + \cos\left(\frac{\pi z}{a}\right)\right)\right\}\right\}^{\frac{1}{2}}$$

so that equation (20) becomes with these fields

$$y/a = \frac{1}{2}\left\{ \frac{1}{R}\left(\frac{\pi^2 A}{2 E_0}\right)^2 \frac{\sin^2\left(\frac{\pi z}{a}\right)}{\left(\frac{\pi z}{a}\right)^2} + \frac{A}{2 E_0}\left(1 + \cos\left(\frac{\pi z}{a}\right)\right)\right\}.$$

This line is shown in Fig. 11 for $R = 25$ and $A/E_0 = 20$, together with the computed particle trajectory. The agreement shows that our description of the non-adiabatic motion of protons in this field geometry is correct, and thus we have shown how the proton current can be distributed throughout a sheet many times as thick as the incoming proton gyrolengths ($R = 25$ for the above computation).

For the above form of the potential (chosen arbitrarily) the particles enter the neutral sheet at

$$y/a \simeq \left\{ \frac{1}{R}\left(\frac{\pi^2 A}{2 E_0}\right)^2 + \frac{A}{E_0}\right\}. \quad (22)$$

Now we found before that the incoming proton gyrolength for a uniform (Alfvén) electric field was ~ 2 km for $N_0 = 0.1$ cm^{-3} and ~ 20 km for $N_0 = 0.01$ cm^{-3}, while the sheet thicknesses

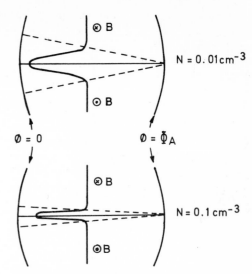

Fig. 12. The form of the maximum localized potentials expected, as discussed in the text. Here the z scale has been magnified by a factor of 10 compared with the y scale.

required by charge neutrality and momentum conservation were ~ 2000 km and ~ 6000 km respectively (corresponding to $R \sim 1000$ and $R \sim 300$). Equation (22) gives us the value of (A/E_0) required, for a given value of R, to prevent a proton from reaching the neutral sheet while moving a distance y/a across the tail. For the maximum effect required we can take y to be the tail diameter, so that $y/a \sim 150$ for $N_0 = 0.1$ cm^{-3} and $y/a \sim 50$ for $N_0 = 0.01$ (diameter $= 50$ R$_E$). From equation (22) we then find that for this distance $A/E_0 \sim 60$ for $N_0 = 0.1$ and ~ 20 for $N_0 = 0.01$. This indicates a fairly large perturbation of the potential in the sheet (see Fig. 12) but the above calculation represents an upper limit on the effect required.

5. SUMMARY

We have considered in some detail the important properties of a field annihilation system where the current in the field reversal region is provided by inflow of plasma contained within the system (i.e. within the lobes of the tail). Self-consistency between the current and magnetic field leads to the value of the total potential across the system. This potential drop is consistent with conservation of energy; the Poynting flux of electromagnetic energy into the sheet is directly converted into particle acceleration in the field reversal region.

Conservation of momentum implies a varying reversal region thickness. This thickness has been calculated using a simple but reasonable model magnetic field structure. The charge density of trapped and accelerating protons is calculated, and is balanced, in the main, by electrons drifting adiabatically in the field reversal region towards the neutral sheet. This implies a sheet thickness for charge neutrality, and using the same model magnetic field as was used in the momentum calculation, gives very good agreement with the latter.

However, the sheet thickness implied by these two calculations is much larger than the incoming proton gyrolengths, assuming Alfvén's uniform electric field across the system. Two effects were then discussed which can remove the inconsistency, both produced by the perturbation of the electric field by charge in the reversal layer. The first is produced by a net positive charge in the sheet, which tends to localize the Alfvén potential drop near the dusk boundary, increasing the electric field and hence the incoming gyrolengths. Secondly, a localized positive potential in the field reversal region can spread the proton current over an area much wider than the incoming gyrolengths. A combination of these two effects is likely to occur in the final self-consistent solution to this problem.

Acknowledgements: I would like to thank Professor J. W. Dungey, both for suggesting the problem and for helpful discussions and encouragement throughout the course of this work. Financial support was provided by the Science Research Council of Great Britain.

REFERENCES

Alfvén, H. 1968. *J. Geophys. Res. 73*, 4379.
Behannon, K. W. 1970. *J. Geophys. Res. 75*, 743.
Camidge, F. P. & Rostoker, A. 1970. *Can. J. Phys. 48*, 2002.
Chandrasheker, S. 1960. *Plasma Physics (Notes compiled by S. K. Trehan)*, University of Chicago Press, Chicago and London.
Cowley, S. W. H. 1971. *Cosmic Electrodynamics 2*, 90.
Fairfield, D. H. & Ness, N. F. 1970. *J. Geophys. Res. 75*, 7032.
Holzer, T. E. Personal communication.
Mihalov, J. D., Sonett, C. P. & Colburn, D. S. 1970. *Cosmic Electrodynamics 1*, 178.
Seymour, P. W. 1959. *Aust. J. Phys. 12*, 309.
Speiser, T. W. 1965. *J. Geophys. Res. 60*, 4219.
Speiser, T. W. & Ness, N. F. 1967. *J. Geophys. Res. 72*, 131.
Speiser, T. W. 1968. *J. Geophys. Res. 73*, 1112.
Stevenson, T. E. & Comstock, C. 1968. *J. Geophys. Res. 73*, 175.
Yeh, T. & Axford, W. I. 1970. *J. Plasma Phys. 4*, 207.

A Theory of VLF Emissions

D. NUNN

Imperial College, London

Abstract: The work attempts a theoretical explanation of the phenomenon of artificially triggered VLF emissions. First resonant particle trajectories in a narrow band whistler wave in an inhomogeneous medium are studied. It is found that second-order resonant particles become stably trapped in the wave. After one or two trapping periods these particles can make a dominant contribution to the resonant particle current. A realistic zero order distribution function is selected, involving a source of potential energy in the form of a loss cone. The resonant particle currents are computed for the case of a constant amplitude whistler crossing the magnetospheric equator. The results tend to explain many of the features of triggering. The equations governing the time development of the wave field due to the presence of a resonant particle current are developed. Resonant particle currents are computed for various generation region type field configurations. These results enable the problem of a self-consistent description of a generation region to be discussed.

1. INTRODUCTION

This work is a theoretical study of the artificial triggering of VLF emissions by whistler morse pulses in the magnetosphere. This fascinating phenomenon has been well documented (Helliwell 1965), and the interested reader is referred to the literature. We will however point out several essential features of the process which a correct theory should be able to explain.

Triggering tends to be confined to cases in which the morse frequency is about 0.5 times the equatorial gyrofrequency along the path of propagation. There is a definite delay – about 70 ms – between the front of the morse pulse and the start of the emission. The emission itself has an amplitude typically two to five times that of the incident morse pulse, and often starts at a frequency 100–300 Hz higher. The fully developed emission usually exhibits a steadily rising or falling frequency, and 'hook-like' forms are not uncommon.

2. SETTING UP THE PROBLEM

Ground-observed whistlers are believed to travel along a magnetospheric field line in a ducted mode (Helliwell 1965). The field-aligned density gradients guide the phase fronts of the wave in such a way that the wave vector k is nearly always parallel to the magnetic field. We thus assume that the whistler morse pulse and the emission together form a continuous narrow band wave train in which k is always parallel to B. When we come to give a more exact description of the emission process it may be necessary to take into account effects such as Landau damping that result from the fact that k is not everywhere exactly parallel to B.

As the wavetrain crosses the magnetospheric equator energetic radiation belt particles become cyclotron resonant with the wave, and give rise to resonant particle currents. Our task is to compute such currents and show that they modify the wave field in such a way as to produce emissions of the kind observed.

3. RESONANT PARTICLE BEHAVIOUR

The first task is to examine the behaviour of resonant particles in a whistler wave when the medium is inhomogeneous. Helliwell pointed out that resonant particles will tend to get quickly forced out of resonance because the resonance velocity will be changing.

Using the usual notation we have for the resonance velocity;

$$\text{Vres} = (\omega - \Omega)/k. \tag{1}$$

A resonant particle will see a time variation in Ω and k because of the inhomogeneity of the magnetic field, and in the field of an emission there will be a steady change in ω. Thus we may write;

$$\frac{d}{dt} Vres = \left(\dot{\omega} - \frac{\partial \Omega}{\partial z} \cdot Vz\right)/k - (\omega - \Omega)$$
$$\frac{dk}{dz} \cdot Vz/k^2. \qquad (2)$$

We also have for the rate of change of velocity along the B_0 direction

$$\frac{dVz}{dt} = -\frac{|V_\perp|^2}{2B} \frac{\partial B}{\partial z} - \frac{eEk}{m\omega}$$
$$|V_\perp| \cos P, \qquad (3)$$

where $|V_\perp|$ is the perpendicular velocity of the particle and P is the phase angle between $V_\perp$ and the electric field of the wave. We are particularly interested in particles which instantaneously satisfy the second-order resonance condition:–

$$\frac{d}{dt} Vz = \frac{d}{dt} Vres; \quad Vz = Vres. \qquad (4)$$

Such particles will clearly be able to stay in resonance with the wave for appreciable periods, and will thus play a dominant role. Substituting expressions 2 and 3 we get

$$\cos P = \frac{-A - B^* |V_\perp|^2}{|V_\perp|}, \qquad (5)$$

where the coefficients A and C are related to the gradients in the system.

$$A = \alpha' \frac{\partial B/\partial z}{|E|} + \alpha'' \frac{\partial \omega/\partial t}{|E|}$$
$$B^* = \alpha''' \partial B/\partial z/|E|$$

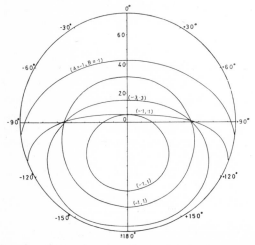

Fig. 1. Some examples of second order resonance lines for various values of the coefficients A and B*.

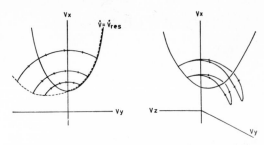

Fig. 2. Trajectories of stably trapped particles showing oscillations about the resonance line. The wave electric field is assumed to be in the x direction. The trajectories shown are the limiting ones, and the volume they enclose is the resonant particle trap.

At a fixed time and place, then, the second-order resonance condition is satisfied along a line in velocity space. The line lies in the $v_\perp$ plane at $Vz = Vres$, and the relationship between relative phase P and $|V_\perp|$ (5), is determined by A and B*. It is interesting to note that if the magnetic field gradient is very large or the wave amplitude very weak it will be impossible to satisfy equation 5 and there will be no second-order resonant particles. Some examples of second-order resonance lines are shown in Fig. 1, using various values for A and B*.

We now pose the question – supposing we take one of these second-order resonant particles and follow its trajectory, does it stay in resonance? The appropriate analysis of the equations of motion has been done in another paper (Nunn 1971). The key result is as follows. In an inhomogeneous medium second-order resonant particles become *stably trapped* in the wave, just as in the homogeneous problem. In velocity space such particles circulate around the instantaneous second-order resonance line, making a kind of ellipse in the coordinates P and Vz. The kind of motion is illustrated in Fig. 2, where again P is the relative phase between $V_\perp$ and E. Another example is shown in Fig. 3, which illustrates the time variation of relative phase P and pitch angle for a stably trapped particle. In an inhomogeneous medium, trapped particles maintain an average relative phase P which is not $-\pi/2$ as in the homogeneous case; consequently they undergo considerable changes in energy and magnetic moment. This can be seen in Fig. 3, as a steady change in the particle's pitch angle.

It is seen from Fig. 2 that trapped particles oscillate about the left-hand branch of the second-order resonance line. It may be shown that if a particle goes beyond the right-hand branch of the

246

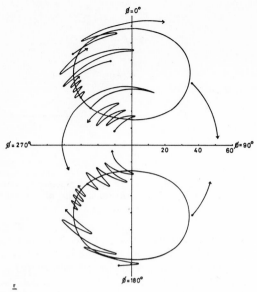

$\phi = 0°$

$\phi = 270°$ 20   40   60 $\phi = 90°$

$\phi = 180°$

r

Fig. 3. Computed examples of the time variation of relative phase P and pitch angle α_p for stably trapped particles. The curves are two separate examples of the resonance line.

resonance line it will fall out of resonance. At any given point we may now construct the region in velocity space that will be occupied by stably trapped particles. One takes the second-order resonance line as defined by the local gradients, and constructs the set of limiting trajectories that just touch the right-hand branch of the resonance curve. The resultant surface encloses the trapping region in velocity space.

A cross section of the resonant particle trap for a particular case is shown in Fig. 4. This illustrates the manner in which the geometry of the particle trap depends upon the second-order resonance line.

It is important to note that this fairly simple picture of trapping behaviour is only valid if the resonance line itself, and thus the wave parameters, is a slowly varying function of time as compared to a trapping period. If this criterion is not met, resonant particle behaviour will be infinitely more complex.

If the wave parameters are in fact slowly varying it is possible to obtain a good deal of information about the resonant particle current without doing a complete computation. Trapped particles which have been in resonance with the wave for long periods will be found in regions of velocity space that are determined by the local gradients at that point. This enables one to make a good estimate

of the very large contribution to the resonant particle current which comes from stably trapped particles.

4. COMPUTATION OF THE RESONANT PARTICLE CURRENT

The component of resonant particle current perpendicular to the **B** direction is obtained by integrating the resonant particle distribution function over the whole of velocity space in the neighbourhood of the resonance velocity.

$$\underline{J_\perp} = - \text{ e } \int (\text{Fres} - \text{F}_0) \ \underline{V_\perp} \ d^3V \qquad (6)$$

Here F_0 (W,μ) is the unperturbed energetic particle distribution function, and is conveniently taken to be a function of energy W and magnetic moment (μ) only.

Each point in the integration represents a particle. If δW, $\delta\mu$ are the changes in energy and magnetic moment undergone by the particle as a result of interacting with the wave field, then we may write using Liouville's theorem

$$\text{Fres} - \text{Fo} \cong - \frac{\partial \text{Fo}}{\partial W} \ \delta W - \frac{\partial \text{Fo}}{\partial\mu} \ \delta\mu.$$

Clearly, in equation 6 the greatest contribution to $J_\perp$ will come from stably trapped particles for which $\delta\mu$, δW are relatively large. Note, however, that stably trapped particles will only dominate the integral if they have been trapped for at least two trapping periods.

It is not possible to compute the resonant par-

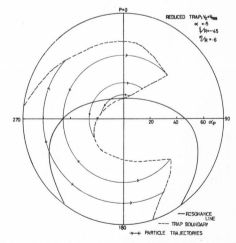

P=0

REDUCED TRAP; $V_z = V_{res}$
$\propto = \cdot 5$
$\frac{1}{R} = \cdot 45$
$\frac{2}{R} = \cdot 6$

270   20   40   60 α_p 90

180

— RESONANCE LINE
---- TRAP BOUNDARY
+-+ PARTICLE TRAJECTORIES

Fig. 4. Cross section of the resonant particle trap in the $V_z = V_{res}$ plane for a particular form of the resonance line. The actual trap size is usually less than the theoretical maximum as particles near the outer edge of the trap are invariably lost.

ticle current without first specifying Fo, and the results obtained will depend entirely upon the choice for Fo. For example, a purely thermal-type distribution function for Fo will be found to give only wave damping. To obtain the growth rates necessary for triggering instability one needs a source of potential energy in the form of a pitch-angle anisotropy or loss cone distribution function.

5. THE INITIAL RESONANT PARTICLE CURRENTS IN THE WHISTLER PULSE

We now enquire – what are the currents which first appear in the whistler morse pulse when it enters the equatorial zone? These will obviously tell us when and how triggering is initiated.

One assumes that the ambient magnetic variation has a parabolic variation with position

$$B = Bo (1 + \tfrac{1}{2} \eta z^2),$$

where z is the distance from the equator measured along the field line (2π units equals one wavelength). The wave field is taken to be that of the unmodified morse pulse, and has a constant amplitude and a frequency fixed at one half the equatorial gyrofrequency. The zero-order dis-

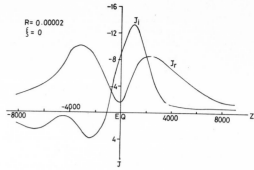

Fig. 6. The in-phase current Jr and reactive current Ji as a function of position for a pulse of constant amplitude and frequency.

tribution function Fo used for the computations is shown in Fig. 5, and is of the loss cone type combined with an overall fall off with energy as E^{-2}. Using a variety of wave amplitudes the resonant particle current is computed as a function of position, using the CDC6600. On the graphs the component of current in-phase with the wave electric field (Jr) and the reactive component of current (Ji) are plotted. The units of current are chosen such that at R = 0.00001 Jr = 1 gives the ordinary linear growth rate for the distribution function chosen.

Fig. 6 plots the currents Jr, Ji for a fairly large amplitude field

$$R = eEk/m\omega^2 = .00002.$$

This corresponds to a wave electric field at the equator of 100 μV/m, and to a full trapping period of about 20 ms. At these amplitudes second order resonant particles are stably trapped in the wave for several trapping periods, and the current is almost entirely due to these trapped particles.

Most of the features of the graph are readily understandable. For $|z| > 8000$ the gradient in magnetic field is sufficiently strong for second-order resonance to be forbidden, and $\underline{J_\perp}$ is consequently small. At Z = 8000 particles become stably trapped. The relative phase of trapping is at first P $\sim$ 0, and the current is antiphase to the electric field at this point. As the equator is approached, the centre of the particle trap moves to P $\sim -\pi/2$, which explains the pronounced peak in Ji. At the equator, phase organisation of the trapped particles ceases, and the current falls to low levels, but on the other side of the equator retrapping takes place to give a new peak in Jr and a generally positive component of Ji.

Fig. 7 is a similar plot for the case R = 0.000005,

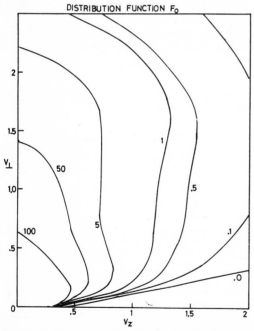

Figure 5. The zero-order distribution function Fo as a function of equatorial Vz and $V_\perp$.

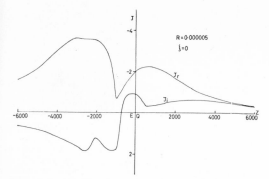

Fig. 7. Computed currents for the intermediate amplitude case.

at which amplitude trapped particles do not dominate the current. However, the form of the curves is still similar to that of Fig. 6.

Fig. 8 shows Jr, Ji for the case R = 0.0000005. This is the weak amplitude case, when the equatorial E field is about 1μ V/m, and the full trapping period is about 200 ms. Stable trapping does not occur and the currents are more or less locally generated. Note the completely different character of the current curves, and that now there is only a single peak in Jr.

6. TIME DEVELOPMENT OF THE WAVE FIELD

We must now develop the equations which show how the whistler wave field is modified by the resonant particle currents of the kind we have been considering.

For the sake of simplicity we suppose that the ambient plasma is of a constant density, and that the magnetic field is a constant. It is reasonable to suppose that the inhomogeneities in the system

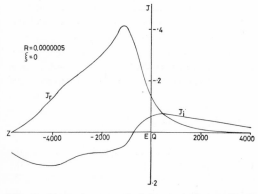

Fig. 8. Currents computed in a weak amplitude pulse.

are only important as far as resonant particle behaviour is concerned.

The governing equations are Maxwell's equations and the equation of motion of the cold plasma particles. Neglecting the displacement current, these reduce to a single differential equation giving the time development of the wave electric field in terms of the resonant particle current.

$$\left[\frac{\partial^2}{\partial z^2} \left(\frac{\partial}{\partial t} - i\Omega \right) - \frac{\Pi^2}{c^2} \frac{\partial}{\partial t} \right] E_\perp = \frac{4\pi}{c^2} \left(\frac{\partial}{\partial t} - i\Omega \right) \frac{\partial}{\partial t} J_\perp. \tag{7}$$

Here $E_\perp$ is the perpendicular electric field vector,

$$E_\perp = E_x + iE_y$$

and $I_\perp$ is the resonant particle current,

$$J_\perp = J_x + iJ_y.$$

At any given time the wave field will have a fast phase variation at a frequency of, say, ω_o and corresponding wavelength k_o. This rapid variation may be factored out, and we deal with slowly varying complex amplitudes ε and J.

$$E_\perp = \varepsilon \, e - i(k_o z - \omega_o t) \tag{8}$$
$$J_\perp = J \, e - i(k_o z - \omega_o t) \tag{9}$$

Here of course k_o, ω_o satisfy the dispersion relation.

$$k_o^2 (\Omega - \omega_o) = \Pi^2 \omega_o / c^2$$

We assume that ε and J are slowly varying compared to the wave frequency.

$$\frac{\partial \varepsilon}{\partial t} \ll \omega_o \varepsilon, \quad \frac{\partial J}{\partial t} \ll \omega_o J$$

We substitute equations 8 and 9 into equation 7 and, neglecting small terms, obtain

$$\left[\frac{\partial}{\partial t} + Vg \frac{\partial}{\partial z} \right] \varepsilon \cong \frac{4\pi \omega_o (\omega_o - \Omega)}{\Pi^2 + k_o^2 c^2} J \tag{10}$$

This is a particularly simple equation and merely says that the current J generates a complex field ε which is advected away at the group velocity. We now divide ε into an amplitude and a phase factor;

$$\varepsilon \cong |\varepsilon| e^{i\varphi}.$$

The current J is expressed in terms of the in phase component Jr and reactive component Ji

$$J = (Jr + i \, Ji) \, e^{i\varphi}.$$

Substituting again we finally obtain

249

$$\left(\frac{\partial}{\partial t} + Vg\,\frac{\partial}{\partial z}\right)|\,\varepsilon\,| = \frac{4\pi\omega_0\,(\omega_0 - \Omega)\,Jr}{\Pi^2 + k_0^2\,c^2} \quad (11)$$

$$\left(\frac{\partial}{\partial t} + Vg\,\frac{\partial}{\partial z}\right)\varphi =$$

$$\frac{4\pi\omega_0\,(\omega_0 - \Omega)}{\Pi^2 + k_0^2 c^2}\,Ji/|\,\varepsilon\,|. \quad (12)$$

As expected, the rate of growth of field amplitude is directly proportional to the in-phase component of resonant particle current. An observer at a given point will see a rate of change of wave number k given by the expression

$$\frac{\partial k}{\partial t} = \frac{\partial}{\partial z}\frac{\partial \varphi}{\partial t} = -Vg\,\frac{\partial k}{\partial z} + \frac{4\pi\omega_0\,(\Omega - \omega_0)}{\Pi^2 + k_0^2 c^2}$$

$$\frac{\partial}{\partial z}\{Ji/|\,\varepsilon\,|\}. \quad (13)$$

As we know, a generation region of the Helliwell type admits of solutions in which k (and thus wave frequency) steadily change. In such a case it is necessary to redefine the quantities k_0, ω_0 as often as it is necessary to ensure that ε, J in fact remain slowly varying.

7. THE TRIGGERING PHASE

The initial time development of the field is found by putting the currents Jr, Ji, computed in the constant amplitude morse pulse, into the expressions 11 and 12.

The strong morse pulse will show two distinct regions of large growth, one on either side of the equator. Either or both of these may develop into a self-sustaining generation region of the Helliwell type, provided that the growth rates are sufficiently great. We shall see that a negative value for Ji in a generation region will cause the wave frequency to rise and vice versa. Thus the region of growth on the downstream side of the equator corresponds to the riser, and that on the upstream side to the faller.

The weaker morse pulse only exhibits a single peak in Jr accompanied by a positive Ji, which suggests that these should only trigger fallers. There is a good deal of observational evidence to suggest that this is in fact the case.

Fig. 9 shows the maximum growth rates in the rising and falling zones as a function of morse amplitude R. It is seen that Jr (max) remains roughly proportional to R over a wide range of amplitudes. Since wave energy losses due to Landau damping and leakage from the duct are also proportional to R, this graph suggests that

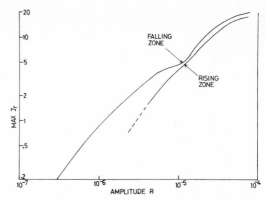

Fig. 9. Maximum initial in-phase current Jr in both rising and falling zones as a function of morse amplitude R.

triggering is just as feasible for weak amplitude signals as for strong. Thus there is nothing surprising about the fact that Omega pulses are able to trigger. It might have been expected that the growth rates would increase very rapidly above R = 0.000005, when stable trapping becomes possible. That this is not the case is due to the fact that the field variation is parabolic and not linear.

The time delay in the production of a triggered emission is readily explained. The currents in Fig. 6, for example, arise as a result of particles interacting with the wave over a distance of about 1000 wavelengths. A resonant particle takes about 60 ms to traverse this distance and it will take about this time for the maximum currents to build up. Another factor is that there is an upper limit to the linear growth rate in the system, in order that the system shall not be absolutely unstable to whistler turbulence (Kennel & Petschek 1966). One thus expects there to be an upper limit also to the non-linear growth rate experienced by the whistler morse pulse.

There is nothing in the theory of wave particle interactions to favour triggering at one half the equatorial gyrofrequency. The fact that such a frequency is favoured is almost certainly a propagation effect. Helliwell has suggested that ducting is most effective at this frequency, when loss of wave energy from the duct and Landau damping will be at a minimum.

8. LONG-TIME DEVELOPMENT OF THE WAVE FIELD

The continued development of the wave field and the production of a Helliwell type generation region is a difficult problem in self-consistent wave particle theory. It is really necessary to do a numerical time integration of equations 11 and 12, computing the resonant particle current at each step. However, each computation of current takes 600 secs on the CDC6600 and this approach is not practicable at present. One must try and understand qualitatively what happens.

One of the most difficult aspects of the problem is the phase behaviour and the fact that the frequency of the emission changes steadily. Two important properties of the resonant particle current make it possible for this to happen. In the strong pulse the current arises from a beam of particles that have interacted with the wave over an appreciable distance. This current is slow to respond to quick changes in wave amplitude or phase, and owing to the inertia of the beam particles the wavelength of the current can only vary slowly. Indeed, if a beam is travelling into a region of decreasing wave amplitude it will become almost independent of the wave field and any distinct phase relationship between the electric field and the current will tend to disappear. In the case of weak amplitude pulses the current tends to be more locally generated and the phase relationship between J and E is much more rigid.

Another important property of resonant particle currents that distinguishes them from those due to, say, cold particles, is that at a given place they are not time proportional to the wave amplitude – in other words the wave field appears first and the currents may appear afterwards.

Inspection of equation 12 reveals that if the resonant particle current J has its phase tied to that of the electric field (as for weak amplitude signals) then the overall time variation of phase φ will be simply that of the incident morse. In this case there will be no frequency changes in the field until the end of the morse pulse is reached. This is known as termination triggering, and is observed in the case of Omega pulses. For the stronger pulses (NAA) the resonant particle current is more flexible in phase and the generated fields can become phase-independent from the incident wave. Thus these pulses can trigger before their end is reached.

One curious phenomenon associated with the early development of the wave field is the offset frequency. The morse field and that of the emission at a slightly higher frequency form a wave train with a beating amplitude. When resonant particles see this beating at the trapping frequency, trapped particles will resonate and be thrown out of resonance. There will then be a choking effect at this point. A full understanding of this problem will really require a full time integration.

9. THE GENERATION REGION

The initial development of the wave field is very difficult to follow because of the rapid variation of parameters which takes place. However, once triggering has taken place, the wave train settles down into a fairly stable configuration of the 'generation region type', with a roughly time-independent wave profile and a steady rate of change of frequency. An obvious line of attack is to attempt a self-consistent wave particle description of a stable generating region.

The first task is to have a look at the currents which appear in the field approximating that

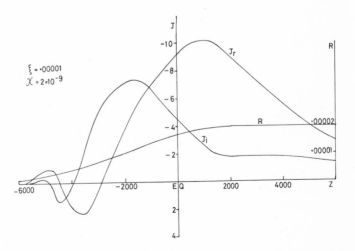

Fig. 10. Currents computed in a Helliwell type generation region with a rising frequency.

251

which might be found in a generating region. The wave amplitude is taken to fall off upstream in a Gaussian fashion, and the location of the g.r. is made to coincide more or less with the known peak in growth rate (Jr). Wave frequency is assumed to be independent of position and to have a linear variation with time, the rate of change being chosen to be a typically observed value. The wavelength is taken to be that which satisfies the local dispersion relation. The first deficiency in such a field is that little is known about the actual profile, and in any case it will not be exactly time-independent. However, it turns out that the exact details of the amplitude profile do not seem significant as far as the current is concerned. Also the wavelength as a function of position will not be exactly as we have chosen it, and there will be some additional phase variations caused by Ji. However our choice of field should tell us about the overall characteristics of the trapped particle beam.

Fig. 10 shows the currents computed in a g.r. with exit amplitude R = 0.00002, in which the frequency rises at a realistic rate:

$$\xi = \partial\omega/\partial t/\omega^2 = .00001.$$

Note that the beam of stably trapped particles is again in evidence. There is now only a single peak in Jr located at the equator, with a pronounced peak in Ji at about $z = -2000$. Note that at about $z < -2000$ the wave field loses control of the trapped particle beam, which then spirals freely, in fact undergoing a wavelength shift at its far end.

Fig. 11 shows the current field for the large amplitude faller. Here Ji is positive at the up-stream end. An interesting point is the secondary peak in Jr accompanied by negative Ji that exists downstream. These are the current fields appropriate to a riser, and if for instance the wave profile of a faller were to slowly slip downstream, it could turn into a riser. Fig. 12 is the case of the weak amplitude faller. The peak in Jr is upstream of the position predicted by Helliwell, and there is an overall positive Ji. The weak riser case is shown in Fig. 13. Here the peak in Jr is well away from the equator, but note that Ji is also positive for this field.

In the strong amplitude case the in-phase component Jr will be a complex function of R, z, and rate of change of frequency ξ. The dependence is illustrated in Fig. 14, which plots Ψ on a z, ξ diagram for R = 0.00002. The quantity Ψ gives the growth rate to be expected from stably trapped particles only. The whole Ψ pattern is linearly proportional to R along both axes. The blank regions on the graphs are where second-order resonance is forbidden. The area labelled 'rising zone' is where Ji is negative, and the falling zone is where Ji is positive. The graph confirms that when stably trapped particles dominate, the maximum growth rate occurs at the equator for rising or falling frequencies, the optimum ratio being $\xi/R = 0.5$.

To achieve a self-consistent picture of a generation region we must first satisfy equation 11. We note first that it is not physically realistic to suppose that the duct is completely free of loss and Landau damping. In practice there will be a substantial loss of energy from the duct, but the rate of this will be difficult to estimate. For a time-independent profile we may write equation 11 as

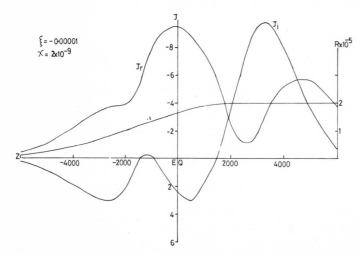

Fig. 11. Currents computed in a large amplitude faller.

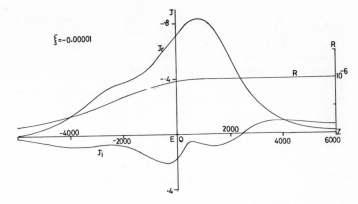

Fig. 12. Current fields for a weak amplitude faller.

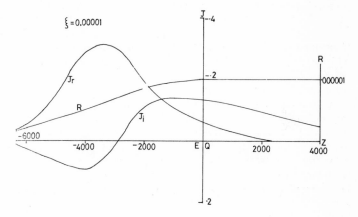

Fig. 13. Current fields computed for the case of a weak amplitude riser.

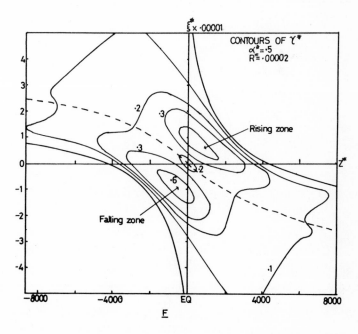

Fig. 14. Plot of Ψ^*, the estimated growth rate due to second-order resonant particles only. It is shown as a function of position z^* and rate of change of wave frequency ξ^*.

253

$$\text{Vg} \, \partial \mid E \mid / \partial z = \frac{4\pi \, \omega_0 \, (\omega_0 - \Omega)}{\Pi^2 + k_0{}^2 \, c^2} \, Jr - \chi \mid \varepsilon \mid.$$

The frequency behaviour of the entire g.r. will be controlled from the furthest point upstream at which the phase of the resonant particle current is still effectively controlled by the wave field. For the large amplitude pulses this will be where the field amplitude is about half the exit amplitude, but for the weaker pulses it will probably be nearer the tip. At this point we may ignore the term in $\dfrac{\partial k}{\partial z}$, and obtain a steady rate of change in wave number. The corresponding rate of change of frequency is then

$$\frac{\partial \omega}{\partial t} = \frac{4\pi \, \text{Vg} \, \omega_0 \, (\Omega - \omega_0)}{(\Pi^2 + k_0{}^2 \, c^2)} \left[\frac{\partial}{\partial z} \, (Ji / \mid \varepsilon \mid) \right]_{cp}.$$

Consulting Fig. 10 we see that $\dot{\omega}$ will be clearly positive provided the field is controlled from a position $z \gtrsim - 2000$. For self-consistency clearly the rate of rise of frequency of the wave field actually caused by the current field must match that originally assumed in computing those currents. For the large amplitude faller we see that fortunately $\dot{\omega} < 0$ provided the control point lies between $z = -1000$ and $z = -3000$. Similarly the weak amplitude faller shows $\dot{\omega} < 0$ for a control point at $z < -2000$. Note that the currents computed in a weak amplitude riser are not of a kind to make the frequency rise and thus a self-consistent picture in this case does not seem possible.

Note that for self-consistency we must satisfy a complex series of interrelating equations. The rate of change of frequency depends strongly on Ji and less strongly on $\mid \varepsilon \mid$. The amplitude behaviour depends on Jr. Both currents Jr and Ji are themselves strong functions of both amplitude and $\dot{\omega}$. Observational evidence seems to point to some kind of stability about the equilibrium condition, as amplitude and $\dot{\omega}$ seem to remain quite stable during an emission. Phenomena such as hooks may presumably be interpreted as being the result of a destabilisation of the g.r. and its rapid change to a more stable configuration.

The present attempt to predict the nature of solutions to equations 11 and 12 is obviously rather unsatisfactory. A full understanding will only be obtained when numerical solutions to these equations are done – either using various trial prescriptions for the current or perhaps computing it in full.

REFERENCES

Abdalla, M. 1970. *Planet. Space Sci. 18*, 799.
Helliwell, R. A. 1965. *Whistlers and Related Ionospheric Phenomena*. Stanford University Press, Stanford, California.
Helliwell, R. A. 1967. *J. Geophys. Res. 72*, 4773.
Kennel, C. F. & Petschek, H. E. 1966. *J. Geophys. Res. 71*, 1.
Nunn, D. 1970. *J. Plasma Physics*. In press.
Nunn, D. 1971. Planet Space Sci., In press.
Stix, T. H. 1968. *The Theory of Plasma Waves*. McGraw-Hill, New York.